JUNIOR ~~~~~~~ LIBRARY
YORK, PENNA.

ASTROPHYSICS

Nuclear Transformations, Stellar Interiors, and Nebulae

By the same author

ASTROPHYSICS

The Atmospheres of the Sun and Stars

A WORK covering both the fundamentals and the major modern developments in the study of the atmospheres of the sun and stars and solar-terrestrial relationships. Topics treated include atomic structure and spectra, gas laws and velocity distribution, ionization, excitation, dissociation of atoms and molecules, and selected aspects of radiation theory.

ASTROPHYSICS

Nuclear Transformations,
Stellar Interiors, and Nebulae

By

LAWRENCE H. ALLER

ASSOCIATE PROFESSOR OF ASTRONOMY
UNIVERSITY OF MICHIGAN

15576

THE RONALD PRESS COMPANY , NEW YORK

IUNIOR COLLEGE LIBRARY
YORK, PENNA.

Copyright, 1954, by

THE RONALD PRESS COMPANY

———

All Rights Reserved

The text of this publication or any part
thereof may not be reproduced in any
manner whatsoever without permission in
writing from the publisher.

Library of Congress Catalog Card Number: 54–6959

PRINTED IN THE UNITED STATES OF AMERICA

QB801 .A5   010101 000
Aller, Lawrence H. (Lawre
Astrophysics nuclear transfor

0 2002 0092132 4

YORK COLLEGE OF PENNSYLVANIA 17403

JUNIOR COLLEGE LIBRARY
YORK, PENNA.

QB
801
A5

To My Students and Colleagues
HERE AND ABROAD, WHOSE HELP
AND ENCOURAGEMENT HAVE MADE THIS
BOOK POSSIBLE

PREFACE

The present volume was prepared as a companion to my *Atmospheres of the Sun and Stars* and treats of nuclear transformations, stellar structure, the origin of the elements, pulsating and irregular variables, stars with extended envelopes, novae and supernovae, gaseous nebulae, and the interstellar medium.

In so far as possible I have stressed not merely the results but also the methods by which they are obtained. For example, the model of a star that derives its energy by the carbon cycle is calculated in detail. The present status of our knowledge of the properties of matter at high temperatures is critically assessed.

Much of the subject matter deals with fields of astronomy that are in a rapid state of flux. Change is particularly rapid in our knowledge of stellar interiors and Cepheid variables while advances in radio astronomy promise to revolutionize the investigation of the interstellar medium.

Many astronomers have supplied helpful comments and suggestions, results in advance of publication, and illustrations. Particular thanks are due to Walter Baade, S. Chandrasekhar, William Fowler, Leo Goldberg, Jesse Greenstein, Emil Konopinski, Edwin Lennox, William Liller, Jean McDonald, Dean B. McLaughlin, Donald H. Menzel, Paul W. Merrill, R. Minkowski, M. Minnaert, Donald Osterbrock, Edwin Salpeter, Allan Sandage, Martin Schwarzschild, Harlow Shapley, Lyman Spitzer, Bengt Strömgren, Otto Struve, H. C. van de Hulst, Edwin Weston, and Olin Wilson. Illustrations have been supplied by the Lick and Mount Wilson and Palomar Observatories. Gordon Newkirk assisted in the preparation of some of the photographs of spectra.

LAWRENCE H. ALLER

Ann Arbor
March 4, 1954

CONTENTS

LIST OF PHYSICAL CONSTANTS

Many of the following values have been taken from "Least-Squares Adjustment of the Atomic Constants, 1952," by Jesse W. DuMond and E. Richard Cohen, *Rev. of Modern Physics* **25**, 691, 1953. Some derived constants of astrophysical interest have been supplied by John K. Wilkinson. A few astronomical constants such as the length of the astronomical unit, light year, and parsec and the number of seconds in a sidereal year are included.

The standard error of many of these numbers is given as a digit preceded by ±. Thus ±8 means that the standard error is 8 in the last significant figure.

Avogadro's number, 1/mol
$N_0 = 6.0247 \times 10^{23}$ ±4
$\log N_0 = 23.779935$

Loschmidt's number, 1/cm^3
$n_0 = 2.68713 \times 10^{19}$ ±16
$\log n_0 = 19.429289$

Planck's constant, erg · sec
$h = 6.6252 \times 10^{-27}$ ±5
$\log h = -26.17880$

Boltzmann's constant, erg/deg
$k = 1.38042 \times 10^{-16}$ ±10
$\log k = -15.85999$

Wien's constant, cm deg
$\lambda_{max} T = 0.28979$ ±5
$\log \lambda_{max} T = -0.53792$
$\lambda_{max}/T = 5.8793 \times 10^{10}$ ±4

Stefan-Boltzmann constant,
    erg/cm^{2}deg^{4}sec
$\sigma = 5.6686 \times 10^{-5}$ ±5
$\log \sigma = -4.24652$

Radiation density constant,
    erg/cm^{3}deg^4
$a = 7.5634 \times 10^{-15}$ ±8
$\log a = -14.12129$ ±4

Saha equation constant,
$\epsilon \, 10^8 \, e$ modulus/$ck = \theta T$
$\theta T = 5040.3$ ±0.2
$\log \theta T = 3.70245$ ±4

Gas constant, erg/deg mole
$R_0 = 8.3166 \times 10^7$ ±4
$\log R_0 = 7.91995$

Rydberg constant for H, 1/cm
$R_H = 1.0967758 \times 10^5$ ±1
$\log R_H = 5.0401178$
$R_H = 3.28805 \times 10^{15}$ ±1/sec

Rydberg for infinite mass, 1/cm
$R = 1.0973731 \times 10^5$ ±1
$\log R = 5.0403543$

Velocity of light, cm/sec
$c = 2.997929 \times 10^{10}$ ±8
$\log c = 10.476821$

Electronic charge, esu
$\epsilon = 4.80288 \times 10^{-10}$ ±21
$\log \epsilon = -9.318498$

Electronic charge, emu
$\epsilon = 1.60207 \times 10^{-20}$ ±3
$\log \epsilon = -19.795319$

Electron rest mass, gm
$m_\epsilon = 9.1085 \times 10^{-28}$ ±6
$\log m_\epsilon = -27.04055$

Radius of the electron, cm
$r_0 = 2.8178 \times 10^{-13}$ ±1
$\log r_0 = -12.55009$

First Bohr radius, cm
$a_0 = 5.29171 \times 10^{-9}$ ±6
$\log a_0 = -8.276404$

Proton/electron mass ratio
$M_p/m_\epsilon = 1836.13 \quad \pm 4$

Mass of the proton, gm
$M_p = 1.67243 \times 10^{-24} \quad \pm 10$
$\log M_p = -23.77665$

Mass of the hydrogen atom, gm
$H = 1.67334 \times 10^{-24} \quad \pm 10$
$\log H = -23.77642 \quad \pm 3$

Mass of unit atomic weight, gm
$M = 1.65983 \times 10^{-24} \quad \pm 10$
$\log m = -23.77994 \quad \pm 3$

$B_\nu(T)$ has its maximum value at
$\nu = T/(4113.3)$ ev
$\nu = (5.8787 \times 10^{10})T$ cycles
     per sec

Electron volt:
$\lambda_0 = 12397.8 \quad \pm 0.5$ Angstroms
$\nu_0 = 8065.98 \quad \pm 0.30$ wave numbers
$T_0 = 11605.7 \quad \pm 0.5^\circ$ K
$\nu_0 = 2.41812 \times 10^{14} \quad \pm 9$ cps

Ergs per electron volt:
$1.60207 \times 10^{-12} \quad \pm 7$
$\log (\text{erg/ev}) = -11.795318$

Energy equivalent of electron mass
$mc^2 = 0.510984 \quad \pm 16$ Mev

Energy equivalent of proton mass
$M_P c^2 = 938.232 \quad \pm 24$ Mev

Conversion factor from atomic mass
     units to Mev
     1 a.m.u. $= 931.162 \quad \pm 24$ Mev

Standard atmosphere (pressure)
     1,013,246 dynes/cm^2/atmosphere

1 barn $= 10^{-24}$ cm^2

Gravitation constant, dyne cm^2/gm^2
$G = 6.670 \times 10^{-8} \quad \pm 5$
$\log G = -7.1759 \quad \pm 3$

Centimeters per light-year
     9.463×10^{17}
     $\log$ cm/ly. $= 17.97603$

Parsec:
     3.084×10^{18} cm/pc
     3.258 light-years/pc
     2.063×10^5 astr. units

Sidereal year
     3.1558×10^7 sec/year

Astr. unit $= 1.49674 \times 10^8$ km
            $= 4.854 \times 10^{-6}$ pc

1 sphere $= 4\pi$ steradians

1 sphere $= 41,253$ square degrees

ASTROPHYSICS

Nuclear Transformations, Stellar Interiors, and Nebulae

CHAPTER 1

STELLAR INTERIORS AND NUCLEAR TRANSFORMATIONS

1. Introduction

At first glance it would appear that no astrophysical topic would remain more concealed from our knowledge than the interiors of the stars. The depth to which we can see into the average star is discouragingly small. The thickness of the gases which produce the dark-line spectrum of the sun amounts to only 2 gm/cm^2, equivalent to the tiniest fraction of the strata that compose the atmosphere of the earth, itself but a negligible fraction of the mass of this planet.

In a few fortunate instances we can find the mass, radius, and luminosity of a star, and from its spectrum we can learn something about the chemical constitution of the surface layers. The problem is: given that the star is stable, and certain basic physical laws, what can we find out about the chemical composition, temperature, pressure, and density in the interior?

We assume that the physical laws governing conditions in stellar interiors are the same as those deduced on the earth from laboratory experiments. Occasional modifications are required, as with the gas laws, under extreme conditions of temperature and density. The nature of these modifications is almost always fairly well indicated by theoretical physics.

The condition that the star must be in a steady state simplifies the problem. Energy produced by nuclear transformations in the deep interior slowly seeps to the surface. The rate of energy generation in the interior must exactly equal the rate of energy emission by the star, i.e., its luminosity. Not only must the star be in a radiative steady state; it must also be in mechanical equilibrium. At each point throughout the interior the pressure must exactly balance the weight of the overlying layers. The pressure, density, temperature, and rate of flow of energy are assumed constant with the time in our treatment of a normal star.

The chemical composition enters in a rather fundamental fashion. Nuclear physics suggests definite mechanisms of energy generation— the carbon cycle and the proton-proton reaction—whereby hydrogen becomes progressively transformed into helium. The hydrogen consumption rate will depend on the amount of hydrogen and, for stars

3

that operate on the carbon cycle, the initial amount of carbon and nitrogen, since the latter cannot be built up from lighter elements. Throughout most of the volume of a typical star, energy is passed from volume element to volume element by radiation. The rate of flow of radiation depends on the opacity of the material—which is fixed by the temperature, density, and chemical composition. The gas pressure at each point depends on the number of particles per gram of material and on the temperature. Completely ionized hydrogen produces more particles (protons and electrons) per gram than does completely ionized oxygen. Since the pressure depends on the number of particles per cm^3, the interior of a hydrogen star would tend to be cooler than that of an oxygen star. On the other hand the radiation would escape more easily through the hydrogen star because of its greater transparency.

In this chapter we shall discuss properties of matter and radiation of especial interest for the general problems of stellar interiors. Let us first find the order of magnitude of the temperature and pressure in the interiors of a star such as the sun.

2. Mean Temperature and Pressure in Stellar Interiors

The condition that the star is in *hydrostatic equilibrium* is expressed as

$$dP = -g\rho \, dr \tag{1}$$

[cf. eqn. (155) of Ch. *7]* where the minus sign arises because the pressure P increases as the distance from the center, r, decreases. We postulate that the star does not rotate. Since the star is spherically symmetrical, the mass of an elementary shell of thickness dr at r will be

$$dM_r = 4\pi r^2 \rho \, dr \tag{2}$$

The acceleration of gravity at r depends only on the mass interior to r,

$$M_r = 4\pi \int_0^r \rho r^2 \, dr \tag{3}$$

in accordance with the law of gravitation

$$g = G \frac{M_r}{r^2} \tag{4}$$

where $G = 6.67 \times 10^{-8}$ in c.g.s. units. Hence

$$\frac{dP}{dr} = -G\rho \frac{M_r}{r^2} \tag{5}$$

---

*All references to chapters in the author's *Astrophysics—The Atmospheres of the Sun and Stars* (New York: The Ronald Press Co., 1953) will be designated in this volume by * before the chapter number.

From eqns. (2) and (5) we get

$$\frac{dP}{dM_r} = -\frac{GM_r}{4\pi r^4} \tag{6}$$

Let us define the average pressure by

$$\overline{P} = \frac{1}{M} \int_0^R P \, dM_r \tag{7}$$

If we integrate by parts we obtain

$$\overline{P} = \frac{1}{M} [P_r M_r]_0^R - \frac{1}{M} \int_0^R M_r \, dP_r \tag{8}$$

where the first term equals zero since P vanishes at the surface of the star, and $M_r = 0$ at $r = 0$ because ρ is everywhere finite. From eqns. (6) and (8)

$$\overline{P} = \frac{1}{M} \int_0^R \frac{GM_r^2}{4\pi r^4} \, dM_r \tag{9}$$

Since r is less than R in the star, we obtain a lower limit to the pressure by replacing r by R under the integral sign. Then

$$\overline{P} > \frac{1}{M} \frac{G}{4\pi R^4} \int_0^R M_r^2 \, dM_r = \frac{GM^2}{12\pi R^4} \tag{10}$$

or

$$\overline{P} > 3.00 \times 10^8 \left(\frac{M}{M_0}\right)\left(\frac{R_0}{R}\right)^4 \text{ atmospheres} \tag{11}$$

where M_0 and R_0 are the mass and radius of the sun. Thus we see that most of the material in stars similar to the sun is under considerable pressure. If we apply these results to the companion of Sirius, for which $M = 0.98$, and $R = 0.02$ in terms of the solar values, we find that the average pressure is greater than 1.8×10^{15} atmospheres.

We may obtain a lower limit to the temperature of a star that obeys the perfect gas law [eqn. (4) of Ch. ★3]. The total pressure includes both gas pressure and radiation pressure,

$$P = P_g + P_r = \frac{\rho \mathfrak{R} T}{\mu} + \frac{1}{3} aT^4 \tag{12}$$

Let us call the ratio of the gas pressure to the total pressure, β.

$$P_g = \beta P \tag{13}$$

$$P_R = (1 - \beta)P \tag{14}$$

We shall define a mean temperature $\overline{T}$ in the same way as we defined $\overline{P}$:

$$\overline{T} = \frac{1}{M} \int_0^R T \, dM_r \tag{15}$$

From eqns. (12), (13), and (15)

$$\overline{T} = \frac{1}{M} \int_0^R \frac{P\mu\beta}{\rho\Re} \, dM_r \tag{16}$$

and from eqn. (2)

$$\overline{T} = \frac{1}{M} \int_0^R \frac{P\mu\beta}{\rho\Re} 4\pi r^2 \rho \, dr \tag{17}$$

If we replace $(\mu\beta)$ by its minimum value $(\mu\beta)_{\min}$, we have

$$\overline{T} \geq \frac{1}{M} \left[\frac{(\mu\beta)_{\min}}{\Re} \frac{4\pi}{3} \right] \int_0^R P \, d(r^3) \tag{18}$$

Integrate by parts and use eqn. (6).

$$\overline{T} \geq \frac{1}{3M} \frac{G(\mu\beta)_{\min}}{\Re} \int_0^R \frac{M_r \, dM_r}{r} \tag{19}$$

We shall obtain a minimum value for the temperature if we replace r by R and integrate. Thus

$$\overline{T} > 3.84 \times 10^6 (\mu\beta)_{\min} \left(\frac{M}{M_0} \right) \left(\frac{R_0}{R} \right) \tag{20}$$

Since for a pure hydrogen star, μ would be $\frac{1}{2}$, and $\beta = 1$ for all but the most massive stars,* $\mu\beta \geq \frac{1}{2}$. Thus

$$\overline{T} > 1.9 \times 10^6 \frac{M}{M_0} \frac{R_0}{R} \tag{21}$$

Most of the stellar interior is at a temperature greater than a million degrees.

A more precise knowledge of the temperature, pressure, and density within a star will require additional physical relationships, e.g., the law of energy generation, gas laws, mode of energy transport, etc. The temperature distribution will depend critically upon how the transfer of energy takes place, whether by radiation from volume element to volume element, or by convection currents wherein large-scale motions of the material carry energy from the deep interior to the surface. If radiative transfer of energy is responsible, the absorption coefficient of the stellar material must be known. If convection currents carry the energy, we need to know the ratio of specific heats. Both modes of energy transfer may play a role in different strata of the same star.

For molecular weight values of practical interest, $(\mu < 1)$, radiation pressure can be neglected as a factor in the equation of hydrostatic equilibrium. The simplest way to justify the neglect of the P_r term is by means of Chandrasekhar's "β Theorem" (see chap. iii, Theorem 7, of his *Stellar Structure*).

3. The Radiative Transfer of Energy

For completeness, we shall derive anew the equation for the radiative flow of energy through a heated gas, and discuss it from a somewhat different point of view than we did in Chapter ★7. Consider a beam of radiation of initial intensity $I(r, \theta)$ passing through a cylinder of length ds and unit area whose axis is inclined at an angle θ with respect to the radius of the star. The amount of energy absorbed in the cylinder in solid angle $d\omega$ is

$$I(r, \theta) \kappa \rho \, ds \, d\omega \tag{22}$$

since $\rho \, ds$ is the mass of the cylinder and κ is the mass absorption coefficient of the stellar material.* The cylinder also emits energy, and the amount re-radiated in solid angle $d\omega$ in any direction will be

$$j\rho \, ds \, \frac{d\omega}{4\pi} \tag{23}$$

Summing up the gains and losses of the incident beam:

$$dI(r, \theta) \, d\omega = -\kappa\rho \, ds \, I(r, \theta) \, d\omega + j\rho \, ds \, \frac{d\omega}{4\pi} \tag{24}$$

From the geometry of the problem

$$dr = \cos \theta \, ds \tag{25}$$

If we define a function

$$u(r, \theta) = \frac{4\pi}{c} I(r, \theta) \tag{26}$$

we can obtain the radiation density, $u(r)$, by integrating eqn. (26) over all angles with r fixed,

$$u(r) = \int_\phi \int_\theta u(r, \theta) \, \frac{d\omega}{4\pi} \tag{27}$$

The transfer equation may now be put in the form

$$\cos \theta \, \frac{du(r, \theta)}{dr} = -\kappa\rho u(r, \theta) + \frac{j\rho}{c} \tag{28}$$

The quantity we shall need is the flux across a sphere of radius r. From Chapter ★5 we recall that the flux is defined by

$$\pi F = \iint I(r, \theta) \cos \theta \, d\omega = \frac{c}{4\pi} \iint u(r, \theta) \cos \theta \sin \theta \, d\phi \, d\theta \tag{29a}$$

*In Chapters 1 and 2 we use κ, rather than k to denote the absorption coefficient.

and the radiation pressure is

$$P_R = \frac{1}{c} \iint I(r, \theta) \cos^2 \theta \, d\omega = \frac{1}{4\pi} \iint u(r, \theta) \cos^2 \theta \sin \theta \, d\theta \, d\phi \quad (29b)$$

With the aid of the definitions (29) we shall now seek a soluton of eqn. (28) valid for the deep interior of the star. First multiply eqn. (28) by $d\omega/4\pi$ and integrate over all angles to obtain

$$\frac{d}{dr}\left(\frac{\pi F}{c}\right) + \kappa \rho u(r) - \frac{j(r)\rho(r)}{c} = 0 \quad (30)$$

Next multiply eqn. (28) by $\cos \theta \, d\omega/4\pi$ and again integrate over all angles. We get [cf. eqn. (23) of Ch. ★5]

$$\frac{dP_R}{dr} + \kappa \rho \frac{\pi F}{c} = 0 \quad (31)$$

since j is independent of angle. We have three unknowns of the radiation field, $u(r)$, $F(r)$, $P_R(r)$, and two differential equations. Fortunately, throughout most of the stellar interior, I is so nearly isotropic that if we expand $u(r, \theta)$ in a series in $\cos \theta$, viz.,

$$u(r, \theta) = \alpha(r) + \beta(r) \cos \theta + \cdots \quad (32)$$

we can neglect the terms depending on higher powers of $\cos \theta$; these assume importance only near the surface of the star. We identify $\alpha(r)$ with $u(r)$ by eqn. (27) while from eqns. (32) and (29b) we have

$$P_R = \frac{1}{4\pi} \iint u(r, \theta) \cos^2 \theta \, d\omega \sim \frac{u(r)}{4\pi} \int_0^\pi \int_0^{2\pi} \cos^2 \theta \sin \theta \, d\theta \, d\phi$$
$$= \tfrac{1}{3} u(r) \quad (33)$$

which is the same relation as for isotropic radiation.

The emissivity in ergs/gm/sec, j, comprises two parts: (1) Thermal emission according to Kirchhoff's law. In order for a steady state to exist, the energy absorbed per gram must equal the energy emitted as thermal radiation. Hence

$$j_1 = \kappa c u(r) = \kappa c a T^4 \quad (34)$$

(2) Energy generation by nuclear processes which depend on the density and temperature, viz., $\epsilon(\rho, T)$ ergs/gram/sec. The total emission is

$$j = j_1 + j_2 = \kappa c a T^4 + \epsilon(\rho, T) \quad (35)$$

From eqns. (30) and (35) we now obtain

$$\pi \frac{dF}{dr} = \rho \epsilon(\rho, T) \quad (36)$$

Now eqn. (31) employed in conjunction with eqn. (33) and eqn. (12) of Chapter ⋆5, $u(T) = aT^4$, gives

$$\pi F = -\frac{4acT^3}{3\kappa\rho}\frac{dT}{dr} \tag{37}$$

as the rate of outward flow of energy.

Let L_r denote the net radiation flow across a sphere of radius r and mass M_r concentric with the star. In a steady state, L_r must equal the total amount of energy generated per second within the sphere:

$$L_r = 4\pi \int_0^r r'^2 \rho(r')\epsilon(r', \rho)\,dr' \tag{38}$$

and the net flux in ergs/cm^2/sec across a sphere of radius r is

$$\pi F = \frac{L_r}{4\pi r^2} = -\frac{ac}{3\kappa\rho}\frac{d(T^4)}{dr} \tag{39}$$

provided radiation, not convection currents, carry the energy.

4. The Stellar Absorption Coefficient

Before much progress can be made in the construction of models in which the energy transport is by radiation, we must have some knowledge of the stellar absorption coefficient. The atomic processes important for opacity of the stellar material are:

(1) Photoelectric absorption (bound-free transitions). Atoms or ions in discrete energy levels absorb sufficient energy to eject an electron and become further ionized. Since any energy greater than the minimum necessary to detach an electron from the atom may be absorbed, a continuous absorption is produced.

(2) Free-free transitions. A free electron moving in an hyperbolic orbit in the neighborhood of an ion may absorb a quantum of energy and move away with a higher speed.

(3) Radiation may be simply scattered by free electrons (Thomson scattering). Electron scattering becomes important at higher temperatures where the material is so highly ionized that photoelectric absorptions can make only a small contribution to the opacity.

(4) Finally, discrete X-ray line absorption may be important at certain temperatures and densities.

The high densities prevailing in stellar interiors have a marked effect upon the absorption coefficient. The energy levels of an isolated atom may be depicted as shown on the left of Fig. 1, where the smooth curve represents the potential curve of the electron in the field of the ion. The high discrete levels gradually coalesce into the continuum as the quantum number increases. In a gas of finite density, high levels which correspond to atomic radii greater than the mean distance between atoms, become smeared out into free states. Physically, what occurs is that the higher the density, the greater the electrostatic shielding produced by the free electrons in the neighborhood until the

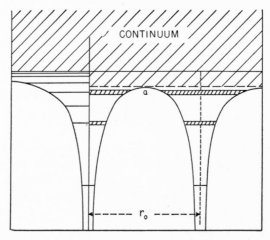

FIG. 1.—ENERGY LEVELS OF A PERTURBED ATOM

In the left third of the figure are depicted the energy levels and potential curve $V = Z\epsilon/r$ of the undisturbed atom.

The right part of the figure illustrates the broadening of the levels when the atoms are separated by a mean distance r_0 of the order of 10^{-7} to 10^{-8} cm. Notice the depression of the lower limit of the continuum as high levels are washed out by the effects of pressure ionization.

nucleus no longer has any effect at distances equal to the radii of the allowed orbits of the bound electrons, and discrete levels cease to exist. For any given density there is a limiting energy above which the originally bound levels are essentially free. As the density increases, the depression of the continuum becomes more and more pronounced and additional states become absorbed into the continuum. This is the phenomenon of *density ionization*. Meanwhile, the initially sharp levels below the depressed continuum become widened out into energy bands, not entirely dissimilar to the energy bands of free electrons in a solid. The dotted line in Fig. 1 shows the point above which all electrons are essentially free.

For a given temperature, pressure, and chemical composition one must compute κ_ν taking into account the negative absorption as a function of frequency and then compute the Rosseland mean coefficient of absorption—which essentially amounts to calculating an average transparency. In eqn. (153) of Chapter *7, K_ν is successively replaced by $\frac{1}{3}J_\nu$, and this in turn by $\frac{1}{3}B_\nu$. This step is justified for stellar interiors where J_ν differs from B_ν by a very small amount. Then

$$\frac{1}{\bar{\kappa}} = \frac{\int_0^\infty \frac{1}{\kappa_\nu} \frac{dB_\nu}{dT}\, d\nu}{\int_0^\infty \frac{dB_\nu}{dT}\, d\nu} \tag{40}$$

The mean absorption coefficient per gram of elements heavier than hydrogen and helium is usually expressed by Kramers' formula

$$\bar{\kappa} = \text{const}\, \frac{\bar{g}}{t}\, \frac{\rho}{T^{7/2}} \tag{41}$$

which gives the dependence on density and temperature. Here $\bar{g}$ is the properly averaged value of the Gaunt correction factor to the law derived by Kramers for X-ray absorption. Eddington humorously called an additional correction for the failure of the Kramers' law, the *"guillotine" factor, t*. The modern procedure is to compute $\bar{\kappa}$ as a function of density and temperature and then choose g/t so that the results can be represented by eqn. (41). If we use the electron density N_ϵ in place of the density ρ, and drop the bar from $\bar{g}$, we get

$$\kappa = \frac{130 N_\epsilon}{t} \cdot \frac{g}{T^{7/2}} \tag{42}$$

per gram of the "heavy" elements. Per gram of the stellar material we have for the "heavy element" contribution

$$\kappa = \frac{130 N_\epsilon}{T^{7/2}} \frac{g}{t} (1 - X - Y) \tag{43}$$

The electron density is given by eqn. (9) of Chapter *3. Therefore

$$\kappa = 3.9 \times 10^{25} \frac{g}{t} \frac{\rho}{T^{7/2}} (1 + X)(1 - X - Y) \tag{44}$$

is the absorption coefficient per gram for the heavy component of the stellar material which includes fractions X and Y of hydrogen and helium respectively.

Per gram, the absorption coefficient of the heavy elements is so much greater than that of hydrogen and helium that most workers have ignored the contributions of the latter. The bound-free absorptions are, of course, negligible because hydrogen and helium are completely ionized throughout the stellar interior, but the free-free absorptions [in spite of the Z^2 factor of eqn. (14) of Chapter *7] cannot be ignored in stars that are composed primarily of hydrogen and helium.*

The contribution of electron scattering to the opacity,

$$\kappa_e = 0.20\rho(1 + X) \qquad (45)$$

is important at high temperatures and low densities. When two or more agencies contribute to the opacity the absorption coefficients cannot simply be added. One may employ, however, a simple empirical rule due to Strömgren. If κ_o and κ_e are the two opacities, κ_{o+e} equals the larger of the pair plus 1.5 times the smaller of the pair. Strömgren calculated the absorption coefficient, assuming hydrogenic levels and taking no account of the effects of electron shielding and pressure ionization. Morse used hydrogenic formulae [see, e.g., eqn. (14) of Ch. *7 and eqn. (98) of Ch. *5] for the free-free and bound-free absorptions with an effective charge Z_{eff} and with the depression of the continuum taken into account. In Fig. 1 we notice that the potential curve has a maximum at some point a which depends on the density. With a given, the amount by which the level of the continuum is lowered may be calculated. He estimated the shielding and Z_{eff} with the aid of the Fermi-Thomas model which assumes that the atomic electrons form a degenerate gas around the nucleus. The absorption contributions of each element are then added and the Rosseland mean computed.

Morse carried out calculations for different assumptions about the proportions of the heavy constituents. The most frequently used blend, called the "Russell Mixture" consists of the following proportions by weight: Fe = 0.125, K + Ca = 0.0625, Na + Mg = 0.25, O = 0.50. At high densities κ varies as T^{-2} and is nearly independent of ρ, while at low densities κ varies as $T^{-7/2}$ to $T^{-9/2}$.

The bound-free absorptions primarily responsible for the opacity in stars like the sun mostly occur from levels associated with X-rays, i.e., they correspond to ionization from the K, L, and M shells. At a given temperature, the K and L shells of different elements are being ionized so that κ varies in an irregular way with the temperature. The roles of the different processes responsible for stellar opacity are best illustrated in the log $\rho(1 + X)$–log T diagram due to Morse. See Fig. 2. If the density is steadily increased, one shell of electrons after another becomes merged into the continuum of free states. Thus, with increasing density, oxygen becomes stripped before iron loses all its electrons.

---

*Within the framework of approximations of the Strömgren theory

$$\kappa(H + He) = 3.31 \times 10^{22}\bar{g}\rho T^{-7/2}(1 + X)(X + 4Y) \qquad (44a)$$

is the expression for the opacity of a mixture of H and He acting alone. In spite of the smaller numerical coefficient, the free-free absorptions would have to be taken into account in a star that was composed of 98 or 99 per cent hydrogen and helium.

Finally, the free electrons become degenerate and the opacity begins to fall off. On the other hand, toward higher temperatures, oxygen becomes completely stripped long before iron atoms are ionized to the core. At high temperatures, all atoms are completely stripped and electron scattering alone determines the opacity. This situation may obtain in some of the hotter stars of the main sequence.

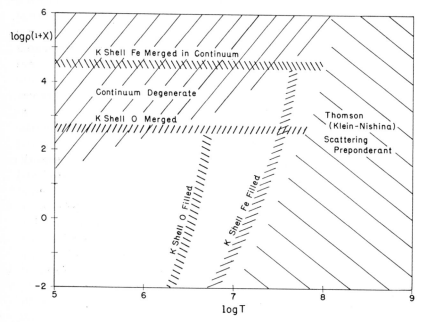

FIG. 2.—EFFECTS IMPORTANT IN THE OPACITY AS A FUNCTION OF ρ $(1 + X)$ AND THE TEMPERATURE

(Courtesy, P. M. Morse, *Astrophysical Journal*, University of Chicago Press, **92**, 36, 1940.)

Although Morse's work represents a distinct advance in the calculation of opacities, there are a number of improvements that need to be made. First, Z_{eff} is different in the initial and final energy levels. The bound electron is held tightly to the nucleus and Z_{eff} approaches Z. The free electron is shielded by the charge cloud around the nucleus and Z_{eff} may be much smaller than Z. The neglect of this change in Z_{eff} makes Morse's opacities too large. Also the Fermi-Thomas charge distribution has to be modified for the fact that the temperature of the gas is not zero; hence the relation between a and ρ is changed. The distortions of the potential are particularly large for hydrogen and helium in the stellar interiors.

Also, the influence of line absorption between greatly broadened energy levels upon the opacity should be taken into account. Calculations show that as the temperature varies from 6 to 15 million degrees and the density from 4 to 70 gm/cm^3, the line absorption increases the opacity of something like the Russell mixture by from 40 per cent to 10 per cent. At lower temperatures, increases in the opacity by a factor of 2 or more might be expected. Iron produces most of the effect.

The opacity depends markedly on the assumed composition of the mixture—pure oxygen will be much more transparent than the Russell mixture. Recent work indicates that elements of the oxygen group are far more prevalent (by weight) than those of the iron group; hence the opacity from this cause alone will be much smaller than Morse's tables would indicate.

Some of the difficulties in Morse's treatment have been eliminated in a recent treatment of the problem by Zirin who allows for the effects of the shielding in calculating the bound-free transitions. He considers a mixture of gases and, although he emphasizes the lighter elements, the heavier ones can be taken into account in an approximate fashion.

The most satisfactory treatment, however, appears to be that by G. Keller and R. E. Meyerott.* Their treatment takes into account the contributions of the bound-free transitions including hydrogen and helium as well. They do not include the bound-bound transitions which may be important under certain conditions—as noted above.

In the degenerate gases of dense stars electronic conduction is more important than radiative processes. Chandrasekhar, Swirles, and Majumdar independently derived expressions for completely degenerate gases while Marshak has treated the intermediate stage.

5. The Convective Transport of Energy

Energy may be transported in stellar interiors not only by radiative processes but also by large-scale motions of the heated gases, i.e., convection currents. Which mode will prevail will depend on the temperature gradient in the region considered. If the temperature gradient required for radiative transport of energy is too high, the layers will be unstable and the slightest disturbance will cause large-scale convection currents to be established.

To ascertain whether a certain zone in a star will be in radiative equilibrium or convective equilibrium, we can proceed thus: Consider a small volume element dV, at a distance r from the center of the star, characterized by a pressure P_1, density ρ_1, and temperature T_1. Imagine that this element is displaced upward a distance dr. Will the forces acting upon it be such as to restore it to its original position? At

---

*See *Argonne National Laboratory Reports*, Nos. 4743, 4771, 4856, and 5008. Detailed tables of opacities are not yet available.

$r + dr$ the surrounding medium is characterized by a pressure P_2, density ρ_2, and temperature T_2, and we want to know the pressure, density, and temperature of the displaced element dV, which we denote by the primed quantities P', ρ', T'. The element dV will expand so that its pressure is equal to the external pressure at $r + dr$, namely P_2. The internal temperature, T'_2, and density ρ'_2 will not necessarily equal T_2 and ρ_2, however. We choose our volume element of such size that it would require minutes or even hours for the energy to escape by radiation or conduction. Now $P_1 = P'_1$, $\rho_1 = \rho'_1$, $T_1 = T'_1$, and $P'_2 = P_2$. Since the change is adiabatic ρ'_2 and T'_2 will be given by:

$$\frac{\rho'_2}{\rho'_1} = \left(\frac{P'_2}{P'_1}\right)^{1/\gamma} \tag{46}$$

$$\frac{T'_2}{T'_1} = \left(\frac{P'_2}{P'_1}\right)^{\frac{\gamma-1}{\gamma}} \tag{47}$$

Here γ is the ratio of the specific heat at constant pressure, c_p, to the specific heat at constant volume, c_v, i.e., $\gamma = c_p/c_v$. The hydrostatic force on any volume element will depend on the difference of density between it and the surrounding fluid. If $\rho'_2 < \rho_2$, the net hydrostatic force is upward and the element is pushed to higher layers. If $\rho'_2 > \rho_2$, the displaced element will sink downward. Thus stability obtains if

$$\rho_1\left(\frac{P_2}{P_1}\right)^{1/\gamma} > \rho_2 \quad \text{or} \quad \left(\frac{P_2}{P_1}\right)^{1/\gamma} > \frac{\rho_2}{\rho_1} \tag{48}$$

For small dr we may expand by Taylor's theorem, viz.,

$$P_2/P_1 = 1 + (dP/dr)\, dr/P_1$$

and

$$\frac{\rho_2}{\rho_1} = 1 + \left(\frac{d\rho}{dr}\right)\frac{dr}{\rho_1} \tag{49}$$

Substitute in eqn. (48) and expand by the binomial theorem

$$\frac{1}{P}\frac{dP}{dr}\frac{1}{\gamma} > \frac{d\rho}{dr}\frac{1}{\rho} \tag{50}$$

Since P and ρ decrease as r increases, we shall write

$$\frac{1}{\gamma}\left(-\frac{1}{P}\frac{dP}{dr}\right) < \left(-\frac{1}{\rho}\frac{d\rho}{dr}\right) \tag{51}$$

Thus the condition for stability is that the actual pressure gradient must be less than the pressure gradient corresponding to the density gradient in adiabatic equilibrium. If γ is small, the left-hand side may become large and the layer will become unstable. Taking the logarithmic derivative of the perfect gas law, we have

$$-\frac{1}{\rho}\frac{d\rho}{dr} + \frac{1}{P}\frac{dP}{dr} = \frac{1}{T}\frac{dT}{dr} \tag{52}$$

and

$$\frac{1}{\gamma}\left(-\frac{1}{P}\frac{dP}{dr}\right) + \frac{1}{P}\frac{dP}{dr} < \frac{1}{T}\frac{dT}{dr} \tag{53}$$

Hence

$$\frac{\gamma - 1}{\gamma}\left(-\frac{1}{P}\frac{dP}{dr}\right) > -\frac{1}{T}\frac{dT}{dr}$$

or

$$(\gamma - 1)\left(-\frac{1}{\rho}\frac{d\rho}{dr}\right) > -\frac{1}{T}\frac{dT}{dr} \tag{54}$$

is the condition for stability. Note that the smaller the temperature gradient, the more stable the layer.

In a medium initially in unstable equilibrium, if a volume element starts to sink it will continue to do so. Likewise a volume element that begins to rise will keep on rising. A rising element has too low a density and hence too high a temperature. In the higher layers it may lose its excess heat. Similarly, the descending element will be warmed up as it sinks. This process tends to cool the inner layers and warm the outer ones. Thus the original temperature gradient which was too steep becomes lowered, and approaches the adiabatic gradient as its limiting value. Notice that the energy is transported by the actual motion of the material itself. The condition

$$(\gamma - 1)\frac{d\rho}{\rho} = \frac{dT}{T} \quad \text{or} \quad \frac{\gamma - 1}{\gamma}\frac{dP}{P} = \frac{dT}{T} \tag{55}$$

represents the limit, on the one side of which the energy transfer is by convection and the other by radiation. That is, if

$$\left[\frac{dT/T}{dP/P}\right]_{\text{ad}} < \left[\frac{dT/T}{dP/P}\right]_{\text{rad}} \tag{56}$$

convection currents will carry the energy. By eqn. (55)

$$\frac{\gamma - 1}{\gamma} = \left[\frac{d \ln T}{d \ln P}\right]_{\text{ad}} \tag{57}$$

For a monatomic gas, $\gamma = \frac{5}{3}$: for a gas with m degrees of freedom, $\gamma = 1 + 2/m$. The smaller the value of γ, the less steep the critical temperature gradient. Now

$$c_p \, \delta T = \delta U + P \, dV \qquad (58)$$

$$c_v \, \delta T = \delta U \qquad (59)$$

where δU represents the gain of internal energy, which can be energy of ionization as well as kinetic energy. If the contribution to δU from ionization becomes sufficiently important, γ can become depressed to the point where the inequality eqn. (55) will hold. For example, when hydrogen is all neutral, $X = 0, \gamma = \frac{5}{3}$, and when $X = 1, \gamma$ will again be $\frac{5}{3}$, but when $0 < X < 1, \gamma$ is less than $\frac{5}{3}$. The addition of small quantities of another element will also depress the value of γ.

Hydrogen, which is the most abundant element, becomes ionized below the level of the photosphere. The γ of the gas becomes depressed to the point where large-scale convection currents may be set up, and mass motion of the gas itself transports the energy. A mass of ionized gas ascending toward the surface recombines. As the ionization energy is liberated, the mass will be heated and will continue to rise until the gas is once more neutral.

The flow of energy in this hydrogen ionization zone must be turbulent, presumably characterized by whirlpools and vortices. New convection units or turbulence cells are set up as the old ones disappear. The actual dimensions of the hydrogen convection zone will depend on the hydrogen content, and it amounts to more than 2000 km for a pure hydrogen atmosphere. Rudkjøbing carried out calculations for the sun, a yellow giant, and an A star. In the former two stars, the convective zone begins at optical depths of 1.1 and 0.8, respectively, but in the A star, the convection zone falls in the atmosphere itself. Eddington argued that the convection zone extended much deeper into the star than the equilibrium theory would predict. This appears to be true for red dwarf stars where Osterbrock's calculations show that the convection zone extends to a large fraction of the stellar radius.

That the influence of the turbulence in the hydrogen convection zone upon the overlying layers could provide a clue to the nature of the granules was suggested by Siedentopf. Half a century ago Benard showed that if a thin layer of liquid is heated uniformly at its lower surface, a steady state of fluid flow in hexagonal cells will occur. The warmer material rises in the center, cools, and descends near the periphery. The same phenomenon was observed by A. Graham and K. Chandra when the experiment was repeated in air. It is tempting to identify each granule with a single convection cell, but such a picture is somewhat of an oversimplification. When a temperature gradient is steep, instability may set in not only through a stationary pattern of motions (i.e., convection) but also in the form of random oscillations of increasing amplitude, a phenomenon sometimes referred to as *over-*

stability (Eddington). Under astrophysical conditions, thermal instability does not lead to convection in the usual sense but to large-scale motions of the type associated with the concept of overstability.

In the structure of model atmospheres, as well as in stellar interiors, convective equilibrium may become important. When convection currents can be maintained, they are much more efficient at the transport of energy than is radiative transfer. The differences between the two mechanisms recalls those between molecular conduction on the one hand, and large-scale currents (hydrodynamical streaming) on the other. Therefore, the temperature gradient required to maintain convection currents is only slightly in excess of the adiabatic gradient. If it dropped strictly to the adiabatic gradient, a mass element would then always be in harmony with its surroundings. Convection currents would stop completely and the energy would have to be transported entirely by radiation. The energy then would not be carried away rapidly enough, the temperature gradient would build up until the adiabatic gradient was exceeded, and convection currents would be re-established. In reality, the convection currents keep going at a steady pace, and the actual gradient exceeds the adiabatic gradient by such a small amount that the relation between density and pressure is sufficiently well given by the adiabatic gas law, $P = K\rho^{\gamma}$.

In the treatment of convection zones in model atmospheres, the direct calculation of the adiabatic temperature gradient becomes complicated because of the variation of γ. If there are two or more abundant ions undergoing ionization simultaneously, e.g., He I and He II, Unsöld proposed that one calculate the entropy S as a function of the state of ionization, P_g, and T for the stellar material by adding the entropies for the separate components. The structure of the convective zone is given without particular numerical integration by the curve $S = $ constant. The temperature gradient is found by numerical differentiation along the $S = $ constant curves. Miss Underhill has pointed out that one must also take into account the entropy of the radiation.

Our main interest, however, is in the deep interiors of the stars. Ionization there is so complete that γ is close to $\frac{5}{3}$. In the practical calculation of any stellar model, at each point it is necessary to compare the temperature gradient with the adiabatic gradient to ascertain whether radiative or convective equilibrium prevails at the point under consideration.

In models where the energy generation depends on a high power of the temperature, say T^{20} (carbon cycle), convection occurs in the core of the star. If the proton-proton reaction rather than the carbon cycle supplies the energy, the convective core may be very small or nonexistent.

In a domain where all energy is transported by convection currents, and radiation pressure can be neglected, the fundamental equations from which the pressure, density, and temperature may be derived as a function of r, would be eqns. (2) and (5) together with eqns. (4) and (10) of Chapter *3. Once a solution of these equations has been obtained, we may improve the solution by computing radiative and convective contributions to the total flux,

$$\mathfrak{F} = \mathfrak{F}_r + \mathfrak{F}_c = \frac{L_r}{4\pi r^2} \tag{60}$$

where L is given by eqn. (38). Here $\mathfrak{F}_r = \pi F$ depends on the temperature gradient according to eqn. (37), whereas $\mathfrak{F}_c$ is the flux carried by the convection currents.

In a large part of the convective core the actual (near adiabatic) temperature gradient is of the same order (although smaller) than the radiative gradient would be. Hence the radiation flux is an appreciable fraction of the total flux. The turbulence adjusts itself automatically so that the resulting temperature gradient gives a convective flux and a radiative flux, which together give the correct total flux.

Chandrasekhar* has discussed the influence of magnetic fields and rotation upon the stability of gaseous layers subject to a temperature gradient. He has derived criteria for the conditions under which instability will set in. Magnetic fields and Coriolis forces can inhibit convection currents. Indeed, the extent of the hydrogen convection zone in the sun appears to be controlled by the solar rotation which is much more important than magnetic fields except in the immediate neighborhood of spots! Future studies of stellar structure will require that the influence of rotation upon the convection zones be taken into account.

6. The Structure of the Atomic Nucleus

The only processes whereby the sun and similar stars may be kept shining are those involving changes in the nuclei of light atoms with the resultant release of energy according to the Einstein relation

$$E = \Delta m \, c^2 \tag{61}$$

where Δm is the loss of mass in grams in the course of the nuclear transformation, c is the velocity of light in cm/sec, and E is the energy in ergs.

In Chapter *2 we mentioned that the tiny "hard" core of the atom,

*See, e.g., *Phil. Mag.*, Series 7, **43**, 1317, 1952; **44**, 233, 1953; *Proc. Roy. Soc.* **A, 210**, 26, 1951; **A, 216**, 293, 1953, for a discussion of some of these and other related topics.

the *nucleus*, contained two kinds of constituent particles, *protons* of mass 1.00759 atomic mass units which carry a positive charge of 4.80×10^{-10} e.s.u. and *neutrons* with a mass of 1.00898 atomic mass units and no charge at all. The total number of protons, Z, in the nucleus determines the chemical element, and the total number of protons plus neutrons fixes the *atomic weight* A. The actual value of A will depend also upon the binding energy which holds the nucleus together. With the mass spectrograph it is possible to find the value of A to one part in a hundred thousand. We include the masses of the electrons in the mass of the atom, A. Consider ordinary carbon ${}_6C^{12}$ of atomic weight 12 and atomic number 6. The binding energy will be

$$6m({}_1H^1) + 6m({}_0n^1) - m({}_6C^{12}) = 6.04884 + 6.05388 - 12.00380$$

$$= 0.09892 \text{ atomic mass units}$$

In this equation, we use the masses of neutral hydrogen (1.00814) and that of neutral carbon (12.00380). Note that the mass of six electrons of the carbon atom is compensated by the mass of the six electrons supplied by the six hydrogen atoms. In order for any isotope to be stable, its mass must be less than the sums of the masses of the constituent particles. This is a necessary but not a sufficient condition for stability.

Nuclear dimensions have been estimated in various ways; from the energies versus decay times of α-particles (helium nuclei) emitted by natural radioactive substances, from the cross-section for elastic scattering of fast neutrons and from a comparison of the binding energies of nuclei of the same mass, one of which contains $(Z + 1)$ neutrons and Z protons and the other of which contains Z neutrons and $(Z + 1)$ protons. For example, ${}_7N^{15}$ with 8 neutrons and 7 protons may be compared with ${}_8O^{15}$ which has 7 neutrons and 8 protons. The nuclei of radioactive atoms tend to have radii, R, in the range of 7–9 $\times$ 10^{-13} cm, while they, and the lighter elements as well, appear to follow the empirical rule

$$R = R_0 \sqrt[3]{A} \text{ cm} \tag{62}$$

where $R_0 = (0.12 \pm 0.02) \times 10^{-12}$ is often identified as the range of nuclear forces, but this is only an approximation.* Eqn. 62 suggests that each nuclear particle occupies roughly the same volume in a large nucleus as in a small one.

The outstanding problem of nuclear physics is the nature of the

---

*That is, $R_0 \sim a = \dfrac{\hbar}{\mu c} = 1.4 \times 10^{-13}$ cm where μ is the mass of the π *meson*. See L. N. Cooper and E. M. Henley, *Phys. Rev.* **92**, 801, 1953.

force or forces that hold together the nuclear particles, or *nucleons* as they are sometimes called.   In view of Coulomb's law of electrostatic repulsion which holds for very small distances, of the order of 10^{-9} cm, as well as for macroscopic dimensions, it might be difficult to see why a nucleus containing two or more protons simply does not blow apart, leaving a monotonous universe of pure hydrogen.   The answer is that the particles within a nucleus are subject to powerful short-range attractive forces that are effective at distances of the order of 10^{-13} cm and weaken rapidly as the distance between the particles increases. The forces between the nucleons are all of the same order of magnitude, whether they are neutron-neutron, neutron-proton, or proton-proton forces.   One nucleon can attract only a limited number of its companions. Such a condition obtains in an ordinary liquid where each molecule attracts only near neighbors.   These considerations lie at the basis of the "liquid drop" model of the nucleus, a crude but useful device for depicting certain nuclear properties.*

An alternative model of the nucleus which is particularly valuable for light atoms is the shell model, in which the nucleons are arranged in shells somewhat analogous to the fashion in which the electrons are arranged in 1s, 2s, 2p, etc., shells in an atom except that the order is 1s, 2p, 3d, 2s, etc.   The central force field is not coulombic but approximates the average of the contributions of the nucleons to the field by a square well or oscillator potential with the range of the order of nuclear radii.

7. Nuclear Transformations

Whatever bonds the constituent particles of a nucleus share among themselves, the nucleus presents a united front to all external, positively charged intruders.   The potential diagram of a typical nucleus is shown in Fig. 3.   For distances, $r < R$, the nuclear particles are tightly bound and an incoming particle will feel the nuclear forces.   For $r > R$, the potential follows the law

$$V = \frac{Z_1 Z_2 \epsilon^2}{r}$$

where Z_1 and Z_2 are the charges on the nucleus and the colliding particle respectively.   If we fire a proton or an α-particle at the nucleus, we might expect the intruder to be simply pushed away unless it had energy sufficient to surmount the barrier and come under the influence of the short-range nuclear forces important for $r < R$.   Penetration can occur, however, even if the impinging particle does not have energy

*The liquid drop model gives only a rough qualitative picture, more satisfactory for heavy nuclei than for the light ones of chief astrophysical interest.

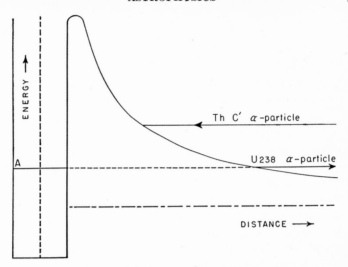

FIG. 3.—PENETRATION OF THE POTENTIAL BARRIER OF A U238 NUCLEUS

The potential curve of this nucleus has a well with a width of about 2×10^{-12} cm. The Th C' α-particle approaches to within 3×10^{-12} cm without showing any influence of a deviation from coulombic scattering. The escaping U238 α-particle must penetrate 6×10^{-12} cm of the barrier (indicated by the dotted line) before it can escape. Zero energy is indicated by the dot-dashed line.

greater than V_0. This penetration of barriers in nuclear physics is probably best illustrated by the phenomenon of radioactive decay. Rutherford bombarded uranium nuclei with α-particles of energy $E = 14 \times 10^{-6}$ ergs from decaying thorium C' and found no departures from coulomb scattering. Yet U^{238} emits α-particles of energy 6.6×10^{-6} ergs corresponding to a distance of closest approach $r = 6 \times 10^{-12}$ cm from the center of the nucleus. Gamow, Condon, and Gurney independently suggested that in accordance with the principles of wave mechanics, there was a finite probability that a particle could "leak through" a potential barrier. Thus the α-particle may be thought of as residing at the level A in the U^{238} nucleus and leaking through the barrier as α-particle of energy 6.6×10^{-6} erg. By a similar token, if we bombard a nucleus with a particle of high enough energy, there is a finite probability that the particle will penetrate the barrier and enter the nucleus. The effective penetration cross-section for a "head-on" collision* turns out to be

$$\sigma = \frac{\pi \hbar^2}{M^2 v^2} \exp\left[-\frac{2\pi \epsilon^2 Z_1 Z_2}{hv} + \frac{4\epsilon(2MZ_1Z_2R)^{1/2}}{\hbar} \right] = \frac{\pi \hbar^2}{M^2 v^2} G \qquad (63)$$

*We mean a collision in which the orbital angular momentum of the incoming particle is zero.

Here,

$$M = \frac{A_1 A_2}{A_1 + A_2} M_0 \tag{64}$$

where A_1 and A_2 are atomic weights (pure numbers) and M_0 is the atomic mass unit, and v is the relative velocity,

$$\hbar = h/2\pi \tag{65}$$

For collisions that are not quite head on, i.e., for which the orbital momentum is not zero, there is still a chance of penetration but the probability falls off very rapidly with increasing angular momentum. The fall-off is less rapid the higher the energy of the incoming particle. Note the rapid decrease of σ with increasing Z_2, and the rise with increasing energy of the bombarding particle. For example, consider protons and α-particles of the same energy. The proton can penetrate a nucleus of approximately four times greater atomic number than can the α-particle. For a given nucleus, the α-particle must have 16 times as much energy.

When the impinging particle succeeds in penetrating the nucleus with moderate energies, it does not excite a particular nucleon, but shares its energy among them all. Following Bohr's liquid drop analogy, we may define a "temperature" of the nucleus in accordance with the relation $E = \frac{3}{2}NkT$, where N is the number of particles. Thus when a new particle enters the nucleus its binding and kinetic energy is shared with the other nucleons and the "temperature" of the assemblage is raised. A neutron which strikes and becomes tightly bound to a lead nucleus adds 6 Mev of binding plus kinetic energy and raises the "temperature" of the latter to 3×10^8 °K! High energy nuclear phenomena, however, are explained by interactions with single particles.

Following Bohr, we think of the nucleus as possessing a great number of energy levels corresponding to possible modes of oscillation. Unlike the atomic problem, wherein the electrons could be excited separately, we regard each excited level of the nucleus as analagous to the superposition of overtones of the fundamental frequencies. In the first approximation, the total energy is the sum of the energies of overtones of all the fundamental frequencies. The net result of these considerations is that a heavy atom will have a great number of possible energy levels close together; in fact the level distribution is almost continuous, because the level breadths are comparable to their separations.

Alternately, using the newer shell model we may think of individual nucleons being excited simultaneously to various energy states. In this picture also, the density of the energy levels of the nucleus as a whole increases strongly with excitation energy and the total number of particles in the nucleus. Only at high excitations will the energy level distribution become nearly continuous. To reach such a level, the nucleus must capture an incoming particle with an energy of the order of 10^7 to 10^8 ev.

In Bohr's picture of a nuclear reaction, the incident particle is first captured, forming a compound nucleus. Only subsequently does the compound nucleus decay into its final state. It should be remembered that even a low-energy incident particle when captured results in a few Mev excitation of the compound nucleus. The compound nucleus is in an energy domain where the density of energy levels is much greater than near its lowest stable state. If an incoming particle has an energy equal to one of the nuclear energy levels, the chance of capture is greatly increased; we refer to such captures as resonance captures. On this picture we can easily understand why slow neutrons often show resonance phenomena in collisions with heavy atoms, such as cadmium, while for light atoms the chance of getting a "resonance capture" is smaller, because the level distribution in the same energy region has a low density.

Nevertheless, even in light atoms resonance effects can occur at relatively low energies of the incident particles. For example, C^{12} has a resonance at 456 kev for proton captures. In the neighborhood of that energy the cross section for proton capture is enormously enhanced over the value one would predict from eqn. (63). The exponential penetration term appears only in the width of the resonance.

Thus, once a particle has been captured by a nucleus, the latter becomes excited to higher energy level. The nucleus may dispose of this energy in a number of ways: (1) A fluctuation may occur in which the energy is given back to the incoming particle which is ejected from the nucleus. This process is indistinguishable from ordinary scattering unless there is loss of kinetic energy. (2) The energy which has been shared among the other nucleons may become collected in one of them and result in the ejection of this particle. On the Bohr picture, the particle emission is analogous to the ordinary evaporation process; enough energy must accumulate in one particle to enable it to escape from the attraction of its fellows. (3) A γ-ray may be emitted. (4) A β-ray may be emitted although this process usually does not happen unless a γ-ray is emitted or another particle is ejected first.

Often, the energy release requires more than one step; e.g., we may have (2) + (3), (1) + (3), or (4) + (3), or (3) may take several steps or cascades. Numerous experiments illustrate each and all of these processes. Inelastic-neutron-scattering experiments wherein the neutrons lose energy rapidly and γ-rays are emitted illustrate (1) + (3).

We define an exoergic process as one in which energy is liberated, whereas an endoergic process is one wherein energy is taken from the incoming particle and stored in the resultant nucleus. The former are of greatest interest in stellar energy-production processes.

With an incident proton, if the emission of an α-particle is sufficiently exoergic it is much more likely to occur than γ-ray emission. For a proton captured by a nucleus of atomic weight $4n - 1$, an α-particle emission is usually quite exoergic. For example,

$$_7N^{15} + {}_1H^1 \rightarrow {}_6C^{12} + {}_2He^4 \tag{66}$$

abbreviated as N^{15} $(p\alpha)C^{12}$, is the last step of the carbon cycle. An additional example is the transmutation of lithium into two α-particles upon the capture of a proton,

$$_3Li^7 + {}_1H^1 \rightarrow 2{}_2He^4 \tag{67}$$

Other examples are:

$$_7F^{19} + {}_1H^1 \rightarrow {}_8O^{16} + {}_2He^4 \tag{68}$$

$$_5B^{11} + {}_1H^1 \rightarrow 3{}_2He^4 \tag{69}$$

The ejection of particles requires not only that the requisite energy conditions be fulfilled but also that certain selection rules be obeyed. When decay by particle emission is not possible, or when the nucleus is left in an excited level after particle emission, γ-radiation may occur. For example, N^{15} captures a proton and ejects an α-particle to decay to an excited level of C^{12}; whereafter it cascades to a lower energy state with the emission of a γ-ray of about 4.4 Mev. The energy of this γ-ray is independent of the proton energy. Hence the γ-emission occurs in the C^{12} atom after the α-particle has been emitted. If, as in proton capture by N^{14}, γ-ray emission alone occurs, the energy of the emitted quantum does depend on the energy of the incoming particle as well as on the mass difference of the nuclei involved.

Consider a nucleus which has captured a proton, but not yet emitted another particle or γ-ray. We call such a nucleus a *compound nucleus*. Eventually it will decay to a lower energy level with the emission of a γ-ray, or possibly it will emit a particle to become another nucleus. We often express the total decay probability in terms of a *disintegration constant*

$$\Gamma = \frac{\hbar}{T} \tag{70}$$

T is the mean lifetime of the compound nucleus. If several alternate modes of decay are available,

$$\Gamma = \sum \Gamma_i \tag{71}$$

where Γ_i represents the disintegration constant for each process. Γ as here defined has the dimensions of energy.

The cross-section for a process wherein a proton is captured and a γ-ray or particle is emitted, is written by Bethe in the form*

$$\sigma = \frac{\pi}{2} \frac{R^2}{E} \frac{A_1 + A_2}{A_2} \Gamma \exp \left[\left(\frac{32R}{a} \right)^{1/2} - \frac{2\pi\epsilon^2 Z_1 Z_2}{\hbar v} \right] \qquad (72)$$

if E is not near a nuclear resonance. Then $A_1 M_0$ and $A_2 M_0$ represent the masses of the interacting particles, R is the nuclear radius, and a is defined by eqn. (87).

In many reactions of astrophysical interest, we can expect eqn. (72) to hold only approximately even when E is not near a nuclear resonance and thus an empirical adjustment of the parameters in this equation is necessary. If E_M is the energy (measured in center of mass coordinates) at which the cross-section σ_M is measured, then (in center of mass coordinates)

$$\sigma_M = \frac{S_M}{E_M} \exp \left(b E_M^{-1/2} \right) \qquad (73)$$

$$b = -31.281 Z_1 Z_2 A^{1/2} \qquad (74)$$

where $A = A_1 A_2 / (A_1 + A_2)$ is the reduced mass in atomic mass units [see eqn. (64)] and E is measured in kev. The cross-section parameter S varies so slowly with the energy that it may be taken as constant over a fair range of velocities. The cross-section at stellar energies σ_0 is

$$\sigma_0 = \frac{S_0}{E} \exp \left(b E^{-1/2} \right) \qquad (75)$$

where E here denotes the relevant kinetic energy in stellar interiors. All energies and cross-section parameters are referred to the center of mass coordinates. The value of S_0 will depend slightly on the central temperature and will not differ greatly from S_M.

If, however, the compound nucleus has an energy level at E_r that does not fall far from the energy of the incoming particle, resonance occurs and σ will be increased. Then

$$\sigma \sim \frac{S_r}{E_r} \exp \left(b E_r^{-1/2} \right) \qquad (76)$$

*That is, σ is the cross-section for a head-on encounter [cf. eqn. (63)], multiplied by the ratio of the reaction probability $\Gamma/\hbar$ [cf. eqn. (70)] to the nuclear frequency $h/M_0 R^2$ (which is identified with the oscillation time of an unobstructed nucleon within the potential well). Actually, the true nuclear frequency is usually quite a bit smaller than $h/M_0 R^2$ since internal collisions between the nucleons increase considerably the time required for a given nucleon to traverse the nucleus. This means that Γ in eqn. (72) is not to be identified with the Γ found in experiments and explains why Bethe's original σ's were too small.

where S_r may be many magnitudes larger than S_0. Resonances that fall in the region of low energies will have a profound effect on the rate of energy generation in stellar interiors (see page 40).

In the neighborhood of resonance one may write

$$\sigma \sim [(E - E_r)^2 + \tfrac{1}{4}\Gamma^2]^{-1} \tag{77}$$

where Γ is defined by eqn. (71).

Frequently a nucleus is still in an unstable state after the emission of a γ-ray. Consider the reaction

$$_6C^{12} + {}_1H^1 \rightarrow {}_7N^{13} + \gamma$$

which we abbreviate as $C^{12}(p\gamma)N^{13}$. The symbol p stands for proton. Now $_7N^{13}$ is short-lived; after about ten minutes it emits an energetic positron or β-ray to form C^{13}, viz.,

$$_7N^{13} \rightarrow {}_6C^{13} + \epsilon^+$$

The positive electron encounters a negative electron and the two annihilate each other. Natural radioactive elements emit only negatrons while artificial radioactive substances emit both positive and negative electrons.

The origin of β-rays provides a fascinating question. From one point of view, both protons and neutrons are regarded as different states of the same particle. A neutron can become transformed into a proton with the ejection of a negative electron. Thus

and

$$\left.\begin{aligned} _1n^0 &\rightleftarrows {}_1p^1 + {}_0\epsilon^- \\ _1p^1 &\rightleftarrows {}_1n^1 + {}_0\epsilon^+ \end{aligned}\right\} \tag{78}$$

Sometimes when such a transition occurs, the excess charge escapes as a fast moving electron. If the energy of an unstable nucleus changes, enough energy must be supplied not only to provide for the rest mass of the electron, mc^2, but also to permit it to escape against the strong coulomb attraction of the nucleus.*

These β disintegrations differ significantly from all other nuclear transformations in that for a transition between two well-defined nuclear energy states, the ejected electron may have any velocity ranging from zero up to the maximum allowed energy. For example, the positrons emitted when N^{13} decays into C^{13} have energies up to 1.20 Mev which correspond to the energy allowed from the mass difference between N^{13} and C^{13}.

*The electron cannot exist within the nucleus; it is created in a transformation and flies away, usually with appreciable speed. Instead of ejecting a positive electron a nucleus will sometimes capture one of its own electrons from the innermost or K shell. Such transitions are called K *captures*.

In order that energy and momentum be conserved, physicists have postulated a small neutral particle (of practically zero rest mass) called the *neutrino*, which is ejected at the same time and carries off excess energy momentum and spin. H. R. Crane has given a summary of the experimental evidence for this process.*

As an illustration of astrophysical interest, let us consider the first step in the proton-proton reaction, the formation of a deuteron in the collision between two protons, viz:

$$_1H^1 + {}_1H^1 \rightarrow {}_1H^2 + \epsilon^+ + \nu + 0.42 \text{ Mev} \qquad (79)$$

where ν denotes the neutrino which carries away about 60 per cent of the energy.

To calculate the probability of deuteron formation, we must consider the following factors:

(1) Collision probability for the two protons and the penetration of their mutual potential barriers. At distances much greater than the nuclear radius the protons repel one another according to Coulomb's law, but at distances comparable with the nuclear radius there come into action also the powerful short-range forces between nucleons. Experimental studies of the scattering of protons by protons permit the determination of the range and magnitude of these short-range forces and provide the necessary background for the theoretical calculation of capture cross-sections. These calculations involve a factor Λ^2 determined by Frieman and Motz, and by Salpeter, which depends on the shape of the potential well of the deuteron; a correction factor, of the order of 1.13, for the finite range of nuclear forces; and the radius of the deuteron, 4.31×10^{-13} cm. A purely radiative collision between two protons would not be possible because He^2 does not exist.

(2) Probability of β-decay. The two protons must remain in close contact long enough for one of the protons to transform itself into a neutron with the ejection of the excess charge as a β-ray. Since the probability of β-decay is always small compared with other nuclear processes, the formation of deuterons will be so infrequent an occurrence in laboratory scattering experiments as to be unobservable. Artificial β-decay is only observable when a radioactive nucleus is produced as the end product of a nuclear reaction.

According to the Fermi theory, the probability of β-emission depends on

$$\Gamma_\beta = gf(W) |M|^2 \qquad (80)$$

where $|M|^2$ involves the summation over possible spin states and the fact that either proton can become a neutron. Numerically $|M|^2$ here

*Rev. Mod. Phys., 20, 278, 1948.

equals $\frac{3}{2}$. Here W is the energy of the β-particle expressed in terms of mc^2 and includes the rest mass of the electron. The Fermi β-decay function $f(W)$ is a known function of the energy of the β-particle. The β-decay constant g bears a somewhat analogous relation to the inter-action between the electron or neutrino and the nuclear force field that the electronic charge ϵ does to the interaction between an electron and the electromagnetic field. According to the discussion by Salpeter,*

$$g = 7.5 \times 10^{-4} \text{ sec}$$

The Fermi β-decay theory agrees well with experimental data on the energy of the emitted electron and the lifetime of the parent nucleus. Aside from the kinetic energies of the colliding particles, the maximum energy available to the positron from the combination of two protons to form a deuteron would be

$$2(M_{proton}) - (M_{deuteron})$$

$$= 2 \times (1.00814 - 0.00055) - (2.01473 - 0.00055)$$

$$= 0.00100.$$

This energy includes the rest mass of the electron, mc^2, in terms of which the maximum energy is 1.83. At a temperature of 15 million degrees the main contribution to the formation of deuterons comes from particles with energies of about 6 kev.

The cross-sections for the proton-proton reaction were calculated first by Bethe and Critchfield, and subsequently by E. Frieman and L. Motz, and by E. Salpeter.

Much emphasis has been placed on the study of light nuclei—lithium to neon ($Z = 3$ to $Z = 10$). The very lightest nuclei, those with 2, 3, or 4 particles, appear to have no excited states of well-defined energy. More than 250 energy levels have been located in nuclei containing from 5 to 20 particles. In heavier nuclei the number of levels becomes greatly increased as the number of participating particles increases. Actually, the nucleons themselves appear to form stable groups among themselves; for example, it is useful to think of the α-particle as existing as a distinct entity within the nucleus of, say N^{15}. Although no law has ever been derived to account for the number, kind, and spacing of these energy levels, some symmetries have been recognized, e.g., the energy level diagrams of isobars are similar.

The identification of the energy levels in a nucleus involves measure-ments of the energies and products of reactions that leave the target

---

*For this reaction the spin of either nucleon has to turn over. This occurs only in the Gamow-Teller type of β-decay. The numerical value of g refers to this type of β-decay.

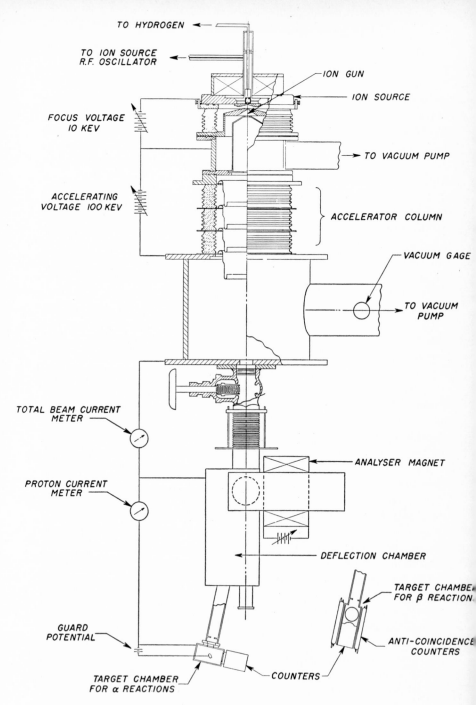

TO HYDROGEN

TO ION SOURCE
R.F. OSCILLATOR

ION GUN

ION SOURCE

FOCUS VOLTAGE
10 KEV

TO VACUUM PUMP

ACCELERATING
VOLTAGE 100 KEV

ACCELERATOR COLUMN

VACUUM GAGE

TO VACUUM
PUMP

TOTAL BEAM CURRENT
METER

ANALYSER MAGNET

PROTON CURRENT
METER

DEFLECTION CHAMBER

TARGET CHAMBER
FOR β REACTION

ANTI-COINCIDENCE
COUNTERS

GUARD
POTENTIAL

TARGET CHAMBER
FOR α REACTIONS

COUNTERS

Fig. 4.—Schematic Diagram of the 100-kev Accelerator at the California
Institute of Technology

Protons from the ion source (top) are accelerated by the electrostatic field and
selected according to energy with the aid of the analyzer magnet and defining slits.
They then impinge upon the target and the reaction rates are measured with suitable
counters.

nucleus in the state X. For example, Be^7 decays by the capture of its own K electron into Li^7 with the liberation of 0.863 Mev of energy, or with the liberation of 0.385 Mev of energy, in which event the Li^7 nucleus is left in an excited level from which it decays with the release of 0.478 Mev. The same 0.478-Mev energy level is found by measuring the energy losses involved in the scattering of α-particles or protons by Li^7. The energy levels in certain nuclei have been mapped in great detail; in other nuclei only portions of the energy range are covered, while in yet others very little information is known.

For an account of the actual experimental techniques by which the basic nuclear reaction parameters are determined, the reader is referred to the literature. The energies of the bombarding protons must be constant; hence, probably the most satisfactory accelerator for the low-energy range is an electrostatic generator or a transformer-condenser rectified voltage generator of the types employed at the California Institute of Technology. See Fig. 4. With the aid of a suitable electrostatic analyzer it is possible to get a beam of one Mev energy with a dispersion in energy of only 200 ev. For thick C^{12} targets one may employ graphite blocks, while for thin carbon targets, Fowler and Lauritsen evaporated paraffin on thin copper supports. The most recent experiments employ carbon foils produced by cracking methane.

Samples enriched in C^{13} have often been employed to measure the cross-sections for this isotope. For nitrogen one must employ rather rare, stable, solid compounds such as titanium nitride in order to withstand heating during bombardment. These can be enriched, if necessary for the isotopes whose properties are to be studied.

Detectors of the reaction products include scintillation counters and Geiger-Müller counters for β-rays. N^{13}, which is formed when C^{12} captures a proton, evolves by β-decay into C^{13}; hence measurement of the β-activity in this reaction gives yields expressed as ratios of positrons to protons. These radioactive isotopes are easier to measure because the accelerator can be turned off to reduce the background during measurements. In all these experiments it is necessary to eliminate the background count by means of anti-coincident counters, etc. At low energies where the yields are small, the background count becomes serious. A pulsed ion source giving large proton yields over short periods was found to be necessary in the study of the (C^{13}, p) reaction which does not produce a radioactive product. The measurement of γ-rays is rather difficult when the yields are low.

The energies of β-rays may be measured by β-ray spectrometers, while γ-ray energies have been determined by measuring their absorption in thin layers of aluminum, lead, or carbon, or from the energies of secondaries torn from atoms by photo-ionization. One method is to measure the ranges of the secondaries, usually with the aid of coincidence counters—another is to measure the electron energy directly from the curvature of its path in a magnetic field. The best method is the measurement of the secondary pulse size in the scintillation counter.

To achieve full resolution of resonance peaks, thin targets are employed to get the position and width, i.e., E_r and Γ_p. If a thick target is used, the increase in yield from below to above resonance will give the area of the curve. Since the height of the thin target peak is $\sim \Gamma_\gamma/\Gamma_p$ and its width is Γ_p, the thick target yield will therefore give Γ_γ. Absolute measures also give the cross-section as a function of proton energy, the influence of the resonances may be estimated and the cross-section evaluated for low energies.

8. Thermal Nuclear Reactions

Years ago, Atkinson and Houtermans suggested that because of the high central temperatures of the stars, protons may acquire sufficient kinetic energy to penetrate the nuclei of light atoms. These processes, however, will be of interest only if energy is liberated from the nucleus.

Following the discussion by Gamow, Bethe, and others we shall derive the dependence of energy generation upon the temperature. Consider two perfect, reacting gases of atomic weights A_1 and A_2, atomic numbers Z_1 and Z_2, and relative concentrations by mass x_1 and x_2, in thermal equilibrium at temperature T and density ρ. For particles with energies (referred to the center of mass) between E and $E + dE$, the kinetic theory gives for the total number of energy-producing collisions per cm^3 per sec,

$$dp = \frac{4x_1 x_2 \rho \sigma}{\sqrt{2\pi A} \; A_1 A_2 M_0^{5/2}(kT)^{3/2}} \, Ee^{-E/kT} \, dE \qquad (81)$$

Here σ is the effective cross-section of the reaction, M_0 is the mass of the proton in grams

$$A = \frac{A_1 A_2}{A_1 + A_2} \qquad (82)$$

where $A_1 = 1$ for a proton, whereas A_2 is the atomic weight (a pure number) of the other particle, e.g., a C^{12} or N^{14} nucleus.

If we substitute eqn. (72) into eqn. (81) we obtain a product of two exponentials; one, $\exp(-E/kT)$ arises from the Maxwellian distribution of the protons, which rises to a maximum at $Mv^2 = 2kT$ and falls off at higher velocities; whereas the other,

$$\exp\left(-\frac{2\pi\epsilon^2 Z_1 Z_2}{\hbar v}\right)$$

due to proton penetration, rises as E increases. Now dp/dE has a sharp maximum at

$$E_0 = \left[\frac{\pi \epsilon^2 \sqrt{A M_0}\, Z_1 Z_2 kT}{\sqrt{2}\, \hbar} \right]^{2/3} \tag{83}$$

whose width is

$$\Delta E \sim \left[\frac{8}{3kT} \right]^{1/2} \left[\frac{2\pi \epsilon^2 \sqrt{M_0 A}\, Z_1 Z_2 kT}{\sqrt{2}\, \hbar} \right]^{1/3} \tag{84}$$

The shape of the dp curve is such that the total number of collisions can be calculated as though the function were the Gaussian error curve of the same height and width. Thus we obtain:

$$p \sim \frac{\pi^{5/6}}{\sqrt{3}} \left(\frac{\epsilon^2 \hbar^2 Z_1 Z_2}{M_0^7 k^2 T^2 A} \right)^{1/3} \frac{x_1 x_2 \rho R^2 \Gamma}{A_1 A_2}$$

$$\exp \left\{ \frac{4\epsilon(2A M_0 Z_1 Z_2 R)^{1/2}}{\hbar} - 3\left[\frac{\pi^2 \epsilon^4 M_0 A Z_1^2 Z_2^2}{2\hbar kT} \right]^{1/3} \right\} \tag{85}$$

Bethe writes the resultant expression for thermal nuclear reactions in the form

$$p \sim \frac{4}{3^{5/2}} \frac{x_1 x_2 \rho}{A_1 A_2 M_0^2} \frac{\Gamma}{\hbar}\, aR^2 e^{4(2R/a)^{1/2}} \tau^2 e^{-\tau} \tag{86}$$

where

$$a = \frac{\hbar^2}{A M_0 \epsilon^2 Z_1 Z_2} \tag{87}$$

and

$$\tau = 3\left[\frac{\pi^2 M_0 A \epsilon^4 Z_1^2 Z_2^2}{2\hbar^2 kT} \right]^{1/3} \tag{88}$$

If we express ρ in grams/cm^3, Γ in electron volts, and T in millions of degrees,

$$p = 5.3 \times 10^{25} \rho x_1 x_2 \Gamma \phi(Z_1 Z_2) \tau^2 e^{-\tau} \tag{89}$$

$$\tau = 42.48 \left[\frac{Z_1^2 Z_2^2 A_1 A_2}{(A_1 + A_2)} \right]^{1/3} T^{-1/3} \tag{90}$$

$$\phi(Z_1 Z_2) = \frac{1}{A_1 A_2 (Z_1 Z_2 A)^3} \left[\frac{8R}{a} \right]^3 \exp \left\{ 2\left[\frac{8R}{a} \right]^{1/2} \right\} \tag{91}$$

The combined radius R is approximately

$$R = 1.2 \times 10^{-13} (A_1 + A_2)^{1/3} \text{ cm} \tag{92}$$

At the present time it appears better to employ eqn. (75) with a value of S_0 estimated for energies of astrophysical interest. The uncertain factors are the cross-section measurements at low energy and the extrapolations to the yet lower energies of astrophysical importance. If S_0 (cf. eqn. 75) is expressed in units of ev *barns* (one barn $= 10^{-24}$cm^2), and Q is the energy emitted in Mev in the reaction between the nuclei of types 1 and 2, the amount of energy in ergs emitted per gram per sec is

$$\epsilon = 4.19 \times 10^{20}(\rho x_1 x_2 S_0 Q)(A_1^2 A_2 Z_1 Z_2)^{-1}\tau^2 e^{-\tau} \text{ ergs/gm/sec} \quad (93)$$

Here Salpeter uses S_0 in laboratory coordinates. We replace S_0 by $\dfrac{A_1 + A_2}{A_2} S_0$ when we use eqn. (75). *In astrophysical calculations we must use the center-of-mass coordinate system values* as indicated by W. A. Fowler. The relation between the laboratory-system values and the center-of-mass-system values is

$$E = E_{CM} = \frac{A_2}{A_1 + A_2} E_{\text{LAB}}$$

$$S = S_{CM} = \frac{A_2}{A_1 + A_2} S_{\text{LAB}}$$

where A_2 is the mass of the bombarded particle in the laboratory experiment.

9. The Proton-Proton Reaction

Some years ago Bethe and Critchfield suggested that in the sun and fainter stars, energy was supplied by the proton-proton reaction, the first step of which is the reaction (79). This reaction has never been observed experimentally, and its reality depends on the correctness of certain selection rules for β-decay. A large amount of experimental data now indicates that these rules, due to Gamow and Teller, are correct, so that appropriate calculations can be carried out. The bottleneck of the process is the collision of two protons to emit a positron and form a deuteron. For temperatures in the neighborhood of 15 million degrees, the lifetime of a proton will be given by

$$p = 3.9 \times 10^{-18}\left(\frac{\rho X}{100}\right)\left(\frac{T}{15}\right)^{3.96} \text{ sec}^{-1} \quad (94)$$

where T is expressed in millions of degrees. The step results in the liberation of 0.42 Mev (of which 0.25 Mev is carried away by the neutrino) plus the annihilation energy of a positron (1.02 Mev).

The next step in the process is the capture of a proton by the deuteron to form a nucleus of He^3, viz.,

$$_1\text{H}^1 + _1\text{H}^2 \rightarrow _2\text{He}^3 + \gamma + 5.5 \text{ Mev}$$

which occurs so quickly that in the interior of most stars the deuteron lasts only a few seconds. The competing process by which the He^3 nucleus captures the deuteron is slower by a factor of at least 50.

It was originally thought that the He^3 nucleus might collide with an α-particle to form Li^7 which subsequently broke down into two α-particles. The process suggested independently by C. C. Lauritsen and W. A. Fowler and by E. Schatzman, viz.,

$$He^3 + He^3 \rightarrow He^4 + 2H^1 + 12.8 \text{ Mev}$$

turns out to be at least a hundred times more frequent. The He^3–He^3 reaction has recently been measured in the laboratory. The cross-section is known to within a factor of 2. Notice that in the proton-proton reaction, 2 deuterons are formed for each α-particle, and 26.2 Mev of energy is liberated. The rate of liberation of energy is given by

$$\epsilon = 2180\left(1 + \frac{5}{12}\tau\right)\left[1 + 0.054\left(\frac{T}{15}\right)^{2/3}\right]\rho X^2 \tau^2 e^{-\tau}$$

$$\sim 5.0\left(\frac{\rho}{100}\right)\left(\frac{X}{0.316}\right)^2\left(\frac{T}{15}\right)^{3.96} \text{ ergs/gm/sec}$$

(95)

in the neighborhood of 15 million degrees. Here T is measured in millions of degrees, τ is given by eqn. (88) and X is the fractional abundance of hydrogen by weight.

In a mass of pure hydrogen at a density of 100 gm/cm³, the rate of liberation of energy would be:

$$T = 5 \quad 8 \quad 15 \quad 30 \quad \text{(millions of °K)}$$

$$\epsilon_0 = 0.2 \quad 3.1 \quad 50 \quad 530 \quad \text{(ergs/gm/sec)}$$

At 15 million degrees the life expectancy of a proton would be 8 billion years! The deuteron, once formed, would last only 4 seconds, and the He^3 nucleus that was formed would endure for a period of the order of half a million years. In spite of the potential barrier, the (He^3–He^3) collisions are more frequent than the deuteron-forming encounters even at temperatures as low as 5 million degrees.

Salpeter suggests that for temperatures in the neighborhood of a temperature T_0 (expressed in millions of degrees), we may write the formula for the rate of energy generation in the form

$$\epsilon = \epsilon_0 \frac{\rho X^2}{100}\left(\frac{T}{T_0}\right)^n$$

(96)

where ϵ_0 is given above and $n = 6.0, 5.0, 4.0,$ and 3.0 at temperatures of 5, 8, 15, and 30 million degrees.

It now appears that the sun derives its energy almost entirely from the proton-proton reaction. This reaction fails to provide sufficient energy only in the hotter main sequence stars where it appears that the carbon (or carbon–nitrogen) cycle may be the principal source of energy generation.

10. The Carbon Cycle

The celebrated carbon cycle is illustrated in Fig. 5. A carbon atom captures a proton (upper left hand corner). If the capture occurs near resonance, 456 kev, the atom will emit a γ-ray of about 2.369 Mev to

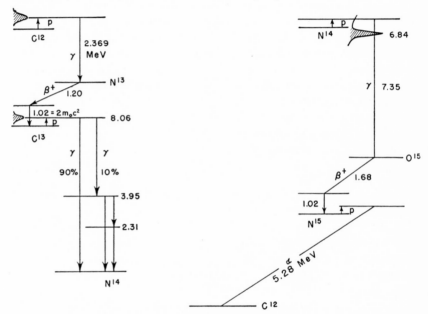

FIG. 5.—THE CARBON CYCLE

The energies are given in Mev. Vertical jumps denote γ-ray transitions. Ejections of positrons (β^+) and α-particles decrease the nuclear charge Z and are represented as diagonal lines. Proton captures are depicted as occurring at resonance except for N^{14} where the captures appear to occur in the tail of the 6.84 Mev resonance. Notice that γ-decay from the excited 8.06 Mev level in N^{14} can occur in different ways. We depict only the most probable mode of α-decay following a proton capture by N^{15}.

form a N^{13} nucleus. The latter is unstable and suffers β-decay into C^{13}, viz.: N^{13} ($\beta^+\nu$) C^{13} (mean life = 10 minutes). The emitted β-particle escapes with a maximum energy of 1.20 Mev. The neutrino takes an average of 0.72 Mev energy so only about 0.5 Mev is normally available to the positron. The annihilation of the positron upon encounter with a negative electron (negatron) releases $2m_0c^2 = 1.02$ Mev.

The C^{13} nucleus captures a proton to become N^{14} in an excited state. The N^{14} nucleus decays to the ground level by γ-ray emission. Ultimately the N^{14} nucleus captures a proton and emits a γ-ray of about 7.3 Mev energy to form O^{15} which decays to N^{15} in the order of two or three minutes with the ejection of a positron and a neutrino; the latter carries off about 0.98 Mev of the 1.7 Mev energy supplied to the two particles. Again 1.02 Mev of energy is supplied as the positron encounters a negative electron and the two annihilate one another. The N^{15} nucleus captures a proton and the resultant compound nucleus breaks down into C^{12} with the ejection of an α-particle. The transformations in Fig. 5 are depicted as occurring at resonance except for N^{14}, but we must remember that under stellar conditions, proton penetrations will occur at much lower energies.

The rate at which energy is produced in the carbon cycle will depend on the temperature, density, and composition of the volume element as well as on the cross-sections for the various steps. These cross-sections can be measured experimentally down to about 100 kev. Under stellar conditions, however, penetrations occur for proton energies in the neighborhood of 25 kev and therefore it is necessary to extrapolate the laboratory data to low energies.

Table 1, due to W. A. Fowler of the California Institute of Technology, summarizes our knowledge of the carbon cycle and the proton-proton reaction (January, 1954). Column (1) gives the parameter b defined in eqn. (74) in $(\text{kev})^{1/2}$ for both the *center of mass* (C.M.) and laboratory coordinates, column (2) gives the reaction. Column (3) gives the energy release (Mev). This is followed by the energy E_M at which the laboratory measures are made and the yield Y_M per incident proton from available targets at laboratory energy. The cross-sections measured at laboratory energies, σ_M, are given in barns (one barn $= 10^{-24}$ cm^2). Column (7) gives the parameter S_M in (kev-barns) in the (C.M.) system. Columns 8, 9, and 10 of the table give the parameters S_0, the energy E_0, and the cross-section σ_0 relevant to a temperature of 13,000,000°K. [See eqn. (75).] Here x denotes the equilibrium by weight at a temperature of 13,000,000°K. The mean reaction times t are calculated for $f\rho X = 1.5 \times 100$ gm/cm^3 for the carbon cycle, and for $\rho X = 100$ gm/cm^3 for the proton-proton reaction. In the last column n is the exponent in the temperature dependence of the reaction probability, including that of the shielding factor [see, e.g., eqn. (96)]. The mean life $t \sim T^{-n}$. Additional comments are given in the notes to Table 1. The tabulated probable errors are about 50 per cent greater than the probable errors of the low-energy laboratory measurement, in order to allow for the errors in extrapolation. The errors will be enormously greater, of course, if a resonance falls near E_0.

The rate of the carbon cycle is affected by two factors which were not important or did not enter in the proton-proton reaction. The

TABLE 1

Stellar Nuclear Reactions, Low-Energy Measurements and Calculations

b(kev)$^{1/2}$ (C.M.) (Lab.)	Reaction	Measurements					Calculations ($T=13\times10^6$ °K)					
		Energy Release Mev	E_M (Lab.) kev	Y_M per proton	σ_M barns	S_M (C.M.) kev-barns	S_0 (C.M.) kev-barns	E_0 (C.M.)	σ_0 barns	Abundance Ratios	t yr	n
181.0 188.4	$C^{12}(p\gamma)N^{13}$ $N^{13}(\beta^+\nu)C^{13}$	1.945 1.502(a)	128(d)	9×10^{-16}	9.3×10^{-10} ±1	1.9 ±0.2	1.2 ±0.2	21.5	7.0×10^{-19}		1.3×10^7 7.0 min(k)	18.3
181.5 188.4	$C^{13}(p\gamma)N^{14}$	7.542	120(e)	5×10^{-15}	4.8×10^{-9} ±1	9.2 ±2	6.1(f) ±2	21.6	3.2×10^{-18}	x_{12}/x_{13} =4.3±1.6	2.7×10^6	18.3
212.3 219.8	$N^{14}(p\gamma)O^{15}$ $O^{15}(\beta^+\nu)N^{15}$	7.347 1.729(b)	124	2×10^{-16}	5.8×10^{-10} ±1	25 ±5	33(g) ±11	23.9	2.1×10^{-19}	x_{14}/x_{12} =26±10(m) $x_N/x_C=21\pm8$ (o)	3.2×10^8 82 sec(k)	20.3
212.8 219.8	$N^{15}(p\alpha)C^{12}$	4.961	99.5	2.5×10^{-14}	5.0×10^{-7} ±1	1.8×10^5 ±0.4	1.1×10^5 ±0.3	24.0	6.3×10^{-16}	x_{12}/x_{15} =110±35(n) x_{14}/x_{15} =2800±1200	1.1×10^5	20.3
	Total	25.026										
22.20 31.40	$H^1(p\beta^+\nu)D^2$ $\beta^+ +e^- \to 2\gamma$	2×0.164(c) 2×1.022(c)	100(h)		2.0×10^{-25}(h)		2.2×10^{-22} ±0.4	5.31	2.8×10^{-27}		14×10^9(l)	4.1
25.63 31.40	$D^2(p\gamma)He^3$ $[D^2(n\gamma)He^3]$	2×5.494(c) –	500(i) Thermal		4.5×10^{-6}(i) 0.57×10^{-3}		8×10^{-5} ±2	6.50	3.4×10^{-10}	x_2/x_1 =2.6×10^{-17}	5.7 sec	4.6
153.66 217.27 38.41 54.31	$He^3(He^3,$ $2p)He^4$ $[T^3(t, 2n)$ $He^4]$	12.847 –	200 200	– –	2.5×10^{-6}(j) 0.032	– 160	1.7×10^3(j) ±1	21.44	5×10^{-16}	x_3/x_1 $\sim10^{-4}$	$\sim10^6$(l)	16.7
	Total	26.207										

Data for proton-proton cycles obtained in part from Salpeter, *Phys. Rev.* **88**, 547, 1952.
(Courtesy, William A. Fowler, Kellogg Radiation Laboratory, Jan., 1954.)

Notes on the opposite page.

(*Notes for Table 1*)

(a) Neutrino energy loss = 0.720 Mev.

(b) Neutrino energy loss = 0.976 Mev.

(c) Neutrino energy loss = 0.257 Mev. Two of these reactions are necessary to complete the proton-proton cycle.

(d) Measured from 96 to 202 kev.

(e) Measured from 116 to 133 kev.

(f) This value will be increased roughly by a factor of 10 if the level at 7.50 Mev in N^{14}, reported as doubtful in the C^{13} $(d n)$ reaction, actually exists and can be produced by s-wave protons in $C^{13}(p\gamma)[E_p = -45$ kev].

(g) Low-lying excited states in O^{15} as indicated in N^{11} $(d n)$ may increase this value by as much as a factor of 20.

(h) Calculated cross section which has a maximum value at 100 kev.

(i) Cross section for p-wave capture followed by electric dipole radiation which is observed at laboratory energies. Cross-section constant for s-wave capture followed by magnetic dipole radiation must be inferred from $D^2(n\gamma)$.

(j) See Good et al., *Phys. Rev.* (in press).

(k) Measured mean lives.

(l) The mean lives of H^1 and He^3 are one-half the mean reaction times respectively.

(m) As a function of temperature $x_{14}/x_{12} = (26 \pm 10)(13/T)^2$.

(n) As a function of temperature $x_{12}/x_{15} = (110 \pm 35)(T/13)^2$.

(o) As a function of temperature $x_N/x_C = (21 \pm 8)(13/T)^2$.

NOTE: In astrophysical computations use energies and constants in center of mass system.

39

first of these, f, may be called the *electron shielding term*. The charge of a heavy nucleus may be screened not only by bound K or L electrons, but also by free electrons. The potential falls off much more steeply than $1/r$, the narrowing of the potential barrier enhances the ease of penetration. The effect is more important at the lower temperatures and higher densities. G. Keller finds that this effect is not important in the theory of stellar structure since the screening factor is unimportant at temperatures where the carbon cycle supplies most of the energy.* The value for σ_0 in Table 1 applies to a stripped nucleus and must be multiplied by $f \sim 1.5$ for the shielding under stellar conditions for the carbon-cycle reactions at 13,000,000°K.

In the carbon cycle the effect of resonances for proton capture may become very serious. C^{12} and C^{13} have well-defined resonances for proton capture at 456 and 550 kev, respectively, while N^{15} has resonances at 880, 1030, and 1200 kev. These particular resonances do not have much influence on our calculations of the rates of reactions in stellar interiors, but real trouble arises if there exist resonances in long-lived C^{12} or N^{14} below the experimentally attainable lower limit of 100 kev for proton energies. In C^{12} it seems likely that there are no such low-lying resonances, but in N^{14} such resonances may occur. In fact, the lifetime of the N^{14} nucleus could be cut down by a factor of 10^4 if the resonances fell near 20 or 30 kev. Hence the rate of the carbon cycle, and the corresponding power output, will depend on the existence or nonexistence of such a resonance.

Such resonances could not be found by direct measurement of the cross-sections at low energies—the yields are too low, but might be located from γ-ray transitions from higher levels. Recent observations of such cascade transitions in $N^{14}(p\gamma)$ reveal no evidence of any such resonances in the stellar region. At the moment it seems legitimate to take the extrapolated cross-sections at their face value and base calculations of energy generation and abundance upon them. An extreme upper limit to the energy production by the carbon cycle can be found if one supposes that nitrogen has a strong resonance and the lifetime of the cycle is fixed by the $C^{12}(p\gamma)$ reaction. In the neighborhood of 13,000,000°K the rate of energy generation by the carbon cycle (assuming the extrapolated cross-sections) is given by

$$\epsilon_{CN} = 235\rho X_H Z_{CN} \frac{\left(\dfrac{13}{T}\right)^{1.2}}{1 + 0.05\left(\dfrac{T}{13}\right)^2} \exp\left[-64.78\left(\frac{13}{T}\right)^{1/3}\right] \times 10^{26}$$

$$= 1.66\rho X_H Z_{CN}\left(\frac{T}{13}\right)^{20.3} \tag{97}$$

*Ap. J. **118**, 142, 1953.

where X is the abundance of hydrogen by weight and Z_{CN} that of carbon plus nitrogen.

11. Other Nuclear Reactions

In most stars, He^4 is the one indestructible ingredient. Light nuclei up to and including boron undergo rapid transformations upon collisions with protons, but all end up as helium. One example is furnished by the reaction

$$B^{11} + {}_1H^1 \rightarrow 3{}_2He^4$$

which has a ten-thousand–fold greater probability than the building up of carbon by the

$$B^{11} + H^1 \rightarrow C^{12}$$

reaction. Except for He, all nuclei between hydrogen and carbon, viz., H^2, H^3, Li^6, Li^7, Be^9, Be^{10}, Be^{11}, can exist in stellar interiors only as long as they are synthesized by nuclear reactions. H^4, He^5, Li^5, Be^6, and B^9 are nonexistent. In particular there is no chance of building up appreciable quantities of carbon from the lighter elements, because any non-radioactive nucleus between He and C, i.e., Li^6, Li^7, Be^9, B^{10}, or B^{11} react with protons, not to build up heavier elements but to give α-particles. The instability of Be^8 causes a gap in the list of stable nuclei because Be^8 is easily formed in nuclear reactions and were it stable there would be some possibility of building up carbon in ordinary stars. The lifetimes of carbon and nitrogen are very long because these elements are constantly being reformed in the carbon cycle.

Among nuclei heavier than nitrogen, transformations occur rather slowly. Under continued proton bombardment, about one O^{16} nucleus in 50 million will ultimately become Ne^{20}. The rest break down into nitrogen by various reactions. These energy transformations proceed so slowly that equilibrium in stars like the sun cannot be reached in times comparable with the age of the earth.

A star of pure hydrogen would operate on the proton-proton mechanism. The carbon which serves as a catalyst for the carbon-nitrogen cycle must have been there "from the beginning," since there is no means of forming it from hydrogen at temperatures prevailing in normal stars. Therefore, we are forced to the conclusion that the carbon and heavier elements are residues of the primitive matter of which ordinary stars were formed.

Salpeter suggests that a star that has exhausted all its hydrogen and has become very dense with central densities and temperatures of the order of 2×10^4 gm/cm^3 and 1.5×10^8 °K, respectively, may derive its energy from the exothermic conversion of 3 He^4 nuclei into one C^{12} nucleus. The C^{12} might eventually be built into yet heavier nuclei such as O^{16} or Ne^{20}. He supposes that in spite of its instability to disintegration into two helium nuclei, a small concentration $\sim 10^{-10}$ of Be^8 will be maintained because of the high temperature and density. This Be^8 easily absorbs a helium nucleus to form C^{12} which can be built up by successive α-particle captures to form O^{16}, Ne^{20}, etc. up to Ca^{40}. Such a process as the building up of C^{12} might occur in Sandage and Schwarzschild's red giant models where high central temperatures and densities in excess of 200,000,000°K may be attained. In these objects some energy might be supplied by the carbon-building reaction, but the main source of energy for quite a while would be the carbon cycle in the thin shell.

If yet higher temperatures could occur in the stars, further building up to the stable elements near iron could take place. Two C^{12} nuclei would collide to give sodium, magnesium, or neon. At temperatures above 10^{10} °K photo-disintegration of nuclei releasing α-particles or protons can occur at a small rate. These liberated α-particles or protons can be absorbed by various nuclei successively to form heavier and heavier nuclei. Nuclear reactions involving elements beyond the most stable region must in general be endoergic.

PROBLEMS

1. A gaseous sphere of the same mass and radius as the sun has a constant temperature of 3,000,000°K. Calculate:

(a) The total energy stored in radiation
(b) The total energy stored in gas kinetic energy assuming the mass to be composed of hydrogen
(c) The total energy stored as energy of ionization.

2. At the center of a model for a star $X = 0.47$, $Y = 0.41$, $T = 20,000,000°K$, $\mu = 0.76$, $\rho = 111$ grams/cm³, $t/g = 16$. Calculate k. Calculate the electron scattering coefficient per gram of material.

3. Assume that at the edge of the convective zone in a star, $T = 15,000,000°K$, $\rho = 81$ grams/cm³, $\mu = 0.76$, $\gamma = \frac{5}{3}$. Suppose the velocity $\bar{v}_t$ of the turbulent element is 0.3 km/sec, and its length l is 1000 km. If the radius of the convective core is 8.4×10^9 cm, and the total energy generated within it, 3.79×10^{33} ergs/sec, is transported to its boundary by turbulent convection, find the required temperature gradient. At the interface

$$\frac{d \log P}{d \log r} = -1.47$$

Hint for Problem 3: Assume that the energy transport F_{turb} depends on the difference between the actual and adiabatic temperature gradients in accordance with the expression

$$F_{turb} = -\rho \bar{v}_t \bar{l} \left[\left(\frac{dT}{dr} \right) - \left(\frac{dT}{dr} \right)_{ad} \right] c_p$$

$$= -\rho \bar{v}_t \bar{l} \left[\frac{dT}{dr} - \frac{\gamma - 1}{\gamma} \frac{T}{P} \frac{dP}{dr} \right] c_p$$

In contrast to the analogous formula for conduction in a gas, c_p occurs here instead of c_v because the intermingling of the vortices with the surroundings and the formation of new eddies occur at a constant pressure.

4. Find the ratio of the turbulent pressure, $P_t = \frac{1}{3}\rho v_t^2$ to the gas kinetic pressure.

5. Assume that the proportion of carbon plus nitrogen to the total amount of the heavier constituents of a stellar interior is 12 per cent. For $X = 0.60$, $Y = 0.35$, $T_c = 20,000,000°K$, $\rho = 100$, calculate the relative energy outputs by the carbon cycle and by the proton-proton reaction.

6. At what temperature, for the preceding values of ρ, X, and Y will the energy output by the two mechanisms be equal?

7. Verify eqn. (85).

REFERENCES

The basic text on problems of stellar structure is:

CHANDRASEKHAR, S. *An Introduction to the Study of Stellar Structure.* Chicago: University of Chicago Press, 1939. See also Chap. xiv in *Astrophysics—A Topical Symposium*, J. A. HYNEK (ed), New York: McGraw-Hill Book Co., Inc., 1951.

The stellar opacity coefficient for normal material is discussed by:

MORSE, P. *Ap. J.* **92**, 27, 1940.

The opacities of degenerate and partially degenerate material is given by:

SWIRLES, BERTHA. *M.N.* **91**, 857, 1931.
CHANDRASEKHAR, S. *Proc. Roy. Soc.* **133**, 242, 1931.
MAJUMDAR, R. C. *Astr. Nach.* **244**, 65, 1931.
MARSHAK, R. E. *Ap. J.* **92**, 324, 1940.

For the nature of convection under astrophysical conditions, see:

BIERMANN, L. *Zeits. f. Ap.* **19**, 1, 1939.
CHANDRASEKHAR, S. *Publ. Astron. Soc. Pac.* **64**, 98, 1952.

An introductory account of the experimental basis of nuclear physics may be found in, for example:

CORK, M. *Radioactivity and Nuclear Physics.* New York: D. Van Nostrand Co., Inc., 1950.

The basic nuclear theory needed for astrophysical applications is treated in:

GAMOW, G., and C. L. CRITCHFIELD. *Atomic Nucleus and Nuclear Energy Sources.* London: Oxford University Press, 1949 (see chap. x).

The most up-to-date atomic masses are those given by:

LI, *et al. Phys. Rev.* **83**, 517, 1951.

Summarizing accounts of energy levels in light atoms are given by:

AJZENBERG, F., and T. LAURITSEN. *Rev. Mod. Phys.* **24**, 321, 1952.

BLATT, J., and V. WEISSKOPF. *Theory of Nuclei.* New York: John Wiley & Sons, Inc., 1953.

The classical papers on the carbon cycle are:

BETHE, H. *Phys. Rev.* **55**, 434, 1939; *Ap. J.* **92**, 118, 1940.

The theory of the proton-proton reaction has been treated by:

BETHE, H., and C. L. CRITCHFIELD. *Phys. Rev.* **54**, 248, 1938.

SALPETER, E. E. *Phys. Rev.* **88**, 547, 1952.

The status of energy-generation reactions in stars is critically discussed by:

FOWLER, W. A. *Mémoires de la Société Royale des Sciences de Liège, 1953—Proceedings of the Symposium on Nuclear Processes in Celestial Objects.*

The building of C^{12} is discussed by:

SALPETER, E. E. *Ap. J.* **115**, 326, 1952.

CHAPTER 2

1. The Fundamental Equations

From the results in Chapter 1 we may now assemble the fundamental equations of the problem of stellar interiors, whose solution will give us the stellar model. We choose r as the independent variable. The dependent variables are the pressure P, the density ρ, the mass inside a sphere of radius r, M_r, the total energy generated within a sphere of radius r, L_r, and the temperature T.

The required physical relationships are:

the equation of state,

$$P = P_g + P_r = \frac{\rho \mathcal{R}}{\mu} T + aT^4/3 \tag{1}$$

the molecular weight,

$$\mu = \mu(\rho, T) \tag{2}$$

the absorption coefficient,

$$\kappa = \kappa(\rho, T) \tag{3}$$

and the energy generation,

$$\epsilon = \epsilon(\rho, T) \tag{4}$$

which is given by nuclear physics.

The molecular weight, absorption coefficient, and energy generation are single-valued functions of the temperature, density, and chemical composition of the material. The latter plays a decisive role, particularly if we change the proportions of hydrogen and helium with respect to the other elements. Significant, although less spectacular, changes occur if the relative proportions of atoms of the oxygen group and those of the iron group are altered. Thus we should have written:

$$\mu = \mu(\rho, T, X, Y, W), \quad \kappa = \kappa(\rho, T, X, Y, W), \quad \epsilon = \epsilon(\rho, T, X, Y, W)$$

where X stands for the abundance of hydrogen, Y for the abundance of helium, and W for the abundance of the heavier elements.

45

The fundamental relations we have established are:

mass distribution:

$$\frac{dM_r}{dr} = 4\pi r^2 \rho$$

$$M_r = 4\pi \int_0^r r^2 \rho \, dr \tag{5}$$

hydrostatic equilibrium:

$$\frac{dP}{dr} = -\frac{GM_r}{r^2} \rho \tag{6}$$

If the star is in radiative equilibrium, i.e., all the energy is carried to the surface by radiation, then

$$\frac{dL_r}{dr} = 4\pi r^2 \epsilon \rho, \quad L_r = 4\pi \int_0^r r^2 \epsilon \rho \, dr \tag{7}$$

and the radiative energy flow is

$$\frac{d(aT^4)}{dr} = -\frac{3\kappa\rho}{c} \frac{L_r}{4\pi r^2} \tag{8}$$

For a star in convective equilibrium, wherein radiation pressure plays a negligible role,

$$P = K\rho^\gamma \tag{9}$$

The following boundary conditions hold

$$M_r = 0, \quad L_r = 0 \quad (r = 0)$$

$$M_r = M, \quad L_r = L, \quad P = 0, \quad \rho = 0, \quad T = 0 \quad (r = R) \tag{10}$$

Actually, T is so small at the surface compared to the value it assumes in the interior that no significant error is made by setting it zero there. From the discussion in Chapter 1, we anticipate that in stars deriving their energy from the carbon cycle, the innermost core will be in convective equilibrium, whereas the outer portions will be in radiative equilibrium. Most of the energy generation occurs in the convective core, and the solution there can be found from eqns. (1), (2), (5), (6), and (9). The part of the star in radiative equilibrium obeys eqns. (5), (6), (7), and (8) in addition to the first four fundamental relations. The over-all structure or model of the star is found by fitting onto the solution of the adiabatic core the appropriate solution of the radiative layers so determined as to insure continuity of pressure, density, and temperature across the boundary.

In the calculation of a model star of given mass from eqns. (1) to (10) three important considerations enter:

(1) Gravitational equilibrium of the star. At each point the weight of the overlying layers must be balanced by the total pressure. $P(\rho, T)$ may become a complicated function when the ionization of some abundant element sets in, or degeneracy occurs.

(2) Composition of the material. Under conditions that must prevail in stellar interiors, the material is mostly ionized. As we have seen, the abundance of hydrogen and helium largely determines the mean molecular weight of the gas, and influences its transparency. The heavier elements of the carbon group and the metals primarily fix the opacity.

(3) The mode of escape of energy from the interior. Throughout most of the star, the transport of energy is by radiation. It is expressed by an equation containing the opacity coefficient. In the central parts of the star, however, convection currents probably are important. In white dwarf stars, the gas is degenerate and energy is transported by conduction.

The atmosphere can have but little influence upon the interior of the star. The surface temperature will so adjust itself that the total energy emitted equals the total energy generated.

We shall describe two models of great historical interest—the *convective model*, wherein all the energy is transported to the surface by large-scale convection currents; and Eddington's so-called *standard* model, wherein the energy flow is by radiation throughout the whole star. Finally we shall compute a stellar model based on the hypothesis that the energy generation varies as a high power of the temperature, as is true for the carbon cycle.

2. Uniqueness of Solution (Russell and Vogt Theorem)

For stars of the same chemical composition, the mass uniquely determines the luminosity and radius.

From eqns. (1) to (10) we can compute a stellar model by quadratures. Suppose we start the integrations at the surface with known values of M, ρ, T, P, and L. From the four differential eqns. (5) to (8), we find the increments dM_r, dP, and dT as we move a short distance Δr. Then we get new values of P, M_r, and T for $r - \Delta r$, and the corresponding density from eqn. (1). With P, ρ, and T we now compute values of μ and κ for the point $r - \Delta r$, employ again the differential eqns. (5) to (8), and proceed (at least in principle) to the center of star. In some regions we may have to use the adiabatic eqn. (9) instead of eqns. (7) and (8), but the principle remains the same.

In general, we would find that at the center of the star, the mass and luminosity would not vanish as they should. We would have to start over again with new values of our parameters, μ and κ_0, and continue until we obtained a solution. The four independent variables, P, T, M_r, and L_r have to satisfy the boundary conditions $M_r = 0$, $L_r = 0$ at $r = 0$, and $P \to 0$, $T \to 0$ at some value of r which corresponds to the radius of the star. Thus, out of a fourfold infinity of solutions, only a single infinity satisfies the three independent boundary conditions.

The model stars of the same chemical composition form a one-parameter family. That is, for stars of the same composition, there exist two exact relations between the three quantities L, M, and R, viz., $R(M)$ or $L(M)$, so that if we plot L against M we should get a curve, not an area. If we find stars of the same mass but different luminosity, or stars of the same mass and different radius, there must be a difference in their composition.* The internal composition of the star may differ from that of its surface layers and cause a spread in L and R for a given M. That is, the M, L, R relationship depends not just on the mean composition but also on any hydrogen/helium ratio or other mean molecular weight discontinuities in the star.

Before the law of energy generation was known, only one composition parameter could be found from M, L, and R, since, as we shall see, there exists only one relation between these three quantities not involving the law of energy generation. The usual practice was to determine X on the assumption $Y = 0$.

Now that the law of energy generation is known for main sequence stars, both X and Y can be found if the proportions of heavier elements are known. By equating L to the total energy produced by the nuclear reactions, we obtain a second equation which also involves L, M, and R (known from the observations), and X and Y which are to be determined from the two equations.

We shall now derive a relation between the mass, luminosity, and radius (mass–luminosity law). This function will be essentially independent of the law of energy generation, if the stars are built on the same model. We accomplish this by means of what is called a *homology transformation*.

3. Homology Transformations and the Mass-Luminosity Law

Bengt Strömgren showed that if the energy generation follows the law

$$\epsilon = \epsilon_0 \rho^m T^s \tag{11}$$

*The result implies that the stars in question have the same equation of state; e.g., they all obey the perfect gas law. We cannot compare the sun and Sirius B, for example, since the latter follows the degenerate gas law.

and the opacity is

$$\kappa = \kappa_0 \rho T^{-(n+3)} \tag{12}$$

the luminosity of a star is given by

$$L = \text{const} \frac{1}{\kappa_0} \frac{M^{s+n}}{R^n} (\mu\beta)^{7+n} \tag{13}$$

provided the radiation pressure is negligible throughout its mass, and the star is in radiative equilibrium. The constant depends on m, s, and n, and if these parameters are the same from star to star, it must follow that L depends on M and R. In the Russell-Vogt theorem we postulated that the energy generation depended in some fashion on the chemical composition, temperature, and density. If the stars have not the same composition, L depends on both M and R and not on just one of them alone.

Following a discussion by Chandrasekhar, we describe models based on two extreme forms of the energy-generation law: (I) Uniform generation of energy throughout the star, i.e., $s = 0$, $m = 0$ and $\epsilon = \epsilon_0$ (e.g., a star of radioactive material). (II) Point source model wherein all the energy is generated at the center, i.e., $s \rightarrow \infty$. All physically possible laws of energy generation fall between these two extremes, $0 < s < \infty$. For a given mass, the point-source model gives the lowest of all luminosities. Without loss of generality in the following discussion we can equate n to $\frac{1}{2}$, so that eqn. (12) corresponds to Kramers' law.

Now, ϵ, μ, and κ all depend on ρ, T, and the composition, and as a consequence of the Russell-Vogt theorem, $L = L(M, \text{comp})$, and $R = R(M, \text{comp})$. Strömgren showed that even if we do not know how ϵ depends on ρ, T, and the composition, we can still find $L = L(M, R, \text{comp})$ provided the energy generation follows the same functional form for all stars. Consider first the model I, wherein $\epsilon = \epsilon_0$. The total amount of radiation flowing through any concentric shell of radius r is

$$L_r = 4\pi\epsilon_0 \int_0^r r^2 \rho \, dr \tag{14}$$

Eqns. (5) and (6) remain valid. We have defined

$$\beta = \frac{P_G}{P}, \quad \text{or} \quad (1 - \beta) = \frac{P_r}{P} = \frac{aT^4}{3P} \tag{15}$$

By Kramers' law,

$$\kappa = \kappa_0 \rho T^{-3.5} \tag{16}$$

eqn. (8) becomes

$$\frac{d(aT^4)}{dr} = -\frac{3\kappa_0\epsilon_0}{c} \frac{\rho^2}{T^{3.5}} \frac{1}{r^2} \int_0^r r^2\rho \, dr \qquad (17)$$

These are the equations that must be solved with the boundary conditions, $M_r = M$, $P = 0$, $\rho = 0$ at $r = R$. Furthermore, $L = \epsilon_0 M_0$. We must have a relation of the form $R = R(\epsilon_0, M)$ or $R = R(L, M)$, so that for a given M only one value of R is possible. Conversely, $L = L(R, M)$; the exact numerical form can be found only by quadratures.

Let us suppose that we have calculated the model for a star of radius R_0, mass M_0, and energy production rate ϵ_0. With the aid of such a solution we can then obtain the solution for another star of radius R_1, and mass M_1, by means of a homology transformation.

Let r_0, P_0, M_{r_0}, ρ_0, R_0, $(\mu\beta)_0$, T_0, ϵ_0, refer to the values for one star and r_1, P_1, etc., refer to the values of the corresponding quantities for the other star. Let us write:

$$r_1 = t^a r_0 , \quad R_1 = t^a R_0 , \quad P_1 = t^b P_0 , \quad \rho_1 = t^c \rho_0 , \quad M_{r_1} = t^g M_{r_0} ,$$
$$(\mu\beta)_1 = t^e(\mu\beta)_0 , \quad (\kappa_0\epsilon_0)_1 = t^f(\kappa_0\epsilon_0)_0 , \quad T_1 = t^d T_0 \qquad (18)$$

In this equation the transformation of β is only approximate. Strictly speaking, the transformation should also be applied to eqn. (15) which would give one more condition. Hence the full homology transformation (with M, R, and μ independently variable) does not apply to stars in which the radiation pressure is important. Now the fundamental eqns. (1) to (8) must be fulfilled in the new variables as they were in the old, and the boundary conditions must be satisfied. That is, certain relations must be fulfilled between a, b, c, d, etc. For example,

$$dM_{r_1}/dr_1 = 4\pi r_1^2 \rho_1$$

whence

$$t^{g-a}\frac{dM_{r_0}}{dr_0} = 4\pi r_0^2\rho_0 t^{2a+c}, \quad \text{or} \quad t^{g-a} = t^{2a+c}$$

implies

$$g - a = 2a + c \qquad (19)$$

since eqn. (5) is fulfilled in the "o" variables. Similarly eqn. (8) gives

$$t^{d-a}\frac{dT_0}{dr_0} = -\frac{3}{4ac}\frac{(\kappa_0\epsilon_0)_0}{r_0^2}\frac{\rho_0^2}{T_0^{6.5}}\int_0^r r_0^2\rho_0 \, dr_0 \; t^{-6.5d+3c+a+f} \qquad (20)$$

from which there results

$$d - a = a + 3c - 6.5d + f \qquad (21)$$

Similarly from eqn. (6) and the expression for P_G we get

$$b - a = g - 2a + c \quad \text{and} \quad b = c + d - e \qquad (22)$$

Thus we have four equations that must be satisfied by our seven variables, r, P, M_r, ρ, $(\mu\beta)$, T, $(\kappa_0\epsilon_0)$, subject to the boundary conditions $\rho = 0$, $T = 0$, at $r = R$, and $M_r = 0$, $L_r = 0$ at $r = 0$. It is usually customary to take r, M and $(\mu\beta)$ as the three fundamental quantities, and therefore the independent parameters will be a, g, and e. Then we get:

$$b = -4a + 2g \qquad (23)$$

$$c = -3a + g \qquad (24)$$

$$d = -a + g + e \qquad (25)$$

$$f = -\frac{1}{2}a + \frac{9}{2}g + \frac{15}{2}e \qquad (26)$$

as the transformation equations for the new star.

Given the variation of ρ, M_r, P, etc., with r for one model star, we can compute these quantities for any other star built on the same model (i.e., with the same assumed law of energy generation, etc.) by means of the transformation eqns. (23) to (26). Let us compare stars for which the radius, mass, and $(\mu\beta)$ have all been changed. First, what will be the effect on the luminosity? From eqn. (14) we have

$$\kappa_0 L_0 = 4\pi(\epsilon_0\kappa_0)\int_0^R r^2\rho\,dr \qquad (27)$$

For another star of luminosity L_1,

$$\kappa_0 L_1 = 4\pi(\epsilon_0\kappa_0)_1\int_0^{R_1} r_1^2\rho_1\,dr = t^{f+3a+c}(\kappa_0 L_0) = t^{-1/2\,a+11/2\,g+15/2\,e}(\kappa_0 L_0)$$

but

$$t^{-1/2a} = \left(\frac{R_0}{R_1}\right)^{1/2}, \quad t^{5.5g} = \left(\frac{M_1}{M_0}\right)^{5.5}, \quad t^{7.5e} = \left(\frac{\mu_1\beta_1}{\mu_0\beta_0}\right)^{7.5} \qquad (28)$$

so we can write

$$\kappa_0 L_1 \sim \left[\frac{(\kappa_0 L_0)\sqrt{R_0}}{M_0^{5.5}(\mu_0\beta_0)^{7.5}}\right]R_1^{-0.5}M_1^{5.5}(\mu\beta)_1^{7.5} \qquad (29)$$

or, dropping subscripts,

$$L = \frac{\text{const}}{\kappa_0}\frac{M^{5.5}}{R^{0.5}}(\mu\beta)^{7.5} \qquad (30)$$

All stars built on the uniform energy-generation model should obey a mass–luminosity law of the form eqn. (30). We quote some of the values of these parameters from the work of Chandrasekhar, viz.:

$$\rho_c = 88.15\bar{\rho}, \quad T_c = 0.968\left(\frac{\mu}{\Re}\right)GM/R, \quad P_c = 20.37GM^2R^{-4} \tag{31}$$

If the luminosity, mass, and radius are expressed in terms of the corresponding solar quantities,

$$L = 1.43 \times 10^{25}\kappa_0^{-1}M^{5.5}R^{-0.5}\mu^{7.5} \tag{32}$$

Now consider model II, the point-source model, in which all the energy is generated at a point at the center of the star. Eqns. (5) and (6) and the gas law obtain as before, but eqn. (8) is replaced by

$$\frac{d}{dr}(aT^4) = -\frac{3\kappa_0\rho^2}{cT^{3.5}}\frac{L}{4\pi r^2} \tag{33}$$

since $L_r = L = $ constant is the total luminosity of the star. Here again, numerical integrations have to be carried out to obtain a specific solution. For other stars built on the same model, we can apply the homology transformations as before, noting, however, that in place of $\kappa_0\epsilon_0$ we have $\kappa_0 L$, and that eqn. (21) is replaced by

$$4d - a = f + 2c - 2a - 3.5d$$

whence

$$f = -\tfrac{1}{2}a + 5.5g + 7.5e \tag{34}$$

If we use

$$\kappa_0 L_1 = t'(\kappa_0 L_0) \tag{35}$$

and eqn. (28) we get

$$L = \frac{(\text{const}')}{\kappa_0}\frac{M^{5.5}}{R^{0.5}}(\mu\beta)^{7.5} \tag{36}$$

which is exactly the same analytical relation as we found for the uniform-source model, except that the value of the constant is different. Since the point-source model gives the lowest luminosity, any physical model based on an energy-generation law of the type indicated by nuclear physics will fall between these two extremes.

Eddington calculated a point-source model for a star five times as massive as the sun and found the luminosity to be 2.5 times lower than the standard model of the same mass, radius, and composition. For star models whose masses range from 0.2 to 20 times that of the sun, the luminosity varies over a range of 16 magnitudes. Hence the luminosity of a star is much more sensitive to the mass and to the molecular weight (i.e., the hydrogen and helium content) than it is to the type of model. An important point in this connection is that if we determine the zero-point of the mass–luminosity relation from the stars themselves, the curves will be the same for a variety of models and the empirical mass–luminosity curve cannot distinguish between the possible basic models the stars might follow.

COMPARISON OF STELLAR MODELS

	Constant	Eddington	Point Source
$\rho_c/\bar{\rho}$	88.15	54.2	37.0
$T_c/(\mu GM/R\Re)$	0.968	0.854	0.900
$P_c/(GM^2/R^4)$	20.37	11.05	7.95

The table, due to Chandrasekhar, summarizes the central pressures, temperatures, and densities for the model with constant energy generation, Eddington's standard model (Sec. 5) and the point-source model. The Eddington model falls between the two extremes.

The importance of the homology transformation is that once we have computed the pressure, density distribution, and temperature for a given mass, radius, and luminosity, we can apply the results to any other star built according to the same model. Furthermore, if we compute a model for a star of a given chemical composition, we can find a model for a different proportion of heavy constituents, hydrogen X, and helium Y, provided the distribution of the heavy elements and, therefore, the opacity law remains the same. An application of this type of homology transformation will be found in (Sec. 7).

4. Polytropic Models

The earliest workers on the problems of large gaseous spheres (stars) realized that the observed flow of energy from the interior to the surface could not take place by gaseous conduction because of the low thermal conductivity of gases. Hence it was assumed that in stellar interiors large convection currents were set up. Under these circumstances pressure and density would be related by the adiabatic gas law

$$P = K\rho^\gamma \qquad (37)$$

provided the radiation pressure is negligible compared with the gas pressure.

The modern view concerning stellar interiors is that energy may be transported either by radiation flow (as Eddington suggested) or by convection currents. The mode operative at any one point will depend on the temperature gradient; hence a given star may be in convective

equilibrium in one region while energy flow takes place by radiation
in another.

Let us now examine the problem of adiabatic or convective equilibrium. We had:

$$dM_r/dr = 4\pi r^2\rho, \qquad\qquad P = K\rho^\gamma$$
$$dP/dr = -GM_r\rho/r^2, \quad P = \frac{\Re}{\mu}\rho T \tag{38}$$

where the constant K is not yet specified. These are the fundamental
equations which we must solve when energy transport is by convection
currents rather than by radiation. We reduce the two first-order
differential equations to one differential equation of the second order,
eliminate M_r and P and use T as the dependent variable. From the
perfect gas law and the adiabatic gas law, we obtain

$$\rho = \left(\frac{\Re}{\mu}\frac{1}{K}\right)^{\frac{1}{\gamma-1}}T^{\frac{1}{\gamma-1}}, \quad P = \left(\frac{\Re}{\mu}\right)^{\frac{\gamma}{\gamma-1}}\left(\frac{1}{K}\right)^{\frac{1}{\gamma-1}}T^{\frac{\gamma}{\gamma-1}} \tag{39}$$

Furthermore,

$$\frac{dP}{dr} = \frac{\Re}{\mu}\frac{d(\rho T)}{dr} = -\frac{GM_r}{r^2}\rho \tag{40}$$

and the first equation of the set (38) yields

$$\frac{d}{dr}\left(\frac{dT}{dr}r^2\right) = -\frac{\gamma-1}{\gamma}\frac{\mu}{\Re}4\pi G\left[\frac{\Re}{\mu}\frac{1}{K}\right]^{\frac{1}{\gamma-1}}r^2 T^{\frac{1}{\gamma-1}} \tag{41}$$

Let us introduce a new variable, y, defined by

$$T = yT_c \tag{42}$$

where T_c is the central temperature. Thus, y is 1 at the center and less
than 1 elsewhere. Since the left-hand side of the equation is homogeneous in r, we may write

$$x^2 = r^2\frac{\gamma-1}{\gamma}\frac{\mu}{\Re}4\pi G\left(\frac{\Re}{\mu}\frac{1}{K}\right)^{\frac{1}{\gamma-1}}T_c^{\frac{2-\gamma}{\gamma-1}} \tag{43}$$

We get

$$\frac{d}{dx}\left(x^2\frac{dy}{dx}\right) + x^2 y^{\frac{1}{\gamma-1}} = 0 \tag{44}$$

as the polytropic equation. The reason for transforming our equation
of equilibrium into this form is to obtain an expression that contains
only the one parameter γ. It is customary to set

$$\gamma = 1 + 1/n \tag{45}$$

where n is called the *polytropic index*. The fundamental differential equation which a gaseous sphere in adiabatic equilibrium must obey is

$$\frac{1}{x^2}\frac{d}{dx}\left(x^2\frac{dy}{dx}\right) + y^n = 0 \tag{46}$$

This expression is called "Emden's Equation." Only for $n = 5$ and the trivial case, $n = 1$, can the equation be integrated analytically. For other values of the parameter n, we must resort to numerical integrations. To tabulate the solution, one starts with the initial conditions, $x = 0$, $y = 1$, $dy/dx = 0$, and calculates the first few values by means of a series expansion. Then one employs numerical integrations until he finds the value of x for which $y = 0$. This point corresponds to the boundary of the star. Emden was the first to compute tables of $y(x)$ for different n's. More recently, the British Association for the Advancement of Science computed tables of Emden functions for polytropic indices of 1, 1.5, 2, 2.5, 3, 3.5, 4, 4.5, and 5. We reproduce here the table for $n = 1.5$, corresponding to $\gamma = \frac{5}{3}$. Here y vanished for $x_0 = 3.65375$. In addition to the solution y as a function of x, certain derivatives of y are given, as well as the following auxiliary quantities:

$$A = y^n, \quad B = y^{n+1}, \quad C = -x^2 y' \tag{47}$$

which are useful in astronomical applications. The parameter n determines the density condensation of the star, the larger the value of n, the greater the concentration of mass toward the center.

With $y \equiv T/T_c$ known from the solution of Emden's equation as a function of x, and x known as a function of r from eqn. (43), we can use eqn. (39) to find the variation of pressure and density throughout the gaseous sphere.

Although the Emden functions are appropriate to those portions of the star wherein the energy transport is primarily by convection currents, workers in stellar interiors have often been tempted to choose their assumptions in such a way that the resultant equation of equilibrium would fall in polytropic form. Thus they sought to avoid troublesome numerical integrations.

5. The Eddington Model

The best known model based on Emden's equation is that due to Eddington. His chief contribution lay in the recognition of the importance of energy transport by radiation and of the role of radiation pressure. Eddington postulated that the star is everywhere in radiative

TABLE 1*

EMDEN FUNCTIONS $n = 1·5$

$x_0 = 3.65375\ 37$ $y'(x_0) = -0.20330\ 13$

x	$\dfrac{x}{x_0}$	y	y'	y''	A	$\dfrac{\delta^4}{10}$	B	$\dfrac{\delta^4}{10}$	C	$\dfrac{\delta^4}{10}$
0·0	0·00000 00	1·00000 00	-0·00000 00	-0·33333 3	1·00000	+1	1·00000	+2	0·00000	-0
0·1	·02736 91	0·99833 46	·03328 34	·33183 5	0·99750	1	0·99584	2	·00033	1
0·2	·05473 82	·99335 33	·06626 80	·32736 7	·99005	1	·98347	2	·00265	1
0·3	·08210 73	·98510 07	·09866 01	·32000 1	·97773	1	·96317	2	·00888	2
0·4	·10947 65	·97365 05	·13017 56	·30985 9	·96074	+1	·93542	1	·02083	2
0·5	0·13684 56	0·95910 39	-0·16054 49	-0·29710 8	0·93929		0·90087	+1	0·04014	-3
0·6	·16421 47	·94158 81	·18951 69	·28195 1	·91367		·86030	+1	·06823	3
0·7	·19158 38	·92125 47	·21686 30	·26463 0	·88424		·81461	0	·10626	3
0·8	·21895 29	·89827 65	·24237 98	·24541 4	·85136		·76476	0	·15512	3
0·9	·24632 20	·87284 56	·26589 23	·22459 5	·81547		·71178	0	·21537	3
1·0	0·27369 11	0·84516 98	-0·28725 55	-0·20248 0	0·77699		0·65669	-1	0·28726	-3
1·1	·30106 02	·81546 99	·30635 57	·17938 7	·73640		·60051	1	·37069	3
1·2	·32842 94	·78397 68	·32311 09	·15563 4	·69415		·54420	1	·46528	3
1·3	·35579 85	·75092 76	·33747 11	·13153 8	·65072		·48865	1	·57033	2
1·4	·38316 76	·71656 31	·34941 73	·10740 4	·60657		·43465	1	·68486	2
1·5	0·41053 67	0·68112 43	-0·35896 02	-0·08352 0	0·56213		0·38288	-1	0·80766	-2
1·6	·43790 58	·64484 99	·36613 87	·06015 8	·51783		·33392	1	0·93731	1
1·7	·46527 49	·60797 33	·37101 73	·03756 2	·47405		·28821	1	1·07224	-1
1·8	·49264 40	·57072 02	·37368 39	-·01595 2	·43116		·24607	1	·21074	0
1·9	·52001 32	·53330 66	·37424 69	+·00448 2	·38946		·20770	1	·35103	0
2·0	0·54738 23	0·49593 68	-0·37283 21	+0·02358 0	0·34925		0·17320 7	-8	1·49133	+1
2·1	·57475 14	·45880 15	·36957 99	·04121 2	·31077		·14258 1	7	·62985	1
2·2	·60212 05	·42207 70	·36464 19	·05728 0	·27421		·11573 9	6	·76487	1
2·3	·62948 96	·38592 39	·35817 84	·07171 3	·23975		·09252 4	4	1·89476	2
2·4	·65685 87	·35048 66	·35035 53	·08446 8	·20749		·07272 4	3	2·01805	2
2·5	0·68422 78	0·31589 26	-0·34134 14	+0·09552 8	0·17755		0·05608 5	-2	2·13338	+2
2·6	·71159 69	·28225 24	·33130 61	·10489 7	·14995		·04232 5	-1	·23963	2
2·7	·73896 61	·24965 98	·32041 74	·11260 1	·12474		·03114 4	0	·33584	2
2·8	·76633 52	·21819 19	·30884 00	·11868 0	·10192		·02223 8	+1	·42131	2
2·9	·79370 43	·18790 94	·29673 37	·12318 8	·08146		·01530 6	2	·49553	2
3·0	0·82107 34	0·15885 76	-0·28425 27	+0·12618 6	0·06331 6	+0	0·01005 8	+2	2·55827	+3
3·1	·84844 25	·13106 64	·27154 47	·12774 0	·04745 0	1	·0^{2}621 91	22	·60954	3
3·2	·87581 16	·10455 15	·25875 07	·12791 3	·03380 6	2	·0^{2}353 45	22	·64961	3
3·30	0·90318 07	0·07931 46	-0·24600 63	+0·12675 7	0·02233 7	$^{+6}_{0}$	0·0^{2}177 17	$^{+21}_{1}$	2·67901	$^{+4}_{0}$
3·35	·91686 53	·06717 24	·23969 37	·12569 1	·01740 9	1	·0^{2}116 94	1	·68996	
3·40	·93054 99	·05534 42	·23344 26	·12429 9	·01302 0	1	·0^{2}72 058	11	·69860	
3·45	·94423 44	·04382 68	·22726 93	·12257 5	·0^{2}917 51	17	·0^{2}40 211	7	·70507	
3·50	·95791 90	·03261 57	·22119 09	·12050 4	·0^{2}589 03	+38	·0^{2}19 212	+1	·70959	
3·55	0·97160 35	0·02170 58	-0·21522 52	+0·11806	0·0^{3}319 79	°	0·0^{6}9413	°	2·71238	
3·56	·97434 04	·01955 95	·21404 73	·11752	·0^{3}273 55	0	·0^{6}5 3505	0	·71275	
3·57	·97707 73	·01742 49	·21287 49	·11696	·0^{3}230 01	0	·0^{6}4 0080	0	·71307	
3·58	·97981 43	·01530 20	·21170 82	·11638	·0^{3}189 29	0	·0^{6}2 8965	0	·71334	
3·59	·98255 12	·01319 07	·21054 74	·11578	·0^{3}151 50	+1	·0^{6}1 9983	-1	·71356	
3·60	0·98528 81	0·01109 10	-0·20939 27	+0·11516	0·0^{2}116 80	+1	0·0^{4}1 2955	-1	2·71373	
3·61	·98802 50	·00900 28	·20824 43	·11452	·0^{3}85 422	14	·0^6 76903	15	·71386	
3·62	·99076 19	·00692 61	·20710 24	·11384	·0^{3}57 641	+27	·0^6 39923	25	·71395	
3·63	·99349 88	·00486 07	·20596 75	·11314	·0^{3}33 889	*	·0^6 16472	-49	·71401	
3·64	·99623 57	·00280 67	·20483 97	·11240	·0^{3}14 870	*	·0^{6}4173 5	*	·71404	
3·65	0·99897 26	0·00076 39	-0·20371 96	+0·11161	0·0^{4}2 1114	*	0·0^{7}161 30	*	2·71405	
x_0	1·00000 00	0·00000 00	-0·20330 13	+0·11128	0		0		2·71406	

*Courtesy, British Association for the Advancement of Science.

equilibrium; i.e., the energy is transported by radiation rather than by convection. From eqns. (7) and (8),

$$L_r = -4\pi r^2 \frac{4acT^3}{3\kappa\rho} \frac{dT}{dr} = 4\pi \int_0^r \rho r^2 \epsilon \, dr \qquad (48)$$

while eqns. (5) and (6) give

$$\frac{dP}{dr} = -G \frac{\rho}{r^2} \int_0^r 4\pi \rho r^2 \, dr \qquad (49)$$

Hence by differentiation,

$$\frac{1}{r^2} \frac{d}{dr} \left(\frac{r^2}{\rho} \frac{dP}{dr} \right) = -4\pi G\rho \qquad (50)$$

Eqns. (1), (48), and (50) should suffice to give us a solution for gaseous stars provided the functional form of μ, κ, and ϵ are known. Cf. eqns. (2), (3), and (4).

Eddington introduced a parameter, called η, by the equation

$$\frac{L_r}{M_r} = \eta \frac{L}{M} \qquad (51)$$

L/M is the mean rate of energy generation throughout the entire star, L_r/M_r is the corresponding average over a sphere of radius r, whereas η is the ratio of the two averages. We find

$$L_r = \eta \frac{L}{M} \int_0^r 4\pi r^2 \rho \, dr \qquad (52)$$

and eqn. (48) becomes

$$-4\pi r^2 \frac{4acT^3}{3\kappa\rho} \frac{dT}{dr} = \eta \frac{L}{M} 4\pi \int_0^r \rho r^2 \, dr \qquad (53)$$

So far, within the framework of the fundamental assumption employed (radiative transfer of energy), the development has been rigorous. In order to cast his equations into polytropic form, Eddington made the assumption

$$\eta\kappa = \text{constant} \qquad (54)$$

With the aid of eqn. (6), eqn. (53) reduces to

$$4\pi \frac{4acT^3}{3\kappa\eta} \frac{dT}{dr} = \frac{L}{MG} \frac{dP}{dr} \qquad (55)$$

Since the radiation pressure is $P_r = aT^4/3$,

$$4\pi \frac{MGc}{L\kappa\eta} \frac{dP_r}{dr} = \frac{d(P_g + P_r)}{dr} \qquad (56)$$

and by integration

$$4\pi \frac{MGc}{L\kappa\eta} P_r = P_g + P_r + \text{constant} \qquad (57)$$

At the surface of the star, P_g and P_r are zero, so that the constant of integration must vanish. Since $\kappa\eta$ is assumed constant, eqn. (57) shows that the ratio of gas to total pressure β must remain constant throughout the star. That is,

$$\beta = 1 - \frac{L\kappa\eta}{4\pi MGc} \qquad (58)$$

Now from eqn. (15)

$$P = P_g + P_r = \frac{\Re\rho T}{\mu\beta} = \frac{aT^4}{3(1-\beta)} \qquad (15a)$$

If the temperature is eliminated from eqn. (15a), the pressure can be expressed in terms of the density by

$$P = K\rho^{4/3} \qquad (59)$$

which is formally identical with the adiabatic gas law, with K given by

$$K = \left\{ \frac{3\Re^4(1-\beta)}{a\mu^4\beta^4} \right\}^{1/3} \qquad (60)$$

Hence the solution is given by Emden's functions for $n = 3$. With x expressed in terms of r by eqn. (43), and $y = T/T_c$ obtained from Emden's table for $n = 3$ as a function of x, we compute ρ and P by means of eqn. (39) for $\gamma = \frac{4}{3}$. Thus we obtain the ρ, T, and P variation with r throughout the star.

The Eddington model exerted such a profound influence on the study of stellar interiors that Milne called it the "standard" model, a term we may still retain to denote stellar models in which β is constant and the energy is transported by radiation.*

The chief criticisms of Eddington's model concern his assumptions about the opacity and energy generation, which are quantities determined from the physical data. Information concerning the stellar absorption coefficient was sketchy in Eddington's time. Nothing was known about energy generation. The assumption that $\kappa\eta$ is constant can be defended only on the grounds of its mathematical convenience. Physical theory fixes κ and ϵ, and therefore η, and we have no right to impose conditions on these quantities.

*Eddington derived the mass–luminosity law and believed it to give strong support to his model. As the homology transformation argument shows, however, the mass–luminosity law arises as a consequence of basic physical laws and does not speak in favor of Eddington's or any other particular model.

In his original work, Eddington assumed that stellar interiors contained little if any hydrogen, and he found a mean molecular weight of 2.1. Since the luminosity depends strongly on the molecular weight [cf. eqns. (30) or (36)], it is not surprising that Eddington's stars were too bright. This difficulty may be easily rectified by supposing that stellar interiors contain great quantities of hydrogen. The great importance of the Eddington model lies in the fact that it approximates most stellar models in temperature and density distribution.

In stars similar to the standard model, the outer portions, although vast in extent, contain very little of the mass. The mathematical treatment of these outer portions of the star is simplified by the fact that there are no energy sources and that the mass of the outer portions is negligible compared with the mass of the star as a whole.

To approach this problem, Chandrasekhar defined a fraction ξ of the stellar radius which contains 0.90 of the mass M; hence ξ gives an indication of the central condensation. For stars built on the same model, ξ, which depends on the luminosity, radius, and mass of the star, must be the same. Chandrasekhar finds that, toward the more luminous stars along the main sequence, the degree of central condensation decreases. That is, the stars become more and more homogeneous. The standard model breaks down at about ten solar masses, above this mass the star could not be built on the standard model and have the observed values of mass, luminosity, and radius.

In the massive supergiant stars, the standard model breaks down in another way; for these objects the central condensation is greater than the standard model suggests. For example, the red component of VV Cephei appears to have 0.9 of its mass concentrated in the first 5 per cent of its radius. Chandrasekhar's method of envelopes is valid for any mass, since the radiation pressure is exactly allowed for, while the usual mass–luminosity treatments neglect it—an approximation valid only for stars less than five times as massive as the sun.

6. The Stability of Stellar Models

After the equations of equilibrium are fulfilled, we have yet to ask if the equilibrium is stable or unstable. Obviously, any model that approximates a real star must be in stable equilibrium with respect to small perturbations. Three essential perturbations are to be considered:

(1) A secular contraction or expansion. If the star begins to contract, will it continue indefinitely or will it pulsate back and forth as the temperature in the interior first is increased and then decreased? If we had a star in which, at any given temperature, the molecules and atoms possessed larger internal than kinetic energy, i.e., $\gamma < \frac{4}{3}$, and this star began to contract, each volume element would be heated. The

internal energy could be, for instance, that of ionization. During contraction, gravitational potential energy would be released, but not in sufficient quantity to maintain the gas in hydrostatic equilibrium. Therefore contraction would continue with increased departure from a state of equilibrium, until γ was greater than $\frac{4}{3}$. Conversely, expansion of the gas, once started, would lower the temperature and release more energy than that required to lift each volume element against the gravitational attraction of the rest of the star. Expansion would proceed until γ exceeded $\frac{4}{3}$ or until the star exploded.

Thus, a gaseous sphere with $\gamma < \frac{4}{3}$ could never exist in stable equilibrium. The result is of little practical interest since polyatomic molecules (for which $\gamma < \frac{4}{3}$) cannot exist in hot stars and the change in effective γ due to ionization can occur only in limited regions—namely, where H and He are becoming ionized. Instabilities of this type, therefore, can occur only in small regions of the stellar interior.

The instability of a star composed of a gas whose internal energy is such that the sum of chemical, ionizational, molecular rotational energy, etc., is greater than the translational energy may be discussed in another way. Consider a volume element dV at a point in a star where the pressure is P. Then

$$\int_0^R P \, dV = PV \Big]_0^R - \int_0^R V \, dP \tag{61}$$

If we integrate this expression from the center of the star to its surface, the first term vanishes at the center, since $V = 0$ there, and at the surface where $P = 0$. Put eqn. (6) into eqn. (61), noting that

$$V = \frac{4\pi r^3}{3}$$

We obtain:

$$\int_0^R P \, dV = \frac{1}{3} \int_0^M \frac{GM_r \, dM_r}{r} \tag{62}$$

The potential energy of a shell dM_r in the field of M_r is $\dfrac{GM_r \, dM_r}{r}$ and we integrate over all dr to get the total potential energy. That is,

$$G \int_0^M \frac{M_r \, dM_r}{r}$$

is the potential of the mass upon itself, Ω. Thus

$$\int_0^R P \, dV = \frac{1}{3} \Omega \tag{63}$$

Suppose radiation pressure to be negligible so that $P = P_g = NkT$. The total kinetic energy of the molecules is

$$\frac{1}{2} N m v^2 = \frac{3}{2} NkT = \frac{3}{2} P_g$$

Thus P numerically equals $\frac{2}{3}$ the kinetic energy of the atoms. The total amount of kinetic energy in the body is

$$E = \frac{3}{2} \int P \, dV = \frac{1}{2} \Omega \tag{64}$$

Now Ω is the amount of energy required to expand the body to infinity against its own gravitational attraction. One-half of this already resides in the kinetic energy of the particles. Therefore the remaining energy store of particles, energies of rotation or vibration, chemical combination, or ionization, must be less than the kinetic energy. Otherwise the star could expand indefinitely and diffuse into space. Now

$$\gamma = \frac{r + 5}{r + 3}$$

where r is the number of internal degrees of freedom. If $r > 3, \gamma < \frac{4}{3}$, an instability of this kind results.

(2) A second type of instability may be called a thermal instability. If a star undergoes a homologous contraction, L will vary as $R^{-\frac{1}{2}}$ in accordance with eqn. (13), but if the rate of energy generation is stepped up by more than this, the star will be stable, because the increase in gas and radiation pressure will cause it to expand to something akin to its original state. On the other hand a star with constant energy generation (e.g., one composed of a uranium-gadolinium mixture) would be thermally unstable, as the rise of temperature would not affect the nuclear processes. An instability of this type would depart only slightly from equilibrium, and the star would continue to shine for millions of years.

(3) Finally, there is "pulsational instability." Suppose that a mass of gas, originally in gravitational equilibrium, is compressed into a smaller volume. The rise in temperature causes the gas to expand beyond the equilibrium condition. It is then too cool and contraction ensues and the cycle of oscillation is repeated. These pulsations will occur until they are damped out by leakage of heat from the hotter to the cooler layers. If, however, the oscillations persisted to the core of the star, they might affect the energy generation if the latter is strongly temperature dependent. Heat would be liberated when the star was smallest, and the resultant impulses would tend to increase the amplitude of the oscillations. Unless the dissipation of energy offset the

increased heat liberation, the amplitude of the pulsations would increase with time until the star blew apart.

The early studies of Eddington and of Jeans suggested that if the energy generation depended more abruptly on the temperature than T^2, the star would be unstable. Cowling, however, showed that if the energy generation increased rapidly with the temperature, the temperature gradient would become so high that the radiative equilibrium would be unstable and a convective zone would be formed in the stellar interior. His work shows that the energy generation may vary as rapidly as T^{20} without causing pulsational instability unless γ is near $\frac{4}{3}$. Ledoux has shown that γ must be $< \frac{4}{3}$ throughout a large volume of the star in order to make the star unstable.

7. A Model for a Star That Derives Its Energy from the Carbon Cycle

With the aid of a procedure due to Schwarzschild, we shall now compute a stellar model by the method of quadratures. The model will be a composite one; the innermost regions will be in convective equilibrium with $\gamma = \frac{5}{3}$. The outer portions, except for the hydrogen ionization zone which we can neglect, are in radiative equilibrium. Hence we must fit a gaseous envelope in radiative equilibrium to a polytropic core. Models of this type were first proposed by T. G. Cowling. The contribution of radiation pressure to the total pressure will be small and may be neglected, thus simplifying our work. We shall assume the composition and molecular weight constant throughout the star.

Our procedure will be to start at the surface of the star and work inward. In the outermost portions the density will be small, and to a considerable depth below the surface the change in M_r will be negligible; i.e., we can assume $M = M_r$ and $L = L_r$, since no energy is generated in the outer zone. Fortunately, pressure and temperature may be expressed as analytic functions of r in the outermost layers. Thus we obtain starting values for the numerical integrations of eqns. (5) to (8) appropriate to a state of radiative equilibrium. Throughout the strata in radiative equilibrium, we shall assume the energy generation to be zero and, therefore, dL_r/dr vanishes. At the bottom of the radiative equilibrium envelope, $r = r_f$, and L_r is then L.

We must emphasize, however, that this approximation will not necessarily, be suitable, for a star that derives its energy from the proton-proton reaction. It may be valid for the hotter stars of the main sequence that derive their energy from the carbon cycle.

We obtain the pressure as a function of the temperature in the outermost layer by dividing eqn. (6) by eqn. (8) to find

$$\frac{\dfrac{dP}{dr}}{\dfrac{d(aT^4)}{dr}} = \frac{-G \dfrac{M_r}{r^2}\rho}{-\dfrac{3\kappa\rho}{c}\dfrac{L}{4\pi r^2}} \tag{65}$$

where $M_r = M$ for the layers under consideration. We shall now adopt an analytic approximation to κ as a function of density and temperature. For the Russell mixture and for the pressure and density ranges valid in stars like the sun, κ can be represented by an equation of the form:

$$\kappa = \kappa_0 \rho^{0.75} T^{-3.5} \tag{66}$$

which corresponds to Kramers' formula with a $(\bar{g}/t)$ factor given by

$$\log\left(\frac{\bar{g}}{t}\right) = -0.6 - 0.25 \log \rho \tag{67}$$

By comparison with eqn. (44) of Chapter 1 we have

$$\kappa_0 = 10^{25}(1 + X)(1 - X - Y) \tag{68}$$

If the heavy constituent of stellar interiors is primarily oxygen, G. Keller finds that the $(\bar{g}/t)$ for the temperature and density of the sun can be represented by

$$\left(\frac{\bar{g}}{t}\right) = 5.9 \times 10^5 (1 + X)^{-0.2} \rho^{-0.2} T^{-1} \tag{69}$$

from which

$$\kappa = 1.70 \times 10^{31} \rho^{0.8} T^{-4.5} (1 + X)^{0.8}(1 - X - Y) \tag{70}$$

and

$$\kappa_0' = 1.70 \times 10^{31}(1 + X)^{0.8}(1 - X - Y) \tag{71}$$

For illustrative purposes we shall carry through the calculations for the Russell mixture. We write the gas law in the form

$$P = \left(\frac{k}{H\mu}\right)\rho T \tag{72}$$

where k is Boltzmann's constant, and H is the mass of the particle of unit atomic weight. With the aid of eqn. (66) and the elimination of ρ by eqn. (72), eqn. (65) becomes

$$\frac{dP}{dT} = \left[\frac{16\pi acGM_r}{3L\kappa_0}\left(\frac{k}{H\mu}\right)^{0.75}\right]\frac{T^{7.25}}{P^{0.75}} \tag{73}$$

which integrates to

$$P^{1.75} = \frac{1.75}{8.25} D(T^{8.25} - T_0^{8.25}) \tag{74}$$

where D denotes the quantity in brackets in eqn. (73).

We neglect the variation of μ and $(\bar{g}/t)$ near the surface of the star. The error made is about the same as that committed in taking T_0 equal to zero instead of T_0 equal to $5000°$K. Below the surface the temperature increases very rapidly. In the layers where we want to apply eqn. (74), $T_0^{8.25} < < T^{8.25}$; we can set $T_0 = 0$ without the sacrifice of accuracy. From eqns. (6), (72), and (73) it follows that

$$\frac{dP}{dr} = -\frac{GM_r}{r^2}\left(\frac{H\mu}{k}\right)\frac{P}{T} = \frac{DT^{7.25}}{P^{0.75}}\frac{dT}{dr}$$

If we eliminate P and T with the aid of eqn. (74) with T_0 as zero, we have

$$\frac{dT}{dr} = -GM_r\left(\frac{H\mu}{k}\right)\frac{1.75}{8.25}\frac{1}{r^2}$$

Then we integrate with respect to r, noting that $T = 0$ when $r = R$.

$$T = GM_r\left(\frac{H\mu}{k}\right)\frac{1.75}{8.25}\left(\frac{1}{r} - \frac{1}{R}\right) \tag{75}$$

For the outer shell down to $\log r = 10.600$, where we can assume M_r equal to M, we use eqn. (75) and then eqn. (74) to compute the temperature and the pressure in terms of r.

The analytical formulae cease to be applicable after a short distance into the star where it is no longer legitimate to set M_r equal to M. Then we must start the numerical integrations. For two or three points near the surface, we calculate values of T, P, r, and $M_r = M$ from eqns. (74) and (75). We then compute the derivatives of P, T, and M_r, and ΔP, ΔT, ΔM_r for an increment Δr and obtain $P(r - \Delta r)$, $T(r - \Delta r)$, $M(r - \Delta r)$. At $r - \Delta r$ we compute a new set of ΔP, ΔT, and ΔM_r and proceed as before. To simplify the computation we shall write:

$$\sigma = \log P, \qquad \tau = \log T$$
$$m = \log M_r, \qquad w = \log r \tag{76}$$

Consider eqn. (5). Since $dM_r/dr = (M_r/r)dm/dw$

$$\log dM_r/dr = \log M_r - \log r + \log dm/dw$$
$$= \log 4\pi + \log \rho + 2\log r$$

but, from eqn. (72),

$$\log \rho = \log P + \log\left(\frac{H\mu}{k}\right) - \log T$$

and with the aid of the definitions, eqn. (76), there results:

$$\log \left[\Delta w \, \frac{dm}{dw} \right] = 3w + \sigma - \tau - m + \log \left[\Delta w \, 4\pi \left(\frac{H\mu}{k} \right) \right] \quad (77)$$

Similarly,

$$\frac{d\sigma}{dw} = \frac{r}{P} \frac{dP}{dr}$$

and from eqns. (6) and (72)

$$\log \left(-\frac{dP}{dr} \right) = \log \left(-\frac{d\sigma}{dw} \right) + \log P - \log r$$

$$= \log \left(\frac{GH\mu}{k} \right) + \log P - \log T + \log M_r - 2 \log r$$

whence

$$\log \left(-\Delta w \, \frac{d\sigma}{dw} \right) = -w + m - \tau + \log \left(\frac{GH\mu}{k} \Delta w \right) \quad (78)$$

From eqn. (76) we have

$$\log \left(-\frac{d\tau}{dw} \right) = \log \left(-\frac{dT}{dr} \right) + \log r - \log T'$$

and since

$$\frac{dT}{dr} = \frac{dT}{dP} \frac{dP}{dr}$$

we use eqns. (6), (72), and (73) to get

$$\log \left(-\Delta w \, \frac{d\tau}{dw} \right) = -w + 1.75\sigma - 9.25\tau + \log \left[\frac{3\kappa_0 L}{16\pi ac} \left(\frac{H\mu}{k} \right)^{1.75} \Delta w \right] \quad (79)$$

Thus eqns. (77), (78), and (79) are the formulae to be solved numerically and simultaneously throughout the radiative layers of the stars. Notice that the parameters used in eqns. (73) and (75), viz., κ_0, D, and

$$\mu = \frac{1}{(2X + \frac{3}{4}Y + \frac{1}{2}Z)} \quad (80)$$

and the constants in the eqns. (77), (78), and (79), all depend on the assumed proportions of hydrogen, helium, and heavy elements. If we suppose the "heavy" constituents of the stellar interior to be primarily oxygen, rather than the Russell mixture, similar equations may be derived. The integrations are carried out numerically until the radiative gradient ceases to be stable. From eqn. (53) of Chapter 1 the condition for stability of radiative equilibrium is

$$\frac{\gamma - 1}{\gamma} \left(-\frac{1}{P} \frac{dP}{dr} \right) > \left(-\frac{1}{T} \frac{dT}{dr} \right) \quad (81)$$

or, in terms of our new variables

$$\frac{\gamma - 1}{\gamma}\left(-\frac{d\sigma}{dw}\right) > \left(-\frac{d\tau}{dw}\right) \tag{82}$$

where γ is $\frac{5}{3}$. When the inequality no longer obtains, we stop the numerical integrations and fit a polytropic solution at the point in question, since the energy transport in the inner layers must take place by convection currents, rather than by radiative transfer. We choose the solution of Emden's equation with $n = 1.5$. At the boundary of the radiative layer, our numerical integrations have given us

$$r_f, \quad M_{rf\,\mathrm{rad}}, \quad P_f, \quad T_f$$

i.e., the values of radius, mass within the radiative layer (mass of star minus mass of radiative layer), pressure, and temperature at the transition surface. Now P_f, r_f, and T_f must be joined to the results from the polytropic solution. If x and y are, respectively, the independent and dependent polytropic variables, the fitting conditions from eqns. (39), (42), and (43) are:

$$x = r\sqrt{\frac{\gamma - 1}{\gamma}\,4\pi G\left(\frac{\mu H}{k}\right)^2 \frac{P_c}{T_c^2}} \tag{83}$$

$$P_f = P_c y_f^{\frac{\gamma}{\gamma - 1}} \tag{84}$$

$$T_f = T_c y_f \tag{85}$$

If we eliminate T_c and P_c from these equations, we obtain

$$[y^{\frac{1}{\gamma - 1} - 1} x^2]_f = \frac{\gamma - 1}{\gamma}\,4\pi G\left(\frac{\mu H}{k}\right)^2 \frac{r_f^2 P_f}{T_f^2} \tag{86}$$

In the table of Emden's functions for $n = 1.5$ we compute the left-hand side of eqn. (86) as a function of x, and find the value of x for which it equals the value of the right-hand side of eqn. (86) computed from r_f, P_f, and T_f. With the aid of y_f and eqns. (84) and (85) we can then find P_c and T_c. The mass of the convective core follows from eqns. (5), (39), (42), (44), and (83):

$$M_{rf\,\mathrm{con}} = 4\pi\left(\frac{r_f}{x_f}\right)^3\left(\frac{\mu H}{k}\right)\frac{P_c}{T_c}\left(-x^2\frac{dy}{dx}\right)_f \tag{87}$$

A necessary condition for the correct solution is

$$M_{rf\,\mathrm{con}} = M_{rf\,\mathrm{rad}} \tag{88}$$

In other words, the mass left over at the end of the quadratures through the radiative equilibrium zone must equal the mass of the convective core. In general this condition will not be fulfilled for an arbitrary choice of X and Y, so we must choose other values of X, say, keeping Y fixed until we get a solution. One procedure is to take Y as zero and try different values of X. A plot of $\Delta \log M = \log M_{rf\ con} - \log M_{rf\ rad}$ against X will enable us to interpolate to obtain the final X for which $\Delta \log M$ is zero, and eqn. (88) is satisfied.

As an illustrative example we shall calculate a model for the sun in which we shall suppose that the energy-producing mechanism depends on such a high power of the temperature that all of it occurs in the convective core. Since the sun derives its energy from the proton-proton reaction, this condition is not actually fulfilled, and for a more realistic model we could have chosen a hotter, more luminous star, such as Sirius. The same principles are involved and we might, in fact, go from our present model to one for Sirius by an homology transformation. The difficulty is that even in Sirius the proton-proton reaction contributes a sizable share ($\sim$25 per cent) of the energy generation. In a yet hotter star where we could be sure that the carbon cycle dominates completely, radiation pressure would have to be taken into account and the opacity would be chiefly due to electron scattering.

We start with a trial value $X = 0.33$, $Y = 0$, and a Russell mixture for the heavy elements. Then from eqn. (80), $\mu = 1.005$ and $\kappa_0 = 0.8911 \times 10^{25}$. The procedure will be:

(1) Carry out the calculations analytically as far as we can go— to $\log r = 10.600$ by eqns. (74) and (75).
(2) Integrate numerically, through the layers in radiative equilibrium, eqns. (77), (78), and (79).
(3) Use eqn. (82) as the criterion for locating r_f. At this point we must fit the Emden function for $n = 1.5$ by eqns. (83) to (85).

The basic numerical constants are:

Total solar mass, $M = 1.985 \times 10^{33}$ gm
Total solar radius, $R = 6.951 \times 10^{10}$ cm
Total solar luminosity, $L = 3.78 \times 10^{33}$ ergs
Constant of gravitation, $G = 6.67 \times 10^{-8}$ dynes cm^2/gm^2
Mass of particle of unit atomic weight, $H = 1.672 \times 10^{-24}$ gm
Boltzmann constant, $k = 1.379 \times 10^{-16}$
Stefan Boltzmann constant, $a = 7.55 \times 10^{-15}$
Velocity of light, $c = 2.9978 \times 10^{10}$ cm/sec

We now compute $\log T$ and $\log P$ for the two values of

$$w = \log r = 10.640 \text{ and } 10.600$$

TABLE 2

Numerical Integration of the Region in Radiative Equilibrium

w	m	$\log \Delta w \frac{dm}{dw}$	$\Delta w \frac{dm}{dw}$	$\frac{1}{2}D'$	σ	$\log\left[-\Delta w \frac{d\sigma}{dw}\right]$	$-\Delta w \frac{d\sigma}{dw}$	$\frac{1}{2}D'$	τ	$\log\left[-\Delta w \frac{d\tau}{dw}\right]$	$-\Delta w \frac{d\tau}{dw}$	$\frac{1}{2}D'$	$\frac{\frac{d\sigma}{dw}\Delta w}{\frac{d\tau}{dw}\Delta w}$
10.640	33.298	7.527	0.003		13.582	9.705	0.507		6.465	9.032			
10.600	33.298	7.779	0.006	0.002	14.055	9.645	0.442	−0.033	6.565	8.972	0.094	−0.007	
10.560	33.290	7.989	0.010	0.002	14.464	9.591	0.390	−0.026	6.652	8.925	0.084	−0.005	
10.520	33.279	8.165	0.015	0.002	14.827	9.540	0.347	−0.022	6.731	8.868	0.074	−0.005	
10.480	33.262	8.318	0.021	0.003	15.152	9.494	0.312	−0.017	6.800	8.842	0.070	−0.002	
10.440	33.238	8.450	0.028	0.004	15.447	9.443	0.277	−0.017	6.867	8.774	0.060	−0.005	
10.400	33.206	8.567	0.037	0.004	15.707	9.397	0.249	−0.014	6.921	8.765	0.058	−0.001	
10.360	33.165	8.666	0.046	0.005	15.942	9.338	0.218	−0.016	6.979	8.684	0.048	−0.005	
10.320	33.114	8.755	0.057	0.005	16.144	9.283	0.192	−0.013	7.022	8.677	0.047	0.00	
10.280	33.051	8.830	0.068	0.005	16.323	9.214	0.164	−0.014	7.069	8.594	0.039	−0.004	
10.240	32.979	8.897	0.079	0.006	16.473	9.146	0.140	−0.012	7.105	8.570	0.037	−0.001	
10.200	32.895	8.953	0.090	0.005	16.601	9.066	0.116	−0.012	7.141	8.501	0.032	−0.003	3.68
10.160	32.800	9.003	0.101	0.006	16.705	8.982	0.096	−0.010	7.170	8.456	0.028	−0.002	3.36
10.120	32.693	9.048	0.112	0.006	16.791	8.888	0.077	−0.009	7.197	8.397	0.025	−0.002	3.11
10.080	32.576	9.091	0.123	0.006	16.859	8.788	0.061	−0.008	7.220	8.342	0.022	−0.002	2.80
10.040	32.447	9.133	0.136	0.006	16.913	8.679	0.048	−0.007	7.240	8.287	0.019	−0.001	2.46
10.000	32.305	9.178	0.151	0.007	16.953	8.558	0.036	−0.006	7.258	8.231	0.017	−0.001	2.13

by eqns. (74) and (75) which become, respectively,

$$\log P = -16.8940 + 4.71430 \log T \qquad (74a)$$

$$\log T = 17.5343 + \log [1/r - 1/R] \qquad (75a)$$

Hence we obtain our starting values for the numerical integrations of σ, τ, and m as a function of w. We assume $m = \log M = $ constant for these first two points. For $X = 0.33$, $Y = 0$, and $\Delta w = 0.04$, the equations to be numerically integrated are:

$$\log \left[\Delta w \frac{dm}{dw} \right] = 3w - m + \sigma - \tau - 8.2130 \qquad (89)$$

$$\log \left[-\Delta w \frac{d\sigma}{dw} \right] = -w + m - \tau - 16.4880 \qquad (90)$$

$$\log \left[-\Delta w \frac{d\tau}{dw} \right] = -w + 1.75\sigma - 9.25\tau + 45.7009 \quad (91)$$

In our integrations we must keep in mind that m decreases with decreasing w, whereas σ and τ increase as w decreases. We compute each new value of m, σ, and τ with the aid of the expression

$$X_{n+1} = X_n + \left(\Delta w \frac{dX}{dw} \right)_n + \frac{1}{2} D' \qquad (92)$$

where X stands for either m, σ, or τ, and D' is the first difference in the $\Delta w \frac{dX}{dw}$ column.

Table 2 illustrates the computational procedure. The σ and τ entries for $w = 10.640$ and 10.600 are taken from the analytic eqns. (74a) and (75a). For example, to obtain σ for 10.560, we compute by eqn. (90),

$$\log \left(-\Delta w \frac{d\sigma}{dw} \right) = -10.600 + 33.298 - 6.565 - 16.488 = \bar{9}.645$$

or

$$\Delta w \frac{d\sigma}{dw} = 0.442$$

The previous entry in this column (obtained from the analytic solution) is 0.507 so that $D' = -0.065$.

Then,

$$\sigma(w = 10.560) = 14.055 + 0.442 - 0.033 = 14.464$$

The values of the other quantities are computed similarly. Proceeding step by step, the integration is continued until

$$\frac{\frac{d\sigma}{dw} \, \Delta w}{\frac{d\tau}{dw} \, \Delta w} = 2.50 \tag{93}$$

at some value, w_f. Then σ_f, m_f, and τ_f are interpolated from their respective columns. In the present example, this point is reached at

$$w_f = 10.045, \quad \tau_f = 7.238, \quad m_f = 32.462, \quad \sigma_f = 16.906$$

The numerical value of the right-hand side of eqn. (86) is 1.649 which must equal $(x^2 y^{n-1})$, a quantity computed from the tabulated solution of Emden's equation for $n = 1.5$. From a table or plot of $y^{n-1} x^2$ versus x, we find $x_f = 1.395$, $y_f = 0.7183$. Then eqns. (84) and (85) give:

$$\log P_c = 17.266 \quad \text{and} \quad \log T_c = 7.382$$

We next interpolate $(-x^2 \, dy/dx)_f$ for $x = 1.395$ from the Emden table, and compute $\log M_{rf \text{ con}}$ from eqn. (87) to be 32.602, which is greater than $m_f = \log M_{rf \text{ rad}} = 32.462$. Hence the condition expressed by eqn. (88) is not fulfilled. This result means we have chosen the wrong composition (hydrogen content) and we must start over with a new value of X, keeping Y zero or varying both X and Y, until we find a solution which satisfies eqn. (88).

Ultimately, we may find a satisfactory model with, say, $X = X_0$ and $Y = Y_0$; but it is not necessarily the model of the star in which we are interested, since we have not included the law of energy generation in the analysis. This law, which is known as a function of temperature, density, and composition, gives an additional relationship which permits a determination of both the hydrogen and helium content of any star whose mass, luminosity, and radius are known, provided we know the relative abundances of the elements comprising the mixture of heavy elements.

In this simplified illustrative calculation we have supposed that the energy generation depends on such a high power of the temperature that it all occurs within the convective core. In a realistic model for the sun and similar stars which operate on the proton-proton reaction eqns. (77), (78), and (79) are supplemented by a relation, eqn. (7), involving the energy generation as soon as the temperature rises above a few million degrees.

8. Schwarzschild's Method for the Determination of the Hydrogen and Helium Content of the Stars

If the energy generation takes place almost entirely by the carbon cycle, it is possible to estimate the hydrogen and helium content of a star in a straightforward fashion. In practice, the considerations apply to stars of the main sequence, somewhat brighter than the sun, e.g., Sirius, but not to stars which are so bright that radiation pressure plays an important role in their structure.

To simplify the integrations of the stellar interior, Martin Schwarzschild introduced four dimensionless variables, p, t, z, and q defined by

$$P = p \frac{GM^2}{4\pi R^4}, \quad T = t \frac{\mu H}{k} \frac{GM}{R}, \quad M(r) = qM, \quad r = zR \quad (94)$$

With these variables the basic differential equations (5), (6), and (8), valid for the layers in radiative equilibrium, become:

$$\frac{dq}{dz} = \frac{p}{t} z^2, \quad \frac{dp}{dz} = -\frac{p}{t} \frac{q}{z^2}, \quad \frac{dt}{dz} = -\frac{C}{z^2} \frac{p^{1.75}}{t^{8.25}} \quad (95)$$

where the constant C is defined by

$$C = \frac{3\kappa_0}{4ac} \left(\frac{k}{\mu H G} \right)^{7.5} \left(\frac{1}{4\pi} \right)^{2.75} \frac{LR^{1.25}}{M^{5.75}} \quad (96)$$

After several trials, Schwarzschild found that $\log C = -5.51674$ permitted a fit between the convective core and the radiative layer. Notice that C contains the two parameters that involve the hydrogen and helium content of the star, viz., κ_0 and μ. Hence a determination of C establishes a numerical relation between κ_0 and μ and therefore between X and Y. At the interface between the radiative layer and the convective core,

$$z_f = \frac{\text{radius of core}}{\text{radius of star}} = 0.121725$$

$$\log p_f = 2.1945, \quad \log t_f = -0.0426, \quad \log q_f = -0.9269 \quad (97)$$

The fitting values of the polytropic variables for $n = 1.5$ are $x_f = 1.1201$ and $y_f = 0.8093$. From eqns. (84), (85), and (94), and the adiabatic gas law, the central temperature and density of the star are derived, viz.:

$$T_c = \frac{t_f}{y_f} \frac{\mu H}{k} \frac{GM}{R}$$

$$\rho_c = \frac{p_f}{4\pi y_f^{1.5} t_f} \frac{M}{R^3} = 79.0\bar{\rho} \quad (98)$$

and if the mass and radius are expressed in units of the mass of the sun,

$$T_c = 25.89 \times 10^6 \mu \frac{M}{R}, \quad \rho_c = 111.6 \frac{M}{R^3} \tag{99}$$

Eqn. (96) may be employed to obtain the mass–luminosity relation. Since the numerical value of C is known, we may substitute the expressions for μ and κ_0, which are given in terms of X and Y by eqn. (68) and eqn. (80), into eqn. (96) to obtain:

$$[2X + \tfrac{3}{4}Y + \tfrac{1}{2}(1 - X - Y)]^{7.5}(1 + X)(1 - X - Y)$$
$$= 1.34 M^{5.75} L^{-1} R^{-1.25} \tag{100}$$

The determination of X and Y requires a second relation between these quantities. The law of energy generation according to the carbon cycle and the proton-proton reaction provides the necessary equation. We modify Schwarzschild's treatment by employing the latest data on the energy generation in the stars. (Cf. Chapter 1.) For a star whose central temperature lies not too far from that of the sun, the energy generation in ergs/cm^3/sec by the proton-proton and carbon-nitrogen cycles are, respectively:

$$\epsilon_{pp} = 0.28 \rho X^2 \left(\frac{T}{13}\right)^{4.1} = \epsilon_1 \rho T^{4.1}$$
$$\epsilon_{CN} = 1.66 \rho X W_{CN} \left(\frac{T}{13}\right)^{20.4} = \epsilon_2 \rho T^{20.4} \tag{101}$$

where the temperature is expressed in millions of degrees, and the abundance of carbon plus nitrogen, W_{CN}, is taken as $0.158(1 - X - Y)$. In accordance with the basic assumptions expressed in the set of eqns. (95), we suppose all the energy is generated in the core so that

$$L = L_{pp} + L_{CN} = 4\pi \int_0^{r_f} \rho(\epsilon_{pp} + \epsilon_{CN}) r^2 \, dr \tag{102}$$

With the aid of eqn. (98), the adiabatic gas law, and the definitions of the polytropic functions we obtain from eqn. (102),

$$\frac{L_{pp}}{M} = \epsilon_1 \rho_c T_c^{4.1} \frac{p_f}{y_f^{1.5} t_f} \left(\frac{z_f}{x_f}\right)^3 \int_0^{x_f} y^7 x^2 \, dx = \frac{\epsilon_1 \rho_c T_c^{4.1}}{15.28}$$
$$\frac{L_{CN}}{M} = \epsilon_2 \rho_c T_c^{20.4} \frac{p_f}{y_f^{1.5} t_f} \left(\frac{z_f}{x_f}\right)^3 \int_0^{x_f} y^{23.4} x^2 \, dx = \frac{\epsilon_2 \rho_c T_c^{20.4}}{58.45} \tag{103}$$

where L, M, ρ, and T are expressed in cgs units. If we now eliminate ρ_c and T_c with the aid of eqn. (99), introduce ϵ_1 and ϵ_2 from eqns. (101), and express L and M in terms of the corresponding solar values, the energy-output equation becomes

$$L = 18.1 X^2 \mu^{4.1} \frac{M^{6.1}}{R^{7.1}} + 3.339 \times 10^5 \times (1 - X - Y)\mu^{20.4} \frac{M^{22.4}}{R^{23.4}} \quad (104)$$

where μ is given by eqn. (80). This equation applies to any star built on Schwarzschild's model. For each star the mass–luminosity eqn. (100) defines one curve in the XY-plane; the energy-output eqn. (104) defines another. The point of intersection, $X = 0.941$, $Y = 0.046$, fixes the hydrogen and helium content for Sirius, according to this model. See Fig. 1. The helium content seems too low. We have

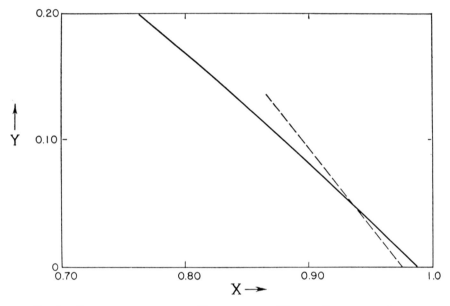

Fig. 1.—Determination of the Hydrogen and Helium Content of Sirius

For Sirius, $M = 2.45$, $L = 36$, and $R = 1.65$ in terms of the corresponding solar values. The point of intersection of the mass–luminosity relation eqn. (100) (solid curve) and the energy-output eqn. (104) (dashed curve) fixes the hydrogen content $X = 0.941$ and the helium content $Y = 0.046$ for this star.

neglected the energy generation outside the core; on the other hand, the temperature dependence of the carbon cycle is too high if T_c is near 20,000,000°K, so that the real central temperature may be higher and the hydrogen content lower. One suspects that the opacity law may be partly at fault.* A further possibility is that the core may be richer in helium and poorer in hydrogen than the envelope (see Sec. 12).

*The investigations of Mrs. M. H. Harrison indicate that for the most likely composition of the heavy stuff, the guillotine factor can no longer be represented by a single straight line of the type of eqn. (67). As an extreme example, G. Keller has considered a stellar model in which there is one heavy element, oxygen.

9. Stellar Models Based on the Proton-Proton Reaction

Calculations by I. Epstein and L. Motz (1953, 1954) and by Peter Naur demonstrate rather conclusively that the proton-proton reaction provides essentially all the energy generation in the sun.

With the red dwarf stars, however, calculations based on the proton-proton reaction with the outer envelopes in radiative equilibrium lead to stellar models that are always too bright.

Strömgren suggested and Osterbrock demonstrated the way out of this difficulty. Below the atmospheric layers in the red dwarf stars lies the hydrogen convection zone in which the Emden eqn. (46) is valid. Instead of being a few hundred kilometers thick, this zone in convective equilibrium may represent a sizable volume of the star. Eventually, near the center, the material switches back to radiative equilibrium. Osterbrock's detailed calculations show that one can get a good fit for the radius, mass, and luminosity of a star such as Castor C or α Centauri B with values of hydrogen, helium, and heavier constituent abundances in good agreement with the results from stellar atmospheres. More precise computations do not appear to be worth while until the status of the opacity calculations is greatly improved.

Naur and Osterbrock found that dwarf G, K, and M stars and probably also the sun must be in radiative equilibrium at their centers. Dwarf stars somewhat earlier than the sun may have convective cores, while main-sequence objects earlier than $F5$ probably have such cores.

Naur, who took into account the effects of the free-free transitions in hydrogen and helium upon the opacity, found that the solar model was extremely sensitive to the assumed opacity law in so far as the existence or nonexistence of a convective core was concerned. His model I had no convective core; his model II a core of radius 0.05. The required composition involved 0.75 per cent of elements heavier than helium, the hydrogen content was about 75 per cent, and the central temperature near 13.5 million degrees. The central density is near 90gm/cm^3. The outer hydrogen-ionization convection zone is much less important than in the red dwarf stars. It extended down only about 200,000 km. The Epstein-Motz model (1954) gives $X = 93.1$ per cent, $Y = 6.7$ per cent, $T_c = 12,850,000°K$, and a convective core radius equal to 0.08 that of the sun.

10. Apsidal Motion in Eclipsing Binaries

Fortunately, in a number of important examples, at least a partial check on the theoretical model is available. In certain eclipsing binary systems it is observed that the interval between primary and secondary eclipse is not constant. The secondary minimum appears to wander back and forth with a period much longer than the orbital revolution period. We interpret this effect as arising from the motion of the stars in elliptical orbits which slowly precess. In general, this precession does not arise because of a third body in the system but rather because the two stars are distorted from their natural spherical shape by their mutual gravitational attraction. Hence they no longer attract one another like point masses. The basic phenomenon depends on the following three effects:

(1) Star A tidally distorts star B.

(2) Because star B is distorted, it will no longer attract as a point mass at its center of gravity.

(3) The fact that B no longer attracts as a point mass means we no longer have a strict two-body problem. The orbits will deviate slightly from Kepler ellipses; the most important feature of this deviation being a slow rotation of the major axis, i.e., a precession of the orbit with an advance of periastron.

Since the stars are gaseous throughout, the figures of their surfaces at any moment will be nearly those appropriate to equilibrium under the instantaneous tidal forces. Hence the problem is more difficult than the corresponding problem of the perturbations of a satellite orbit by the equatorial bulge of a rapidly spinning planet.*

The amount of distortion of star B will depend on the masses of the two stars, their relative separation, the size of B, and the mass concentration or the model of B. Likewise, star A will be distorted by star B. Cowling and Sterne's investigations show that the ratio of the orbital period to the length of time it takes the major axis or line of apsides to rotate completely around will be:

$$\frac{\text{orbital period}}{\text{apsidal period}} = 15K_2 \frac{R_2^5}{A^5} \frac{1 + \frac{3}{2}e^2 + \frac{1}{8}e^4}{(1 - e^2)^5} \frac{M_1}{M_2}$$

$$+ 15K_1 \frac{R_1^5}{A^5} \frac{1 + \frac{3}{2}e^2 + \frac{1}{8}e^4}{(1 - e^2)^5} \frac{M_2}{M_1} \qquad (105)$$

where A is the semi-major axis of the orbit, R_1 and R_2 are the radii of the stars A and B, M_1 and M_2 their masses, and e is the eccentricity, while the K's are constants that depend on the mass concentration to the center of the distorted star. For a homogeneous star, K is 0.750, whereas for a star whose mass is essentially all concentrated at the center, with a vanishingly small amount in the rest of its volume, K would be 0.00 since the stars would then be point masses and the

---

*Chandrasekhar's investigation of the equilibria of distorted polytropes constitutes the fundamental work on this problem. (*M.N.* **93**, 449, 1933.)

two-body solution would hold. For other density models, the value of K naturally falls between 0 and 0.75. On the assumption that the stellar internal density distribution can be approximated by polytropic models, Chandrasekhar computed the following table, which gives K and the ratio of central to mean density. For comparison with these

Polytropic Index	0	1	1.5	2	3	4
K	0.750	0.260	0.1446	0.0741	0.0144	0.00134
$\rho_c/\bar\rho$	1.000	3.290	5.991	11.403	54.18	622.41

calculations we take the observed rates of apsidal motions for eight eclipsing binary stars with well-determined orbits and K values, see Table 3. For each star Russell lists the spectral class, period in days,

TABLE 3

BINARIES WITH MOVING APSIDES*

Star	Spectrum	P	R_1/A	R_2/A	e	$P^1_{aps}/1000P$	K
Y Cyg	$O9.5$	2.996	0.206	0.206	0.14	5.6	0.014
GL Car	Bp	2.422	0.215	0.215	0.16	3.8	0.017
AG Pers	$B3$	2.029	0.263	0.184	0.05	9.6	0.0045
CO Lac	F	1.542	0.24	0.24	0.03	9.5	0.004
V523 Sgr	$A5$	2.324	0.22	0.22	0.17	31	0.0018
HV 7498	$A0$	3.471	0.123	0.147	0.55	63	0.009
YY Sgr	$A0$	2.629	0.127	0.127	0.17	49	0.018
RU Mon	$A5$	3.584	0.13	0.11	0.44	61	0.018

*Courtesy, H. N. Russell, *Ap. J.* **90**, 650, 1939.

ratio of stellar radius to orbital radius for each component, the eccentricity of the orbit, and the period of apsidal motion P^1 divided by 1000 times the period, and finally K. Notice that K is always small; in no instance is it larger than 0.02. Observational selection would work in the opposite direction, since rapid apsidal motions, and therefore larger K's would be easier to detect. Thus there is strong evidence that the density concentration within the stars is high. It is also likely that the stars are not all built on the same model. GL Carinae (Bp) and V523 Sag ($A5$) have nearly the same orbital period and radii, while the respective apsidal periods are 25 and 200 years.

The density and temperature distribution in the average star model is well represented by the standard model (polytrope for $n = 3$), and it is satisfying to see how closely the predicted and observed central density concentrations of the stars agree.

11. Stellar Rotation

A star in static gravitational equilibrium will be radially symmetrical; i.e., the pressure, density, and temperature will depend on the single variable, r, and the problem of its internal structure will be readily soluble if the basic physical data are given. Now imagine such a star to be set in rotation. There will be a centrifugal force and the pressure, density, and temperature will depend not only on r but on the latitude as well. In general, the angular velocity will not be constant throughout the star but may vary from point to point.*

The problem is complicated because the star does not rotate as a solid body, and the fundamental equations are much more complex than those valid for a static star. For example, the equation of hydrostatic equilibrium (6) becomes replaced by two expressions, viz.:

$$\omega^2 r(1 - \mu^2) = +\frac{1}{\rho}\frac{\partial P}{\partial r} + \frac{\partial \Phi}{\partial r}$$

$$-\omega^2 r^2 = \frac{1}{\rho}\frac{1}{\mu}\frac{\partial P}{\partial \mu} + \frac{1}{\mu}\frac{\partial \Phi}{\partial \mu}$$

(106)

where ω is the angular velocity, μ is the sine of the latitude, and Φ is the gravitational potential. Similarly, the equation of transfer has to be written for two components, r and μ.

In that portion of the star in radiative equilibrium, the viscosity is negligible and therefore the angular velocity may vary with the distance from the center and also with the latitude. The effect of meridional currents is negligible.

Since the original work of von Zeipel, who showed that a star cannot rotate as a solid body, Milne, Eddington, Jeans, Rosseland, Biermann, Randers, Krogdahl, M. Schwarzschild, and others have contributed to the problem. G. Randers studied the most general state of steady motion possible in a rotating symmetrical star of viscous material, and derived a number of theorems concerning the circulation of the material. Among the most interesting recent investigations is M. Schwarzschild's study of stellar rotation for stars similar to the sun.

---

*One might expect yet another difference between a rotating and non-rotating star. We have no reason to anticipate large-scale internal currents in the latter; we may expect only a disorderly mixing of material between adjacent layers in a convective zone. Various writers have suggested that, in a rotating star, large-scale currents circulate in meridional planes. A detailed discussion by Schwarzschild has indicated that such currents may not play an important role in energy or momentum transport.

Schwarzschild's treatment of the equations of equilibrium for the sun takes advantage of the fact that rotation amounts to only a small perturbation. Therefore, we may start with the static (i.e., non-rotating) solar model and apply a perturbation method. We write: $P = P_0 + P'$, $L = L_0 + L'$, $T = T_0 + T'$, etc., where the subscript 0 applies to the static model. If these equations are substituted in the equilibrium equations, and the second and higher powers of the perturbations are neglected, two sets of equations follow. One set involves only P_0, L_0, T_0, etc., and corresponds to the equilibrium conditions for a non-rotating star, a problem which has already been solved. The second set involves only linear terms in the perturbation. The resultant six differential equations must be solved with due regard to conditions of continuity at the interface between the convective core and the radiative envelope, and to the appropriate boundary conditions at the center and surface.

Schwarzschild supposed that in the strata in radiative equilibrium, the star tries to distribute the angular momentum in such a way that it needs no large-scale currents to assist in the transport of energy to the surface. Thus he attempted to find a possible dependence of the angular velocity on r and ϕ, such that the equations of equilibrium are fulfilled and the net flux is constant.

A check on the theory follows from a comparison with the observed rotational velocity of the sun. If v_E is the equatorial velocity, and $\mu = \sin \phi$, the predicted linear velocity at any latitude ϕ will be

$$v = v_E \sqrt{1 - 0.97\mu^2 + 0.06\mu^4} \sqrt{1 - \mu^2} \qquad (107)$$

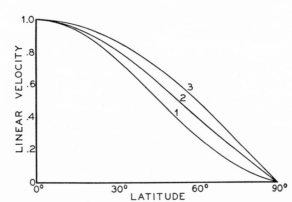

FIG. 2.—THE ROTATIONAL VELOCITY AT THE SURFACE OF THE SUN

The curve (1) is the relation found by Schwarzschild's analysis, (2) is the observed rate of rotation, and (3) corresponds to a solid body. For all three curves the velocity is expressed in terms of the linear velocity at the equator as 1. (Courtesy, M. Schwarzschild, *Astrophysical Journal*, University of Chicago Press, **106**, 456, 1947.)

A comparison with the observations (see Fig. 2) shows that the actual linear velocity of the solar surface falls in between the speed for solid-body rotation and the velocity distribution predicted by theory. In other words, the predicted equatorial acceleration of the sun is about twice the observed equatorial acceleration.

It is of interest that the Schwarzschild theory, wherein large-scale convection currents are ignored in dynamic and thermal considerations, gives the correct qualitative picture of the solar rotation. If we postulated that convection currents played an important role in the transport of energy in rotating stars, there should exist an equatorial deceleration instead of an acceleration, because convection currents tend to preserve angular momentum. Schwarzschild suggests that the quantitative discordance between observation and theory may mean that the inner part of the radiative zone also rotates as a solid body, and slow convection currents may penetrate this region and carry a portion of the energy flux. The currents may be so slow as to have little influence on the dynamics of the problem, but their effects on the transport of energy could be appreciable.

Whether a star is distorted by tidal forces or by its own rotation, the gravity g will vary from point to point on the surface. Von Zeipel showed that the surface brightness at any point is proportional to the surface gravity. In particular, the equatorial regions of rapidly spinning stars would appear dimmer than their poles. This phenomenon of gravity darkening assumes considerable importance in the interpretation of precise photometric observations of close eclipsing binaries.*

12. The Giant Stars and Stellar Evolution

Although chemically homogeneous models that derive their energy from the carbon cycle or proton-proton reaction give an adequate interpretation of the main sequence, they fail for the giant and super-giant stars. The derived central temperatures are so low that the only possible nuclear reactions would be those involving the terrestrially rare elements such as lithium, beryllium, boron, or deuterium. Such energy sources are extremely unlikely. The liberation of energy by gravitational contraction is quite inadequate.

The way out of these difficulties seems to lie in chemically inhomogeneous models, in which the outer portions of the star have very nearly a "normal" hydrogen-rich composition whereas the inner core is depleted of hydrogen. Öpik was the first to suggest chemical inhomogeneities as the explanation of the large radii of giant stars. Subsequently, G. Gamow and G. Keller proposed a model in which the

---

*An account of von Zeipel's theorem is given in Eddington, *Internal Constitution of the Stars* (Cambridge: Cambridge University Press, 1926), p. 287.

energy is generated in a thin shell surrounding an isothermal core wherein all the hydrogen has been exhausted. F. Hoyle and R. A. Lyttleton and, more recently, Li Hen and M. Schwarzschild treated models wherein the core and inner portion of the radiative envelope had a molecular weight μ_1, whereas the outer radiative envelope had a molecular weight μ_2. A suitable model for a supergiant star could be obtained by a judicious choice of μ_1 and μ_2. Extensive contributions to the problem have been made also by A. Reiz, P. Ledoux, C. M. and H. Bondi, J. G. Gardiner, M. Schonberg, and S. Chandrasekhar, and others.

Particular mention should be made of the family of models recently calculated by J. B. Oke and M. Schwarzschild. They assume a hydrogen-rich envelope ($X = 0.92$) in radiative equilibrium, an intermediate zone in radiative equilibrium, and a core in convective equilibrium. Hydrogen is poor ($X = 0.01$) in both of the latter regions but still suffices to supply energy. They calculated a family of solutions which differ from one another in the fraction of mass (14 per cent to 70 per cent) included in the convective core. The resultant models, for masses 1, 2, and 4 times that of the sun give dimensions and luminosities appropriate to giant stars but are sensitive to the assumed opacity law. The masses turn out to be lower than those required by the mass–luminosity law.

The physical justification for such non-homogeneous models is to be sought in the evolution of the stars. The lifetimes of highly luminous stars is short compared to the age of the galaxy. The sun produces energy at the rate of 2 ergs/gm/sec while the O-type main-sequence eclipsing binary Y Cygni generates 1200 ergs/gm/sec. Hence, stars such as Y Cygni will have consumed all their hydrogen in a couple of hundred million years. The lifetime of a less luminous star is longer but even objects such as Sirius, thirty or forty times as luminous as the sun, must be younger than the galaxy.

The evolution of a star will depend very much on whether it keeps itself well mixed or whether the mixing is confined to the convective core.

Let us consider first the evolution of a star that keeps itself well mixed by internal large-scale motions so that the star remains chemically homogeneous. As hydrogen is converted into helium, the mean molecular weight increases and the star gradually becomes more luminous, consuming its diminishing supply of fuel at an ever increasing rate. For purposes of illustration let us trace the evolution of a star of the same mass, radius, and luminosity as the sun. Employing Schwarzschild's model with an initial $X = 0.47$, $Y = 0.41$, and utilizing eqn. (100) together with his energy-output equation, analogous to our eqn.

TABLE 4

EVOLUTION OF A STAR THAT REMAINS CHEMICALLY HOMOGENEOUS
(*Schwarzschild Model*)

X	Y	T_{eff}	R/R_0	L/L_0
0.47	0.41	5700	1.00	1.00
0.40	0.48	6460	1.035	1.73
0.30	0.58	8830	1.062	4.00
0.20	0.68	9750	1.100	10.3
0.15	0.73	11000	1.12	17.36
0.05	0.83	14720	1.13	57.2
0.025	0.855	16300	1.11	83.0
0.020	0.860	16600	1.10	88.0
0.015	0.865	17100	1.09	95.5
0.010	0.870	17600	1.07	104.0
0.005	0.875	18350	1.04	115.5

Successive columns give the hydrogen content X, helium content Y, effective surface temperature T_{eff}, and finally the radius and luminosity in terms of the initial values of these quantities. The model is based on the carbon cycle as the source of energy generation. Hence the results are only of qualitative significance.

(104), we obtain the results given in Table 4. As hydrogen is depleted, the radius increases and then decreases slightly, but the luminosity and temperature steadily rise. The star moves up the main sequence at an ever increasing rate until the hydrogen is all consumed. After that it may shrink with gravitational contraction supplying all the energy (Kelvin process) and eventually develop into a white dwarf—or if its mass exceeds a certain critical limit (see page 88), it may shed material violently as in supernovae or more slowly as perhaps in Wolf-Rayet stars.

Unless the star is rotating rapidly, there appears to be no means whereby it can keep itself everywhere well mixed. Normally, mixing will occur only in the convective core; the radiative envelope will retain its initial composition. Thus as time goes on, the hydrogen in the core becomes converted into helium and a pronounced difference in composition between core and radiative envelope develops. In our discussion of Sirius by the Schwarzschild model we obtained an improbably high abundance of hydrogen due to our neglect of the difference in composition between envelope and core. Eventually all the hydrogen is gone; the star develops an inert, isothermal core; and the energy generation takes place in a thin shell at the boundary between the convective core and the radiative envelope. Schonberg and Chandrasekhar showed that the isothermal core could grow until it included about 12 per cent of the mass. By this time the star would have left the main sequence and brightened about one magnitude. Beyond this point the star cannot be stable, and Sandage and Schwarzschild suggest that the core contracts gravitationally. Their detailed calculations of the evolution of such stars assume that all nuclear energy is developed in a thin shell at 30 million degrees. At the same time energy is released in the contraction of the core. The stellar model consists of a hydrogen-rich envelope ($X_e = 0.596$, $Y_e = 0.384$) and a hydrogen depleted core ($Y_i = 0.98$), both in radiative equilibrium. The mass of the core gradually grows as it shrinks in size, the hydrogen-rich envelope expands, and each step of the evolution can be followed in detail.

For the sequence of models they calculated that the objects very nearly follow the mass–luminosity law for main-sequence stars, that the radius of the hydrogen-exhausted core shrinks from about 6 per cent of the stellar radius to 0.14 per cent, and that the central density rises from 3000 times the mean density to a thousand million times the mean density. The models reproduce the large radii required for giant stars and sufficiently high internal temperatures for nuclear processes to occur. Ninety per cent of the energy is produced in a thin shell of 0.4 per cent radius. The central temperature rises above

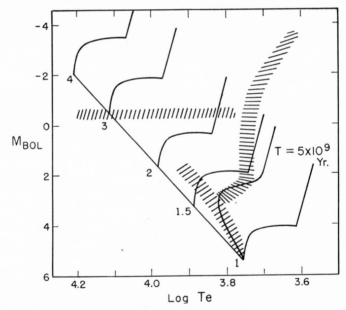

FIG. 3.—THE EVOLUTION OF THE STARS

The lines give the speculative evolutionary tracks for stars of masses 1, 1.5, 2, 3, and 4 times that of the sun. It is assumed that the conversion of helium into carbon sets in at about 1.1×10^8 °K. The cross-hatching shows schematically the distribution of stars in a globular cluster, while the heavy line gives the theoretical appearance of the diagram 5×10^9 years after the formation of the stars. (Courtesy, A. R. Sandage and M. Schwarzschild, *Astrophysical Journal*, University of Chicago Press, **116**, 475, 1952.)

30 million degrees because part of the gravitational energy goes into the increase of internal energy. The calculations show that once the contraction of the core sets in the star moves rapidly away from the main sequence into the giant region of the Russell diagram.

Sandage and Schwarzschild were particularly interested in interpreting the color magnitude arrays observed by Arp, Baum, and Sandage in the globular clusters. In Sandage's color-magnitude plot for Messier 3 (cf. Fig. 6 of Ch. *1*) notice that the stars form a continuous sequence from $M_v = -3$ and color index $= +1.5$ to $M_v = 5.5$ and color index $= +0.6$. This sequence may represent an evolutionary path—at least in part. Suppose that in the beginning, about 5×10^9 years ago, the cluster started out with main-sequence stars of all spectral classes. The O and early B stars would burn out quickly and disappear, next the A stars would go until the main sequence would have been eliminated almost to the sun. In the allotted time, a star about 1.4–1.5 solar masses would have exhausted its hydrogen core and would have turned off the main sequence. Fainter stars will not yet have reached the turn-off point which occurs at $M_{bol} = +3.3$ by theory. The observed turn-off point is at $M_{bol} = +3.6$ and corresponds to the sharp turn at $M_v = +3.7$, color index $+0.35$ in Fig. 6 of Chapter *1. The good agreement between theory and observation shows that the assumed age of the cluster is approximately correct. The star then rapidly moves to the right in the color–magnitude array, and theory would lead us to expect a gradual brightening and reddening. Although the internal temperature rises and the size of the star increases, the luminosity does not change very much. The observations, however, show a break near a color index of $+0.5$ and a sequence of stars of nearly constant color and steadily increasing luminosity. This break-off point appears to correspond to a central temperature slightly over 10^8 °K and the onset of Salpeter's carbon-building process wherein helium is consumed. Calculation shows that this would give an evolutionary development in the right direction. Also, rotation might affect the later stages by affecting the mixing and retarding envelope development. The stars appear to swell in size and gradually rise in luminosity until the nuclear sources are exhausted. The subsequent Kelvin contraction may produce the horizontal branch of blue stars in the color–magnitude array.

Thus the color–magnitude array for a globular cluster represents an evolutionary picture. Each point represents a star that was once on the main sequence. If this concept is true, the luminosity function,

*All references to chapters in the author's *Astrophysics—The Atmospheres of the Sun and Stars* (New York: The Ronald Press Co., 1953) will be designated in this volume by * before the chapter number.

i.e., the distribution of stars as a function of absolute magnitude, should be predictable from the density of stars in the main sequence on the color–magnitude diagram. The stars should pass through the high-luminosity phases quickly, those of low luminosity relatively slowly. Sandage finds the observed luminosity distribution to be exactly that predicted on the evolutionary picture.

Turning to stars in the neighborhood of the sun, we may expect the brighter ones which have exhausted the supplies of hydrogen and helium in their cores to evolve into subgiants, giants, or even supergiants, depending on their masses.

As long as there is no mixing between the surface layers and the energy-producing interior, the stellar spectra will not reveal the profound composition changes that may occur in the interior. Stars whose spectra may reflect such changes appear to include the faint blue stars discovered by Humason and Zwicky and studied by Greenstein and Münch, the Wolf-Rayet stars, and perhaps objects such as Bidelman's helium star, HD 160641. An analysis of Mount Wilson and Palomar coudé plates of the latter shows that the proportions of C, N, O, Si, and Mg are not greatly different from the values for an ordinary B star, but hydrogen appears to have been replaced completely by helium.

Much work on problems of stellar evolution remains to be done before a fully satisfactory picture will emerge. Interesting problems are posed by eclipsing binary systems which are presumably of the same age and initial chemical composition and in which a bright main-sequence star often is associated with a less luminous, less massive subgiant.

The final stage of the evolution of many stars, however, appears to be represented by the remarkable white dwarf stars, whose properties we shall now consider.

13. The White Dwarf Stars

The white dwarf stars have low luminosities, masses comparable with that of the sun and densities of the order of 10^4 to 10^6 times that of water.

The companion of Sirius is the most famous of all these objects. A century ago, Bessel noted from meridian circle observations that Sirius did not move in a straight line but oscillated back and forth with a period of about 50 years as though it had an invisible companion. In 1862 Alvan Clark discovered the companion near its predicted position. Orbital measures revealed its mass to be 0.98 that of the sun, a somewhat surprising result since its luminosity was about 1/400 that of the sun. The star aroused little interest, however, until W. S. Adams, in 1915, found its spectrum to be $A5$ and its temperature therefore near 8500°K. The absolute photovisual magnitude is 11.42, and since the bolometric correction is 0.32, the absolute bolometric magnitude is 11.10, as compared with 4.62 for the sun. Hence Sirius B is 1/390 as luminous as the sun. Consequently each cm^2 of its surface must radiate $(8500/5712)^4 = 4.92$ times as much energy as does the sun. Therefore the surface area must be $(1/390) \times (1/4.92) = 1/1920$ that of the sun. Thus the radius would be 0.023 that of the sun. Since a mass 0.98 that of the sun is compressed into a volume 0.023 that of the sun the density will be 1.2×10^5 gm/cm^3, or more than two tons per cubic inch! The precise value of the density will depend on the assumption made about the surface temperature. If we take the surface temperature as 8000°K, we get a radius of 17,000 km and a density of 97,000 gm/cm^3. A temperature as low as 2500°K would be required to give a density equal to that of the sun, and such a star would certainly not have an A-type spectrum.

Eddington pointed out that since, according to the theory of relativity, the observed frequency of a spectral line depends on the difference of the gravitational potential between the emitting atoms and the observer, the spectral lines of Sirius B should show a red shift of the order of 20 to 30 km/sec. In 1925 Adams measured the radial velocity of the star and, after allowing for its orbital motion, he found an Einstein shift of about 23 km/sec in accord with expectations. This result checks our conclusions about the density of the star and also seems to put a limit on its temperature. For, if the temperature were greater than 9000°K, the predicted value of the Einstein shift would appreciably exceed the observed value.

The efforts of Luyten and of Kuiper have added many new white dwarfs to our lists. They are more numerous in space than supergiants, giants, or subgiants, comprising perhaps as much as 3 per cent of the total numbers of stars in the neighborhood of the sun. In addition to the white dwarfs, yellow and red stars thousands of times fainter than main-sequence stars of the same color appear to exist. Perhaps they approach the last stages of a degenerate star—the "black dwarf" state.

The spectra of the white dwarfs have been investigated most thoroughly by Kuiper and by Luyten. Kuiper found some showed broad hydrogen lines with no metallic lines; others showed only continuous spectra, while van Maanen 2 showed only strong H and K and the ultraviolet iron lines, although its color corresponded to that of an A star. The most complete survey is that by W. Luyten, who obtained spectral classes for 44 white dwarfs and color indices for these and many more. Most of the stars are classified as A; i.e., they show the Balmer lines, but a number show the H and K lines, while others show continuous spectra in which no features can be distinguished. Luyten found two stars that showed helium and no hydrogen lines; these stars were not so blue and therefore presumably not so hot as others which showed the Balmer lines with no trace of helium. With the aid of all available parallaxes and color indices, Luyten finds the white dwarfs to occupy a single sequence roughly parallel to the main sequence in the Russell diagram but about 8 or 9 magnitudes below it.

The role of white dwarfs as components of visual binaries may be of great cosmogonic interest. Stars in which main-sequence primaries are accompanied by white dwarf companions include Sirius, Procyon, 40 Eridani B, and Wolf 672. Some of the more recently discovered objects are components of wide doubles which ultimately may give us information on the masses. In this connection, a double star discovered by Luyten wherein both components are white dwarfs is of particular interest. Both stars are 1600 times less luminous than the sun, with diameters less than that of the earth, densities of the order of a million times that of water, and an orbital period of the order of 250 years with a separation of 50 astronomical units.

The quantities of main interest in white dwarf theories are the radius and the mass. The mass can be found for components of binary systems, but the radius can be determined only from the total luminosity and effective temperature. Our knowledge of the latter depends mostly on the studies by Luyten, who finds that most white dwarfs have diameters that lie between that of the earth and Uranus, and on the investigations of G. P. Kuiper, who demonstrated that by combining spectrophotometric determinations of the energy distribution in the continuous spectrum with measures of the Balmer line profiles, as interpreted by the Verwiej theory, it was possible to estimate the mass of a white dwarf of known distance to within a factor of about two. At Palomar, J. L. Greenstein has recently secured excellent spectra of these stars.

14. The Theory of the White Dwarfs

In 1924 Eddington suggested that the high densities of the white dwarf stars could be explained by the fact that in the hot stellar interiors, the atoms must be completely stripped of electrons and hence the bare nuclei could be closely jammed together. R. H. Fowler, in 1926, showed that such a gas, as a consequence of the Fermi-Dirac statistics, would obey the degenerate gas law. Just as H_2O can exist as ice, water, or steam, gaseous matter can exist in the perfect gas or degenerate gas state. The white dwarf material is what it is because of the pressure under which it is kept.

For densities of the order of 10^6 gm/cm^3 and temperatures less than 20,000,000°K the electron gas is degenerate, while the heavy particles follow the perfect gas law. The pressure exerted by the degenerate electrons so much exceeds that supplied by the nuclei, that in our equations of equilibrium we neglect the contribution of the latter completely.

White dwarf stars are not entirely composed of degenerate material. A thin stratum of normal substances overlies the degenerate gas core. The thermal conductivity of a degenerate gas is high and its opacity is low, because an electron can absorb a quantum of energy only if it can pass to an allowed state, i.e., one that is not already filled. This means that only electrons of high energy will be able to absorb quanta. The others will be unable to obstruct the outward flow of radiation. Hence no large temperature gradients can exist within the body of the degenerate gas. The star consists of a nearly isothermal core overlaid by a shell which supports almost the entire temperature gradient. It thus resembles a metallic sphere enclosed in an insulator.

Let us now examine the equations governing the structure of the white dwarf stars. Throughout most of the star the material will be degenerate, and the relation between the mass and radius will depend on the degenerate gas law.

In general we will have to use Chandrasekhar's parametric equations of state: eqns. (38), (39), and (40) of Chapter *3. The equation of mechanical equilibrium, in the form of eqn. (50), may be transformed by means of the substitutions:

$$r = \left(\frac{2A}{\pi G}\right)^{1/2} \frac{1}{By_0} \eta$$

$$y = y_0 \phi, \quad y = \sqrt{1 + x^2}$$

$$(108)$$

(where x is defined by eqn. (39) of Chapter *3) into Chandrasekhar's differential equation

$$\frac{d^2\phi}{d\eta^2} + \frac{2}{\eta}\frac{d\phi}{d\eta} = -\left(\phi^2 - \frac{1}{y_0^2}\right)^{3/2}$$

$$(109)$$

Notice that the constant, y_0, which fixes the units of the solution, does not drop out as it did in Emden's equation. This equation is not homogeneous in any power combination of the independent and dependent variables. If the whole star is degenerate, the solution of eqn. (109) will tell us how the pressure and density vary as a function of the distance from the center.

If we substitute the parametric equation of state [(38) of Chapter *3], into eqn. (6) and make use of eqns. (39) of Chapter *3, and eqn. (108) we get

$$M_r = -4\pi\left(\frac{2A}{\pi G}\right)^{3/2} \frac{1}{B^2}\left[\eta^2 \frac{d\phi}{d\eta}\right]$$

$$(110)$$

At the center of the star M_r must vanish, $d\phi/d\eta = 0$, and $\phi = 1$ at $r = 0$. At the boundary of the star the density ρ vanishes. Further, $\rho = Bx^3 = 0$ implies $x = 0$ or $y = y_0 = 1$. If η_1 corresponds to the boundary $r = R$, $\phi(\eta_1) = 1/y_0$.

For each value of y_0 there is only one solution. Since both mass and radius must be functions of the parameter y_0, there exists a mass–radius relationship which is of the nature that the greater the mass, the smaller the star, and the greater its density.

Chandrasekhar has computed the solution for a series of values of $1/y_0$ in the range $0 < y < 1$. We give a few of his results in Table 5.

TABLE 5

COMPLETELY DEGENERATE CONFIGURATIONS*

$1/y_0^2$	$M/M(0)$	ρ_c gm/cm³	ρ_m gm/cm³	Radius (cm)
0	5.75	∞	∞	0
0.01	5.51	9.85×10^8	3.70×10^7	4.13×10^8
0.1	4.33	2.65×10^7	2.10×10^6	9.92×10^8
0.5	2.02	9.82×10^5	1.34×10^5	1.93×10^9
0.8	0.88	1.23×10^5	1.92×10^4	2.79×10^9

*The values apply to $\mu' = 1$. For other values of μ', M should be multiplied by $1/\mu'^2$, R by $1/\mu'$, and ρ by μ'. $M(0)$ denotes the mass of the sun. Courtesy, S. Chandrasekhar, *An Introduction to the Study of Stellar Structure* (Chicago: University of Chicago Press, 1939), p. 427.

They show that the mean density, mass, and radius of these degenerate gas configurations fall in the observed ranges of the known white dwarfs.

In some respects the most interesting result is that the mass of a white dwarf star must be less than $M = 5.75/\mu'^2$. A star with a greater mass than this must get rid of the excess (possibly by a supernova or Wolf-Rayet process) before it can settle down to the white dwarf state.

We do not obtain greatly different results for the μ–M–R relationship whether we assume the degenerate core extends to the surface of the star, or whether we fit onto this core a perfect gas shell. Kuiper applied the Chandrasekhar theory to Sirius B. With an adopted effective temperature of 9000°K the corresponding radius is 0.021 that of the sun. Since the mass is 0.98 that of the sun, we find from interpolation in Chandrasekhar's table that

$$\mu' = 1.35 = \frac{1}{X + \frac{1}{2}(1 - X)}$$

which implies $X = 0.48$. An effective temperature of 10,000°K will give an $X = 0.38$ with $\mu' = 1.46$, but there seems no obvious way of making X' much smaller than about 0.4.

Such large hydrogen contents lead to difficulties in connection with the mechanism of energy generation. If we suppose the luminosity is correct and estimate the internal temperature in the usual way, we find that with this temperature and with $X = 0.4$, the star would explode. A logical procedure would be to estimate the hydrogen content necessary to reproduce the observed energy output, calculate μ' and then R from the known mass of the star. The radius computed in this way turns out to be smaller than that found from the effective temperature and observed luminosity. Marshak found the same discrepancy in subsequent calculations. The difficulty may lie in the observational data themselves. The observed spectrum of Sirius B may be affected by the overpowering brilliance of its companion. Hence the actual temperature of the star may be appreciably higher than the 9000°K usually assigned. Possibly it is as high as 25,000°K. The observed Einstein shift may be too small if the spectrum is affected by scattered light from Sirius A.

The degenerate matter does not lie far below the surface. Schatzman finds degeneracy to set in at $\Delta R/R = 0.05$ in Sirius B and $\Delta R/R = 0.0072$ in van Maanen 2. He finds that under the influence of the strong gravitational field of a white dwarf, hydrogen is separated almost completely from the heavier elements, the thickness of the layer where the two are mixed together depending sharply on the temperature and surface gravity. Possibly the atmospheres of the white dwarf stars that show metallic lines are kept stirred up by convection currents.

The white dwarf theory may be applied not only to stars but also to find the maximum size of a cold body such as a planet. If we start with a cold body of small mass and add more and more material, the size will increase as the added material takes up more and more volume. Eventually the pressure becomes so great that pressure ionization sets in and the electrons become degenerate. Then as more mass is added, the gravitational forces compress it yet further, and the greater the amount of material, the smaller the volume it occupies. When degeneracy is widespread throughout the mass, the mass–radius relation for white dwarfs holds until the critical mass is reached. Thus there will exist a maximum size that a cold body in equilibrium can have. Kothari derived the relationship between the mass, radius, and molecular weight for a cold body. He carried out calculations for the two extremes of a mass composed of hydrogen and iron and found that the planets fell between the two limits (see Fig. 4). Notice that, for a mass a little greater than that of Jupiter, the radius will begin to decline.

If the white dwarfs represent the final state of stellar evolution, it is

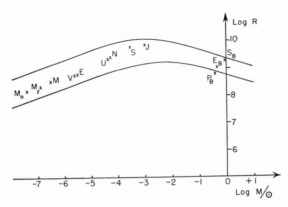

FIG. 4.—THE RELATIONSHIP BETWEEN THE MASS AND RADIUS OF A COLD BODY

The solid curves give the theoretical mass-radius relationship for hydrogen (upper curve) and iron (lower curve). The radius R is expressed in centimeters, the mass M is given in terms of that of the sun.

M_n = Moon	E = Earth	J = Jupiter
M_y = Mercury	U = Uranus	S_B = Sirius B
M = Mars	N = Neptune	E_B = σ_2 Eridani B
V = Venus	S = Saturn	P_B = Procyon B

(Courtesy, D. S. Kothari, *Monthly Notices*, Royal Astronomical Society, **96**, 833, 1936.)

difficult to understand why normal stars such as Sirius should have white dwarf companions, unless the latter were originally massive objects that long ago consumed their hydrogen fuel and collapsed to their present stage with the ejection of the excess mass. Occasionally we should observe a massive star undergoing a transition to a white dwarf state; perhaps the supernovae and Wolf-Rayet stars represent such metamorphoses (Ch. 4), although Schatzman has suggested that Type II supernovae originate from catastrophic readjustments in the superficial layers of white dwarf stars in the course of their evolution. Additional observational data are needed, especially white dwarfs whose masses can be found, to test the theoretical mass–radius relationship. For this reason observational programs, such as those of Kuiper, Greenstein, and Luyten, are of highest importance.

15. The Origin of the Chemical Elements

An outstanding astrophysical problem is the relative abundances of the chemical elements in the universe. A plot of the cosmic abundance against the atomic weight shows a maximum at hydrogen and a jagged distribution that falls off more or less steeply to silver, and then declines slowly thereafter. There is a deep minimum at Li, B, and Be. The irregularities can be accounted for by the differing stability of the various isotopes of a given element, and the details therefore depend on natural β-decay. Of prime interest are the broad features of the distribution; why does the abundance decline so slowly beyond silver— why does not the exponential decay persist to uranium?

Two different hypotheses have been proposed to account for the varying abundances of the elements. In one the distribution was assumed fixed during the pre-stellar stage of the universe. The other hypothesis is that the elements originated in dense stars. The present distribution of the elements cannot have originated in ordinary main-sequence stars since their central temperatures and densities suffice only for the transformation of hydrogen into helium and the destruction of rare light elements such as lithium, boron, and beryllium. Atoms heavier than oxygen would be left intact. If we seek a stellar origin for all the elements, we are forced to postulate objects with very high internal densities and temperatures far in excess of even the Sandage-Schwarzschild models.

Earlier attempts to explain the origin of the elements postulated an equilibrium pre-stellar state in which the relative proportions of different nuclei were fixed by their stability at the prevailing temperature and density. A nucleus $_Z X^A$ of charge Z and atomic weight A may change to one of charge Z' and weight A' by the capture (or emission) of a neutron, a proton, or an α-particle. By the emission of a β-ray it may change to an isobar. For example, Chandrasekhar and Henrich considered the equilibrium between protons, neutrons, α-particles, electrons, positrons, and various atomic nuclei. Thus protons and electrons may combine to form neutrons, $p + \epsilon^- \rightleftarrows n$, and vice versa, while positive and negative electrons may combine to form a γ-ray

$$\epsilon^- + \epsilon^+ \rightleftarrows \gamma\text{-ray}$$

Nuclei may be transformed by the absorption and emission of protons and neutrons, at the high densities and temperature presumably prevailing at the time of the formation of the elements. Under equilibrium conditions the concentration of protons, free neutrons, electrons, and α-particles can be found by statistical mechanics and the abundances of the various nuclear species derived. By choosing the neutron abundance so that the oxygen/argon ratio was the same as that given in Goldschmidt's work on the composition of the earth's crust, Chandrasekhar and Henrich found $T = 8 \times 10^9$ °K and $\rho = 10^7$ gm/cm^3. The predicted abundance of hydrogen and helium was much too large, partly because no attention was paid to excited nuclear states which become important in the heavier atoms. The formation of elements beyond carbon requires more drastic conditions. Chandrasekhar and Henrich suggested that in the initial state of the universe the tempera-

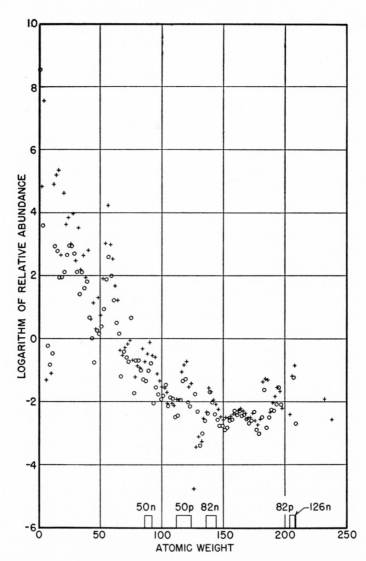

FIG. 5.—RELATIVE ABUNDANCES OF THE ELEMENTS IN THE UNIVERSE

The relative abundances of nuclear species are given as a function of atomic weight according to the data of Harrison Brown. All isotopes of a given element have been added together, and silicon is taken as 10,000. Nuclei of odd and even atomic weight are denoted as o and +, respectively. (Courtesy, R. C. Alpher and R. C. Herman, *Reviews of Modern Physics* **22**, 155, 1950.)

ture was 10^{10}–10^{11} °K and the densities ranged from 10^7 gm/cm³ to nuclear densities. The heavier nuclei were formed under these conditions and as the mixture cooled a small proportion presumably were left intact.

Gamow pointed out that equilibrium theories of element formation encounter severe difficulties.

The binding energies per nucleon increase up to iron and thereafter decrease. The ratio A/Z increases strongly for the heavy nuclei. On these equilibrium theories it seems impossible to find conditions under which correct abundances for both intermediate and heavy elements are found. Furthermore, heavy nuclei would not be frozen out in a slowly cooling mass but would break up into lighter nuclei. To preserve the heavy nuclei, the change in density and temperature of the material must have been very abrupt. Gamow suggested that the elements were formed during the early stages of the expansion of the universe.

According to Alpher, Bethe, and Gamow the primordial substance from which the elements were formed, called the *ylem*, was a highly compressed neutron gas. As the gas pressure fell as the result of the expansion of the universe, the neutron gas decayed into protons, neutrons, and electrons.*

Radiative captures of neutrons by the protons led first to the formation of deuterium nuclei which, in turn, captured additional neutrons. Gradually all the elements were built up. The present distribution was obtained after β-decay had increased the charges of many of the heavier nuclei. Alpher points out that the observed abundance of a given kind of nucleus bears an inverse relationship to its neutron-capture cross-section. Common nuclei have small capture cross-sections, and vice versa. It is well known that elements of even atomic weight are about ten times as abundant as elements of odd atomic weight. A nucleus will more easily capture a neutron if the resultant nucleus has an even atomic weight. Cross-sections for neutron capture increase fairly rapidly with increasing A up to an atomic weight of about 100 and remain roughly constant after that. The abundances decrease exponentially with A up to about 100 and then change slowly with increasing A.

Hence the element-forming process may have been one of successive neutron captures. The final abundance of an element will depend principally on its cross-section for the capture of neutrons. Furthermore, the neutron captures must have occurred at high temperatures, since there is no preponderance of elements such as cadmium or gado-

---

*A neutron left to itself will decay into a proton and an electron in about 1800 seconds. A gas of pure neutrons could exist only under extremely high pressure.

linium which have high cross-sections for the capture of slow neutrons. In this process the rate of increase of nuclei of atomic weight i is equal to the difference between the rate at which nuclei of atomic weight $i - 1$ capture neutrons and become nuclei of atomic weight i, and the rate at which i-nuclei capture neutrons to become nuclei of atomic weight $i + 1$. The differential equations for this situation may be written for each nucleus and solved for various assumptions about the early stages of the expansion of the universe (the cosmological model). In order to get agreement with the observed abundances of the elements, Alpher found it necessary to suppose that in the early stages, the universe consisted mostly of radiation with only a trace of matter present. In this picture the element-building process started 200–300 seconds after the beginning of the expansion, when the temperature was of the order of 10^9 °K, and the density was about 10^{-3} gm/cm^3. The elements must have been formed in a period of time comparable with a neutron lifetime, about 30 minutes. That is, within an hour or two, the present distribution of the elements was established.

In the element-building process, all free neutrons disappeared. Thereafter, lithium, beryllium, and boron, which have high target areas for proton capture, were to a large measure destroyed to form helium. Heavier elements such as carbon or nitrogen were scarcely affected in the short time that elapsed before the density and speeds of the protons had fallen to such a low value as to make proton captures unimportant.

The non-equilibrium theory does reproduce the observed relative abundances, at least semi-quantitatively. There are some stumbling blocks, such as the non-existence of stable nuclei with atomic weights 5 and 8. The gap at mass 5 means that He^4 cannot absorb a proton or a neutron because neither He^5 nor Li^5 exists. Some process must be found for adding more than one particle at a time! So far, no satisfactory bridge over the mass 5 (and to a lesser extent the mass 8) difficulty has been found. Nevertheless, as a working hypothesis the non-equilibrium theory seems attractive.

The possibility remains that some heavy elements may be formed in the hot, dense cores of certain abnormal stars. If heavy elements show abundance differences from star to star, as recent work by Merrill, Greenstein, Bidelman, Keenan, and others would suggest, a strong argument is provided for the stellar origin of at least some fraction of the heavy elements.

PROBLEMS

1. Derive the mass–luminosity law for a star composed only of hydrogen and helium. Assume a law of energy generation of the form:

$$\epsilon = A \rho X^2 T^{3.5}$$

and that the star is in radiative equilibrium throughout.

2. Suppose that $X = 1$ when $t = 0$ for the star described in Problem 1. Calculate the radius R and luminosity L, when $X = \frac{1}{2}$, and when $X = 0.1$ in terms of the initial radius R_0 and luminosity L_0.

3. Verify eqn. (87).

4. Consider an isothermal sphere of radius R in hydrostatic equilibrium. Derive the differential equation relating the density and independent variable r, and put it in a form analogous to the Emden equation in which the gas constant $\mathfrak{R}$ and the molecular weight μ do not appear explicitly.

5. A star radius R, mass M, and luminosity L generates energy in a thin shell of infinitesimal thickness and radius R_c. In the region $r > R_c$, $X = X_1$, $Y = Y_1$, and radiative equilibrium holds. In the domain $r < R_c$, $X = 0$, and $Y = X_1 + Y_1$. The opacity is given by Kramers' law. Write down the relevant equations for each region and the boundary conditions.

6. Verify eqns. (109) and (110).

7. What is the theoretical radius of a white dwarf of the same mass as the sun and composed completely of helium?

8. Calculate a table, similar to Table 4, for Sirius. Give the time scale.

REFERENCES

1. *The standard text and reference is:*

CHANDRASEKHAR, S. *An Introduction to the Study of Steller Structure.* Chicago: University of Chicago Press, 1939. The theory of Emden's equation, homology transformations, white dwarfs, and the interpretation of the Russell diagram are given in full detail.

The "classical" book on stellar interiors is

EDDINGTON, A. S. *Internal Constitution of the Stars.* Cambridge: Cambridge University Press, 1926. Eddington treats the "standard model" fully. Although out of date in most respects, this book gives a good account of many of the fundamentals.

For tables of the Emden Functions see *Mathematical Tables of the British Association for the Advancement of Science*, Vol. 2, London, 1932.

2. *Stellar Models*

(a) Main-Sequence Stars:

CHANDRASEKHAR, S., and L. HENRICH. *Ap. J.* **94**, 525, 1941.

Chandrasekhar and Henrich considered stellar models with isothermal cores and envelopes in radiative and polytropic equilibrium. In models of the first type not more than 35 per cent of the mass can be retained in the core. L. Henrich, *Ap. J.* **93**, 483, 1941, treated a convective model with radiation pressure; in *Ap. J.* **96,**

106, 1942, he considered a point-source model with convective core and envelope in radiative equilibrium, wherein the opacity is given by Kramers' law and radiation pressure is taken into account. He has also computed point-source stellar models with appreciable radiation pressure and opacity due to electron scattering. This model gives a limiting extreme to the mass–luminosity relation. *Ap. J.* **98**, 192, 1943.

Mrs. M. H. Harrison has calculated a stellar model whose energy is derived from gravitational contraction, i.e., $\epsilon \sim T$, *Ap. J.* **102**, 216, 1945.

Models of the sun in which the mean molecular weight, μ_1, of the core differs from that of the radiative envelope μ_2 have been treated by P. Ledoux, *Ann. d'Ap.* **11**, 174, 1948, and by Shu Mu Kung.

Our discussion of the Schwarzschild model in which all energy is produced in the convective core is taken from:

Schwarzschild, M. *Ap. J.* **102**, 203, 1946.

See also:

Keller, Geoffrey. *Ap. J.* **108**, 347, 1948 (model of sun with oxygen as the heavy constituent).

Harrison, Marjorie H. *Ap. J.* **108**, 310, 1948 (models of the sun for varying proportions of oxygen and the Russell mixture).

Epstein, I., and L. Motz. *Ap. J.* **117**, 311, 1953 (model of the sun for proton-proton reactions). A revised model is in press (*Ap. J.*).

P. Naur's model is discussed by B. Strömgren in chap. ii of volume I, *The Sun*, in G. P. Kuiper's *The Solar System*, Chicago: University of Chicago Press, 1953.

See also:

Naur, P. and D. E. Osterbrock. *Ap. J.* **117**, 306, 1953.

Models for faint dwarf stars in which deviations from the perfect gas law become serious are given by:

Wares, G. W. *Ap. J.* **100**, 158, 1944.
Duff, G. F., and R. E. Williamson. *M.N.* **109**, 46, 55, 1949.

Models for red dwarf stars were discussed by:

Oke, J. B. *J.R.A.S. Canada* **44**, 135, 1950.
Aller, L. H. *Ap. J.* **112**, 207, 1950.

The failure of models with envelopes in radiative equilibrium (*Ap. J.* **115**, 328, 1952) led to the convective envelope model of:

Osterbrock, D. *Ap. J.* **118**, 529, 1953.

(b) Shell-Source, Isothermal Core, and Giant Models:

Schonberg, M., and S. Chandrasekhar. *Ap. J.* **96**, 161, 1942.
Gamow, G., and G. Keller. *Rev. Mod. Phys.* **17**, 125, 1945.
Harrison, M. Hall. *Ap. J.* **103**, 193, 1946; *Ap. J.* **105**, 322, 1947.
Reiz, A. *Ann. d'Ap.* **10**, 301, 1947; *Arkiv for Astronomi* **1**, 7, 1949.
Schwarzschild, M., and Li Hen. *M.N.* **109**, 631, 1949.
Hoyle, F., and R. A. Lyttleton. *M.N.* **102**, 218, 1942; **109**, 614, 1949.
Motz, Lloyd. *Ap. J.* **112**, 434, 1950.
Schwarzschild, M., and J. B. Oke. *Ap. J.* **116**, 317, 1952.

3. *Stellar Rotation*

Schwarzschild, M. *Ap. J.* **95**, 441, 1942; **106**, 427, 1947.
Krogdahl, W. *Ap. J.* **96**, 124, 1942; **99**, 191, 1944.
Cowling, T. G. *M.N.* **105**, 166, 173, 1945.

4. *Apsidal Motion in Eclipsing Binary Systems*

The theory is given by:

STERNE, T. E. *M.N.* **99**, 451, 662, 670, 1939.
COWLING, T. G. *M.N.* **98**, 734, 1938.

An observational test of the theory is due to:
RUSSELL, H. N. *Ap. J.* **90**, 650, 1939.

5. *Stability of Stellar Models*

COWLING, T. G. *M.N.* **96**, 42, 1936; **94**, 768, 1934.
BIERMANN, L., and T. G. COWLING. *Zeits. f. Ap.* **19**, 1, 1939.
LEDOUX, P. *Ap. J.* **104**, 333, 1946.

6. *White Dwarf Stars*

For an account of the basic data on temperatures and spectra see Kuiper's paper in *Symposium on Novae and White Dwarfs*, Actualities Scientifiques et Industrielles, No. 903. Paris: Herman and Cie, 1939.
See also:
LUYTEN, W. J. *Ap. J.* **116**, 283, 1952.
MILNE, E. A. "The White Dwarf Stars," Halley Lecture, Oxford, 1932.
CHANDRASEKHAR, S. *Stellar Structure.* Chapter xi gives a complete account of the basic theory we have only mentioned.
STRÖMGREN, B. **7**, *Handbuch der Astrophysik.* Berlin: Julius Springer, 1934.
MARSHAK, R. E. *Ap. J.* **92**, 321, 1940.
CRITCHFIELD, C. L. *Ap. J.* **96**, 1, 1942, discusses the theoretical properties of dense hydrogen.
SCHATZMAN, E. *Ann. d'Ap.* **8**, 143, 1945; **10**, 19, 1947; *Ap. J.* **110**, 261, 1949. "Le spectre des naines blanches et leur debit d'energie," Academy of Science. Copenhagen, 1949.

The maximum size of a cold mass was discussed by:
KOTHARI, D. S. *M.N.* **96**, 833, 1936.

Application of the Kothari theory to the possible planet-like companion of 61 Cygni discovered by Strand (*Publ. Astron. Soc. Pac.* **55**, 29, 1943) is made by Russell, H. N. (*Publ. Astron. Soc. Pac.* **55**, 79, 1943).

7. *Stellar Evolution*

The possible evolutionary role of rapidly rotating stars and close binaries (which are often surrounded by extensive clouds of gas) is discussed by:
STRUVE, OTTO. *Stellar Evolution.* Princeton: Princeton University Press, 1950.

The evolutionary paths of massive stars that remain well mixed throughout their existence are discussed, for example, by:
GAMOW, G. *Ap. J.* **98**, 498, 1943; *Phys. Rev.* **65**, 20, 1944.

The evolution of stars whose cores become exhausted of hydrogen is traced by:
SANDAGE, A., and M. SCHWARZSCHILD. *Ap. J.* **116**, 475, 1952.

Color–magnitude arrays for globular clusters are discussed by:
ARP, H. C., W. A. BAUM, and A. R. SANDAGE. *Astron. Journ.* **58**, 4, 1953.
SANDAGE, A. R. *Astron. Journ.* **58**, 61, 1953.

8. *Origin of the Elements*

Summarizing accounts of the various theories (with full bibliographies) are contained in:
ALPHER, R. A., and R. C. HERMAN. *Rev. Mod. Phys.* **22**, 153, 1950.
TER HAAR, D. *Rev. Mod. Phys.* **22**, 119, 1950.

CHAPTER 3

The Cepheids and Long-Period Variables

1. Introduction

In the last chapter our problem was—given the observed mass, luminosity, and radius of a star, and some information on the composition of the surface layers—to find what we could about the stellar interior or, more specifically, the variation of density, temperature, and energy generation with radius. We saw that a reasonable picture of the main-sequence stars could be obtained, although adequate models for giants and supergiants is still lacking. Some information on the density concentration in main-sequence stars could be obtained from eclipsing binary systems which showed a motion of the line of apsides. It would be useful to have additional clues to the internal structure of the stars.

Now the periods and amplitudes of mechanical systems in oscillation give data on their structure that could not be obtained otherwise. Raman spectra reveal modes of vibration of complicated molecules. Hence they give information on the binding forces that hold such structures together, that might never be found by traditional chemical procedures. Similarly a study of pulsating stars may give information on stellar interiors that could not be found from objects in static equilibrium.

In this chapter we shall deal with stars that are believed to vary because of an over-all pulsation of the star. The observational data provide a wealth of material that is only now beginning to pay rich dividends not only in questions of stellar interiors but stellar atmospheres as well. By studies of the strange and exotic we throw new light on the unsolved problems of the atmospheres and interiors of giant and supergiant stars.

2. Cepheids, RR Lyrae Stars, and Long-Period Variables

The classical Cepheids, cluster Cepheids (or more precisely the RR Lyrae variables), the W Virginis stars, the long-period variables, and the RV Tauri stars are examples of stars which are believed to owe their variability to a single cause, probably pulsation. The stars of this group range in period from an hour and a half to more than two years and show a great spread in luminosity, dimensions, and presumably in mass. They are subject to cyclical changes in brightness, radial velocity, spectrum, and color.

These stars belong to both kinds of stellar populations. In order of increasing period, the Type I population is represented by the classical Cepheids and the long-period variables with periods of the order of a year. The Type II population includes the RR Lyrae stars, the Cepheid-like W Virginis stars, the RV Tauri stars, and the shorter-period long-period variable stars. Fig. 1a shows very schematically the relation between the luminosity, expressed on a magnitude scale, and the logarithm of the period for some of these different types. The Type II stars form a continuous sequence from the RR Lyrae stars through the W Virginis stars to the RV Tauri stars.

The classical Cepheids also form a group in which the luminosity increases as the period increases, but this family of variables appears to fall 1.3 to 1.5 magnitudes above their analogues in the Type II population. The long-period variables which fall in spectral classes Me, Se, and N, and whose periods are greater than 50 days, do not form a continuation of either the Type I or Type II sequences. Bolometrically, the long-period variables of shortest period are three magnitudes, or more, fainter than classical Cepheids of the same period.

Both long-period variables and classical Cepheids show a well marked relation between period and median spectrum in the sense that the longer periods are correlated with the later spectra.*

Visual light range and period show a conspicuous correlation in that stars of longer period have greater amplitudes. Thus the visual ranges of long-period variables are greater than those of Cepheids, although the bolometric ranges are similar. The wave-length range to which the eye is sensitive happens to include the maximum of Cepheid radiation, but is far to the short wave-length side of the energy maximum of the long-period variables. Hence small temperature changes in cool stars can produce huge changes in the output of visual light.

Some confusion in terminology has arisen from the recent practice in some quarters of referring to the Type II Cepheids as "W Virginis Stars." Actually, the W Virginis group comprises only the Type II Cepheids with periods between 12^d and 20^d, whereas Type II Cepheids with periods between 2^d and 12^d and with periods longer than 20^d are

*G. Miczaika, from a study of the long-period variables in the great cloud in Cygnus found that the longer the period, the fainter the star. This correlation originates principally from the increasing influence of the TiO bands on the spectra of the variables. The elimination of this effect shows that the true luminosity is not a function of the period. Infrared work by Hetzler suggests that the period–luminosity relation for these stars is only a consequence of molecular bands in their atmospheres.

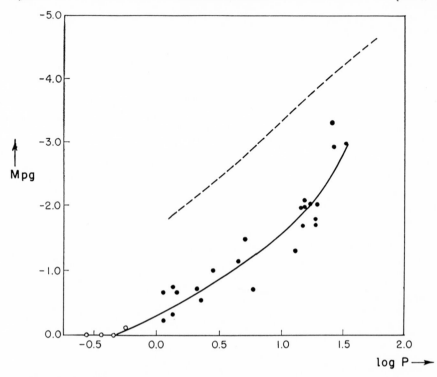

FIG. 1a.—THE PERIOD–LUMINOSITY CURVE FOR CLASSICAL CEPHEIDS, RR LYRAE
STARS, AND TYPE II CEPHEIDS

The absolute photographic magnitude is plotted against the logarithm of the
period for RR Lyrae stars (circles), Cepheids of Type II population (dots), and
classical or Type I population Cepheids (indicated by the dotted line). In this
diagram, drawn by Harlow Shapley from observations made of eleven globular
clusters, the zero-point of the period-luminosity curve for the Large Magellanic Cloud
Cepheids is arbitrarily adjusted by 1.3 magnitudes. The fact that the classical
Cepheids are of the order of 1.3 magnitudes brighter than previously supposed has
been established primarily by the work of Walter Baade. Compare this figure with
that given by S. C. B. Gascoigne and G. E. Kron for the Small Magellanic Cloud,
Publications of the Astronomical Society of the Pacific **65**, 35, 1953.

well known.   The emphasis on the W Virginis stars has arisen from
the fact that these particular stars can be distinguished from Type I
or classical Cepheids by their light-curves alone, whereas for the other
stars no obvious differences in the light-curves occur for the two populations.   Thus we should speak of classical Cepheids or Cepheids of
population I on the one hand, and Cepheids of population II on the
other.   The two groups show different dependences of the form of the
light-curve on the period, the differences becoming very pronounced
between 12^d and 20^d.   Cecilia Payne-Gaposchkin attempted to separate

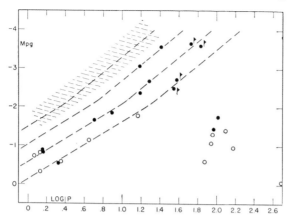

FIG. 1b.—PERIOD–LUMINOSITY DIAGRAM FOR TYPE II CEPHEIDS

Mean absolute photographic magnitudes for thirteen Cepheids in the globular clusters M2, M3, M5, M10, M13, and M15 are plotted with filled circles. Open circles are six Cepheids taken from Martin's work in Omega Centauri. The flagged points represent Cepheids with the RV Tauri behavior of alternating deep and shallow minima. They are all plotted with their longer period. The shaded region indicates the position of the classical Cepheids with the new zero point of −1.5. Points in the lower right-hand corner are long-period variables, predominantly around 100-day period, as present, in these globular clusters.

Dashed lines drawn through the points are all exactly similar but translated horizontally by a factor of two in the period. Color indices indicate that Type II Cepheids at a given luminosity are equivalent to each other regardless of which line they fall on; i.e, whatever period they have. Joy's spectra of these Type II Cepheids correspond to the spectra of classical Cepheids of the *same* luminosity. Finally, the particular dashed line on which these Cepheids fall seems to be identifiable from the shape of their light-curve. (Courtesy, Halton C. Arp, Mount Wilson and Palomar Observatories.)

the light-curves of the two varieties of Cepheids by means of Fourier analyses.*

3. Light-Curves and Intrinsic Luminosity

The most easily observed characteristic of a variable star is usually its light-curve, and far more data have been accumulated on the light-curves of variables than on any other parameter, e.g., color, spectra, or parallax.

The classical Cepheid light-curves show a considerable variety in form. Some rise rapidly from minimum to maximum and then decline more slowly (e.g., δ Cephei), while others show humps on the declining branch (e.g., η Aquilae), or less obvious humps on the ascending part (e.g., Z Lacertae). Hertzsprung called attention to an interesting relation between period and shape of light-curve for the Type I (classical)

*Astron. J. **52**, 218, 1947.

Cepheids. If we arrange the best observed light-curves in order of increasing period, we find that for each period a definite light-curve prevails, and as we proceed to longer periods, the form of the light-curve changes. The progression of shape change with period shows discontinuities near $0^d.43$, $1^d.2$, $2^d.8$, and 10^d; as one group fades out another sets in. Kukarin and Parenago, on the other hand, find four separate groups.

The most striking characteristic of the classical Cepheids is the constancy of their periods and the faithfulness with which they repeat them. For example, measures of light or radial velocity variations in δ Cephei taken in different years agree as well as those obtained in successive cycles. Some Cepheids, however, do show fluctuations in light-curve and period, although there is increasing evidence that these fluctuations themselves are periodic in character.[*]

The continuous sequence of Type II variables extends from the RR Lyrae star HD 223,065, for which Eggen finds a period of 80 minutes, to RV Tauri stars with periods of the order of 80 days. The analogues of the classical Cepheids are the Type II Cepheids. The best-known example, W Virginis, whose period is 17 days, resembles the classical Cepheids in amplitude and steadiness of its light-curve. The form of its light-curve is markedly different from that of classical Cepheids of the same period and its spectrum is strikingly different. The Type II Cepheids outside the 12^d–20^d range show no appreciable differences in their light-curves from Type I Cepheids.

The light-curves of the semi-regular RV Tauri stars show striking variations from period to period. The light-curve of RV Tauri shows a 78.534^d period with two maxima of almost equal height and two unequal minima, whose relative depths may change from cycle to cycle. In addition, these double fluctuations are superposed on a 1300-day oscillation. J. van der Bilt has recently suggested an even longer period of 8000 days. Other stars of this type may or may not possess the long-period fluctuations. In some objects, e.g., U. Monocerotis, the minima interchange from time to time and the periods show fluctuations.

The long-period variables are among the best-known variable stars, since their deep-red color and large fluctuations in visible light make them easy to detect. Ninety per cent of the known ones belong to spectral class Me (TiO bands plus emission lines), while the others are divided among the Se stars (ZrO) and carbon stars.[†]

---

[*]L. Campbell and L. Jacchia, *Story of Variable Stars* (Cambridge: Harvard University Press, 1941).

[†]There is a powerful selection effect in favor of the Me variables since many of them were discovered by objective prism surveys from their spectra.

The Gaposchkins find the average light-curves for the long-period variables to be much more nearly symmetrical than for average Cepheids or W Virginis stars. Among the Me variables the shorter-period stars tend to have symmetrical light-curves; the longer-period light-curves become increasingly asymmetrical. Among the Se or carbon stars, those of longest period tend to show the most symmetrical curves; but on the whole the R, S, and N stars have more symmetrical curves than have the Me variables.* The light-curves of long-period variables may show considerable variations from cycle to cycle. Mira Ceti is often appreciably brighter at one maximum than at another.†

What can be said of the intrinsic luminosities and dimensions of these different types of variables? The classical Cepheids are pure Type I objects, confined closely to the galactic plane, to the Large Magellanic Cloud, to the spiral arms of the Andromeda nebula, and to other Type I populations.

The relative luminosities of the classical Cepheids are well known, thanks to Miss Leavitt's period–luminosity relation. From a study of the light-curves of these variables in the Small Magellanic Cloud she found that the period was related to the apparent brightness in the sense that the longer the period, the brighter the star. Since all these stars are at essentially the same distance, this relationship must indicate a correlation between intrinsic luminosity and period. The establishment of the zero-point of the period–luminosity law; i.e., the absolute magnitude corresponding to a particular period, turns out to be extremely difficult. Parallaxes and proper motions of nearby Cepheids have been employed, and until recently it was thought that the period–luminosity curve of the Cepheids fitted onto that of the RR Lyrae stars. Much evidence has now been accumulated to show that the classical Cepheids are about 1.5 magnitudes brighter than previously supposed.‡

To establish the zero-point of the period–luminosity relation for the classical Cepheids, Blaauw studied 15 of these objects for which accurate proper motions had been determined from the meridian circle observations. He made a careful analysis of the influence of space absorption on the distance determination. From an analysis of

*See Campbell and Jacchia, *op. cit.*, for details.

†See L. Goldberg and L. H. Aller, *Atoms, Stars and Nebulae* (Cambridge: Harvard University Press, 1943), Fig. 70.

‡In this connection we must mention the work of H. Mineur (*Ann. d'Ap.* **7**, 160, 1944; *Comptes Rendu* of the Paris Academy **235**, 1607, 1952). In contrast to all previous investigators, he realized that, since absorption had to be taken into account statistically, the final solution would be very sensitive to errors in the adopted pole of the galaxy because of the very strong concentration of the Type I Cepheids to the galactic plane. He therefore derived a new value for the position of the pole from the Cepheids and obtained a position in good agreement with that found by Oort and by the radio observers.

the proper motion and radial velocity data he concluded that a correction of -1.4 magnitudes was needed for the previously accepted zero-point. Thus, at minimum, δ Cephei, whose period is 5.366 days, has an absolute magnitude of -3.0.

The RR Lyrae stars, whose periods are less than one day, are found not only in globular clusters, where they were first discovered by S. I. Bailey, but also in great numbers in all galactic latitudes, although they show a strong concentration to the galactic central bulge. Baade estimates there are 85,000 RR Lyrae stars within 3 kiloparsecs of the center. They appear to be pure Type II objects; those found in the neighborhood of the sun are all high-velocity stars. The establishment of their intrinsic luminosity is a matter of considerable importance for the determination of the distances of globular clusters and the scale of our galaxy. Sandage's careful comparison of the Russell diagrams for the clusters and for the stars in the neighborhood of the sun gives an absolute visual magnitude of $M_v = -0.09 \pm 0.2$.

An adequate study of the variables in a globular cluster requires a very large telescope. The most detailed investigation was that carried out by H. C. Arp at the Mount Wilson and Mount Palomar Observatories. He was able to get photovisual and photographic light-curves and correct for the effects of the interstellar absorbing medium. The Type II Cepheids show a different relationship between period and shape of light-curve than do the Type I Cepheids. The colors of Type II Cepheids show very little change with period; they are always very much bluer than Type I Cepheids of the same period. Also, there is no unique period–luminosity relationship for the Type II Cepheids as exists for the classical Cepheids. In fact, there may be two or even three groups. Finally, if the two classes of Cepheids are interpreted in terms of the pulsation theory, the kinematics of the pulsation must be completely different for the two classes. The two RV Tauri stars found by Helen Sawyer Hogg in globular clusters have bolometric magnitudes near -4.5.

From a spectroscopic study of 35 variables of high luminosity in globular clusters, Joy finds that in addition to the RR Lyrae stars, four distinct groups exist. The first group with periods 1.4 to 2.8 days, although distinct from RR Lyrae stars, shows the same range of spectral class. It appears to form an offshoot of the RR Lyrae type, quite distinct from classical Cepheids of the same period. The variables of period 13-19 days resemble W Virginis. Those outside this range have light-curves resembling those of classical Cepheids. The stars of periods between 25 and 90 days show emission lines and are earlier in spectral class than classical Cepheids of the same period. Some may be RV Tauri stars. There are also irregular and semi-regular variables of types that have large space motions and low galactic concentrations. *Me* variables are found in 47 Tucanae. It is significant that although the RR Lyrae stars are prominent in globular clusters, classical Cepheids are nonexistent there.

Thus, spectroscopically, the Type II Cepheids differ markedly from the Type I Cepheids. For a given period they are always earlier in spectral class as their colors would indicate.

Various investigators have studied the luminosities and motions of the long-period variable stars. From radial velocities and proper motions, Wilson and Merrill find that variables of type $M1e$ (period $\sim$ 175 days) have absolute visual magnitudes of -2.7, while $M8e$ variables with periods $\sim$ 450 days have absolute magnitudes of 0.8. Wilson and Merrill find that the *Me* and *Se* stars, as a group, have absolute magnitudes of -1.0. From radial velocities, proper motions, and interstellar lines Wilson and Sanford find an absolute magnitude between -0.4 and -0.8 for R stars, and -1.8 and -2.3 for the N stars. Irregular M-type giants have an absolute magnitude of -0.9, according to Joy and Wilson, while Keenan finds -0.5. The supergiant irregular M variables have absolute magnitudes between -2.0 and -4.5 (Joy). Keenan, who also applied spectroscopic criteria, finds M to be -4.5 while Wilson gets -3.4 from the radial velocities and proper motions.

The long-period variables live up to the most literal interpretation of supergiant stars. Thus Mira Ceti has a mean diameter of the order of 220,000,000 miles, so that if Mira Ceti were to replace the sun, the orbit of the earth would lie well below the surface. This well-observed star is probably typical of long-period variables.

The space motions may be of great help in distinguishing Type I and Type II objects. Many long-period variables are high-velocity objects that are found in all galactic latitudes and longitudes. There is a remarkable dependence of motion on period of light variation. For example, the average space motion decreases from 139 km/sec for a group of 14 variables having a mean period of 173 days to 40 km/sec for 16 stars with a period of 440 days. The kinematics of irregular variables appear similar to those of long-period variables. Class R stars also have high velocities, while Sanford finds evidence of effects of differential galactic rotation in the observed radial velocities of the class N stars.

In addition to the light variations, RR Lyrae stars, classical Cepheids, W Virginis stars, RV Tauri stars, and long-period variables show simultaneous variations in velocity, color, and spectrum. The velocity curves provide crucial data for the interpretation of the variation. In the classical Cepheids such as δ Cephei or η Aquilae, the greatest velocity of recession falls at minimum light. This relation is fulfilled closely for Cepheids with periods less than 10 days, but Joy finds that stars with longer periods show a tendency for velocity minima to come later than light maxima. In the RV Tauri stars the lag of velocity minimum after light maximum is greater than in Cepheids.

The Cepheids and long-period variables are bluer in color and earlier in spectrum at maximum than at minimum. For example, the spectrum and color of δ Cephei at maximum matches that of α Persei $F5\,Ib$ (supergiant) and at minimum it resembles that of β Draconis $G2\,Ib$ (supergiant), while Mira at maximum is $M5$ and sinks to $M9$ because of the enormous strengthening of the TiO bands at minimum. From minimum to maximum light, W Virginis shows the Balmer lines in both emission and absorption; the relative intensities of neutral and enhanced lines show pronounced variations with phase. The lines also show a doubling near minimum. At maximum, RV Tauri shows a K-type spectrum, but becomes redder as it fades and shows TiO bands at minimum in a spectrum that seems from its atomic lines, too early for these bands.

Mention should be made here of the work of Olin Eggen. He accurately established the relations between period, color amplitude, and light amplitude among the three well-known groups of classical Cepheids: (A) δ Cephei-like, which show a rapid rise and a slow decline, (B) η Aquilae-like, which show bumps on the descending branch, (C) ζ Geminorum-like, which show nearly symmetrical curves. The constancy of spectral class at maximum, observed by Arthur Code, is not confirmed by the colors. At minimum the colors check Struve's suggestion that Cepheids belong to Morgan's Class Ib and resemble normal stars.

4. Radial Pulsations and Stellar Variation

Any interpretation of the Cepheids, long-period variables or related objects must explain the correlation between light variation, color, and spectrum changes. So far, the only hypothesis that appears to give a coherent interpretation of the observations is that these stars are pulsating. If the pulsation hypothesis is correct, the relation between the bolometric luminosity, the effective temperature, and the radius, viz.:

$$L = \sigma T_e^4 4\pi R^2 \tag{1}$$

must be fulfilled at each point in the cycle. That is, suppose we are given the light-curve and compute the radius variation from the radial velocity curve. If we know the radius at some one epoch, we may then calculate T from R and L. Will the predicted temperature variation be consistent with the observed changes in color and spectrum?

First let us apply this criterion to the Cepheids. Stebbins determined the light-curve of δ Cephei at six different effective wave lengths, viz., λ3530, λ4220, λ4880, λ5700, λ7190, and λ10,300. With a temperature standard chosen as 5500°K for a $dG5$ star, he derived the color temperature from a comparison of the relative intensities at λ4220 and λ10,300. Since the amplitude varies with wave length, the color temperature changes through the cycle from 6500°K at maximum light to 4920°K at phase 0.7, just before the light minimum. Stebbins also found a progressive retardation of phase with increasing wave length, amounting to 0.05 over the extreme range. At points of equal magnitude on the ascending and descending branch, the star is bluer as it brightens. These observations are to be understood in terms of the equivalent of eqn. (1) for monochromatic radiation, viz., $L_\lambda = 4\pi B_\lambda(T)\pi R^2$, where $B_\lambda(T)$ is the Planckian function. At maximum the color agrees with the supergiant α Persei $F5$ Ib(Morgan-Keenan-Kellman), while at minimum it corresponds to that of a supergiant $G2$ star.

The spectral class variations agree closely with the color variations. From a comparison of Cepheid variables with standard supergiants of MKK Classes Ia, Ib, II, Arthur Code at Yerkes Observatory found

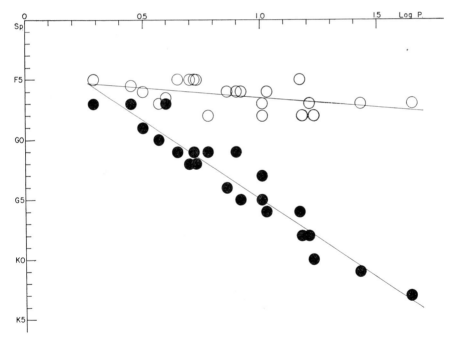

FIG. 2.—THE SPECTRAL VARIATIONS IN CEPHEIDS

Open circles show the spectral types at maximum; filled circles show the spectral classes at minimum. (Courtesy, Arthur Code.)

that at maximum the spectral type was nearly the same for all Cepheids, but with increasing period the type at minimum becomes later and later (see Fig. 2). At maximum the hydrogen lines are abnormally strong, as Struve and others had noted, while at minimum λ4215 is abnormally weak.

The agreement between spectral class and color variations suggests that, in the first approximation, it is legitimate to treat the atmospheres of these stars as similar to those of other supergiants, in so far as the radiation laws are concerned.

To derive the effective temperature variations for comparison with the color temperature variations, one must know the radius and bolometric luminosity at each phase. Integration of the radial velocity curve gives the variation in R, but to get the absolute value of R and the bolometric luminosity, one must know the absolute visual magnitude M_{vis} and the temperature at one phase. In his discussion of the pulsations of δ Cephei, Martin Schwarzschild chose $M_{vis} = -2.36$ at maximum light, on the basis of the period–luminosity curve. In view of the revision of the zero-point of the period–luminosity curve we shall take $M_{vis} = -3.66$. For the temperature at maximum, 5700°K will serve our purposes for an illustrative calculation. Then the radius R at maximum light will be 47.6 solar radii or 33.144×10^{11} cm. From the integration of the radial velocity curve, Martin Schwarzschild found $r - \bar{R}$ to be -1.505×10^{11} cm at maximum light; hence the average (median) radius $\bar{R}$ was 34.649×10^{11} cm. For any other phase, the value of $r - \bar{R}$ may be found from the integration of the velocity curve.

Our next task is to find the luminosity at each point in the cycle. The light-curves give the apparent magnitude, m_{vis}, and since we know M_{vis} at maximum light, we can find M_{vis} at any phase. To obtain L we must apply the appropriate bolometric corrections, which

TABLE 1

EFFECTIVE TEMPERATURES OF δ CEPHEI

Phase	$-m$	B.C.	M_{bol}	$\log L$	$(r - \bar{R}) \times 10^{-11}$	$R \times 10^{-11}$	T_e
0.10	−3.526	−0.190	−3.716	36.898	−0.294	34.36	5570
0.20	−3.380	−0.275	−3.655	36.860	+0.611	35.26	5430
0.30	−3.261	−0.350	−3.611	36.838	+1.169	35.82	5330
0.40	−3.147	−0.410	−3.557	36.818	+1.371	36.02	5250
0.50	−3.046	−0.450	−3.496	36.790	+1.226	35.88	5180
0.60	−2.958	−0.500	−3.458	36.768	+0.769	35.42	5160
0.70	−2.895	−0.520	−3.415	36.744	−0.015	34.63	5175
0.80	−2.961	−0.472	−3.433	36.759	−1.137	33.51	5280
0.90	−3.302	−0.320	−3.622	36.840	−2.194	32.46	5610
1.00	−3.660	−0.120	−3.780	36.934	−1.505	33.14	5750

we derive from Kuiper's table (Table 6 of Ch. ★6*) for $M_{vis} = -4.0$ and the color temperature given by Stebbins. We then compute the effective temperature from eqn. (1) for various phases throughout the cycle.†

In Table 1 we give for each phase the visual brightness on a magnitude scale, $-m$; the empirical bolometric correction interpolated as a function of color temperature from Kuiper's table; the bolometric absolute magnitude, $\log L$ in c.g.s. units; $(r - R)$ and R in cm; and the effective temperature computed from eqn. (1). Our effective temperatures differ from those in Schwarzschild's paper because we have chosen a different $\bar{R}$. The qualitative agreement of the phases of the variations in the effective and color temperatures is good. Both show a maximum at

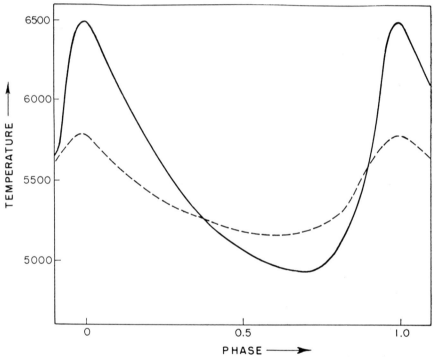

FIG. 3.—THE COLOR TEMPERATURE AND EFFECTIVE TEMPERATURE AS A FUNCTION
OF PHASE IN δ CEPHEI

The solid curve represents the variation of the color temperature as measured by Stebbins; the dashed curve represents the effective temperature derived in Table 1.

*All references to chapters in the author's *Astrophysics—The Atmospheres of the Sun and Stars* (New York: The Ronald Press Co., 1953) will be designated in this volume by ★ before the chapter number.

†In the numerical illustrations in this chapter we have used a zero-point correction of -1.3 magnitudes, whereas a correction of about -1.5 magnitudes seems more likely on the basis of the most recent work (January, 1954).

about the same phase (although the minimum effective temperature precedes the minimum color temperature) and for both the rise is sharper than the decline. Notice that the radius of the star near maximum and minimum light is almost the same and near the minimum value. The range in light variation is to be attributed to changes in the surface temperature; radius changes only modify the form of the light-curve.

Quantitatively, the agreement between T_e and T_c is poor, but here we must recall that a color temperature is merely the parameter chosen to fit Planck's formula to the observed energy distribution over a limited wave-length range. We can interpret the color temperature only if we know something about the temperature gradient in the atmosphere and the absorption coefficient. If the star is pulsating, the temperature and density may vary in the atmospheric layers in such a way that the calculation of the relationship is difficult. W. Becker's studies suggest that the use of the color temperature to compute the radius is inappropriate. From the maximum and minimum of a number of Cepheids, Becker finds T_c to be related to a quantity he calls the "radiation" temperature. For a specified spectral region, the radiation temperature is the temperature a black body of the same size would have to have in order that it emit the same amount of energy in the given spectral interval. This quantity differs from the color temperature and has a smaller amplitude of variation. If it is employed in conjunction with the light-curve at any phase, the computed radius agrees more closely with the relative radius derived from the velocity curve. Hence we conclude that the pulsation hypothesis is worth further examination. Let us see how it fits the long-period variables.

In the long-period variables, most of the radiation is emitted in the infrared and to derive bolometric luminosities the character of the infrared radiation must be examined. The most important study of the radiation of these stars was that carried out by Pettit and Nicholson with a thermocouple at the 100-inch telescope. If one junction is exposed to the stellar radiation and the other is shielded, the e.m.f. developed will depend on the total energy (summed over all wave lengths) falling upon the thermocouple. The energy received depends on the atmospheric absorption and the reflectivity of the telescope mirrors, quantities which must be determined independently. If a cell containing water is placed before the thermocouple, much of the infrared radiation is cut out. By a comparison of the total energy received without any filter with that measured when the far infrared is extinguished by the water cell, it is possible to estimate the temperature, provided we can suppose that the star radiates like a black body in the infrared.

To interpret their measurements, Pettit and Nicholson drew black-body curves for various representative temperatures. From these curves they subtracted: (a) the energy removed by atmospheric absorption and mirror reflectivity, and (b) this energy loss plus the energy absorbed by the water cell. (See Fig. 4.) The lower the temperature, the larger will be the fraction of the energy concentrated in the far infrared, and the greater will be the proportion of energy removed by the water cell. Thus the ratio of the areas under the two curves, one of which involves the water-cell transmission, while the other does not, is a function of the temperature. It can be represented by the empirical formula:

$$\log T = 3.477 - 0.6231 \log w \tag{2}$$

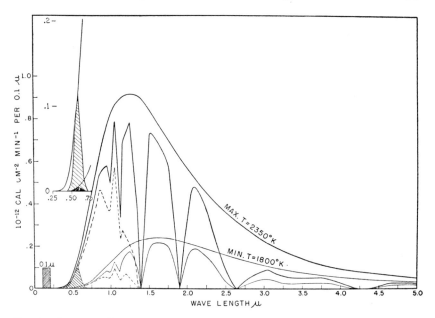

Fig. 4.—Spectral Energy Curves of Long-Period Variable Stars at Maximum
and Minimum of Temperature and Light

The smooth Planckian curves drawn for temperatures of 1800°K and 2350°K are multiplied by the atmospheric transmission for average conditions at Mount Wilson and by the coefficients of reflection for 2 freshly silvered mirrors. The resultant jagged curves show the spectral distribution of the energy reaching the thermocouple. The dotted curves show the energy distribution after passage through the water cell.

The energy curve in the visual region multiplied by the sensitivity function of the eye is shown on a magnified scale in the upper left-hand part of the diagram. Notice that the huge range in visual brightness corresponds to a much smaller range in the total energy output.

The scale of the ordinates refers to the amount of energy received per cm² per minute outside the earth's atmosphere for a star of zero radiometric magnitude. (Courtesy, E. Pettit, and S. B. Nicholson, *Astrophysical Journal*, University of Chicago Press, **78**, 333, 1933.)

where the water cell absorption w is the ratio of the two afore-mentioned areas expressed in magnitudes. Here T is the temperature of the Planckian energy distribution that most nearly fits the energy distribution in the star.

To reduce the radiometric magnitudes to bolometric magnitudes, it is necessary to find the ratio of the area under the black body-curve to the area corrected for atmospheric transmission and reflection losses by the mirror, i.e., the ratio of the energy in the beam outside the atmosphere to the energy received at the thermocouple. Pettit and Nicholson were able to express the bolometric corrections in magnitudes in terms of the water-cell absorption by the empirical formula

$$\delta m_r = 0.252 + 0.234w, \quad m_b = m_r - \delta m_r \qquad (3)$$

where m_r is the observed radiometric magnitude and m_b is the apparent bolometric magnitude.

The energy received from the star outside of the earth's atmosphere, as expressed by m_b, depends on the angular diameter of the star, d, and the temperature which is a function of the water-cell absorption. We may write

$$\log d = 5.276 - 2 \log T_e - 0.2m_b \qquad (4)$$

It is found empirically that the effective temperature T_e is not the temperature derived by fitting a black-body curve to the stellar energy distribution, but is related to T by $T = 1.044T_e$. Hence d is proportional to $1.09T^{-2}$.

The amplitude measured in total energy is much smaller than the visual amplitude. Thus eleven long-period variables with a mean visual range of 5.9 magnitudes had a bolometric amplitude of only 0.89 magnitudes, while the famous red star, χ Cygni has a thousand-fold greater amplitude in visual than in total light. The temperatures, as measured from the water-cell absorptions, ranged from 2640°K at visual maximum to 1920°K at minimum for Mira Ceti, while χ Cygni varied from 2240°K at maximum to 1640°K at minimum. The coolest star measured, V Cygni, had a temperature of 1500°K.

Pettit and Nicholson found the temperature to be greatest at the time of greatest visual brightness rather than at the time of greatest total radiation, indicating that not only the temperature but also the diameter of these variables changed during the cycle. From the observed radiometric magnitude m_r and water-cell absorption w, one can find both the diameter and temperature variations with the aid of eqns. (2), (3), and (4). The diameter of the average long-period variable fluctuates about 37 per cent of its mean value. The radiometric measures show that the light maximum in the infrared comes systematically later than the maximum in visual light. The bolometric maximum comes about 50 days after the light maximum when the star has faded 1.5 magnitudes. Like the classical Cepheids, the long-period variables are bluer on the rising branch of the light-curve than at the same magnitude during the decline.

The spectra of the long-period variables show complex and, to some degree, startling changes. Mira, which Joy studied in great detail, may serve as a typical example of an Me variable. At maximum the spectrum is near $M5$ and, as the star fades, the spectral class advances as the TiO bands strengthen until at minimum it is near $M9$. Low-level atomic lines such as λ4227 of Ca I also strengthen. These changes are all consistent with the temperature variations indicated by the bolometric observations.

Somewhere on the rising branch of the light-curve, bright hydrogen lines appear and strengthen as the star rises to maximum, only to decline again as the star fades. Their behavior is not symmetrical with the light maximum, however. The intensity ratios of these lines are bizarre; before maximum Hδ is strongest, Hγ is weaker, Hε is very weak, and Hβ is usually missing. As the cycle advances, the Hγ/Hδ ratio increases until Hγ is stronger than Hδ. Now Hγ falls in an absorption band of TiO and Hβ in an even stronger band, Hε is superposed on the Ca II H line, while Hδ falls in a relatively unobstructed region of the spectrum. Thus the observations suggest that before maximum the TiO and Ca II absorption occurs above the level where the hydrogen emission is produced.* That is, as time advances, the Balmer decrement tends more and more closely to its normal value.

The fact that spectroscopic effects are observed from different strata at the same time complicates the interpretation of long-period variables. The bright lines appear to originate deep in the atmosphere, whereas the dark lines seem to be formed in the upper layers. Nowhere are complications introduced by stratifications better exhibited than in the radial velocity data.

Fig. 5, due to Paul W. Merrill, illustrates the changes observed with high dispersion in the spectra of the $M8e$ variable R Leonis. The bright lines, Fe II, H, Si I, and λ4202 Fe I give a systematic velocity of approach as compared with the dark lines, a phenomenon noted long ago by W. W. Campbell. The velocities of the emission lines of hydrogen and ionized iron decrease with advancing phase, while those of neutral iron, λ4202, and Si I increase with advancing phase. The absorption-line velocities show little change with phase. Similar data are obtained for other Me variables.

*In unusually bright maxima, Hγ becomes stronger than Hδ, and Hβ is strong as though the overlying TiO bands were weaker.

Is it possible to interpret the radial velocity, radiometric, and temperature variations of the long-period variables in terms of the pulsation theory? From their radiometric observations, Pettit and Nicholson computed the diameter variations as a function of phase. From these diameter variations it is possible to calculate the velocities of expansion or contraction of the star. It is difficult, however, to correlate these predicted velocities with any observed feature of the spectrum.

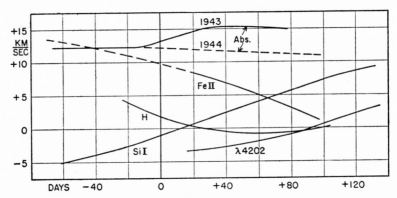

FIG. 5.—COMPARISON OF VELOCITY CURVES DERIVED FROM VARIOUS LINES IN THE SPECTRUM OF R LEONIS

(Courtesy, Paul W. Merrill, *Astrophysical Journal*, University of Chicago Press, **103**, 286, 1946.)

R. M. Scott suggested that the photosphere of the star associated with the radiometric measurements is near the region where the emission lines are produced, rather than near the layers where the absorption lines and the titanium oxide bands are formed. The radius variations, computed from emission-line velocities derived long ago by Joy from low dispersion spectrograms of Mira, seemed to agree in phase with the radii computed by Pettit and Nicholson. Recent high dispersion (coudé) studies of similar stars, however (cf. Fig. 5), show that no unique velocity may be assigned to the emission lines, and that different elements behave in different ways. The general behavior of the emission lines strongly suggests that the emitting gases move continuously outward; there is no clear-cut indication of an actual atmospheric pulsation. The agreement found by Scott, therefore, appears to have been fortuitous; at the present time the long-period variables permit no decisive judgment to be rendered on the pulsation hypothesis. The observed velocity variations may represent the passage of running waves through strata at different depths, but a quantitative analysis would be difficult. As a working hypothesis, however, we shall assume pulsations as the basic cause of variation in these long-period stars.

5. The Theory of Adiabatic Pulsations

August Ritter, in 1873, was the first to suggest that Cepheid variation was due to a pulsation and showed that for a homogeneous star the period of pulsation would be inversely proportional to the square root of the density. The pulsation hypothesis was ignored, however, in favor of the interpretation of Cepheids as double stars until Shapley, in 1914, showed the latter theory to be untenable. The size of the orbit of the supposed companion to the Cepheid would be too small to leave room for the primary and the companion would have to move within the principal star.

Eddington developed the modern mathematical theory of Cepheid pulsation which we shall now consider. If a star in hydrostatic equilibrium becomes suddenly compressed, the gas pressure will more than compensate the weight of the overlying layers, and the upper strata will be pushed violently upward past the equilibrium position. The diminishing pressure cannot support the weight of these layers which gradually slow down, come to rest, and fall back into the star. The falling material overshoots the equilibrium position, the gas is compressed, and the cycle is repeated, until it is damped out by dissipative forces, unless power is supplied from some source.

If, for each instant of time we can specify the pressure, density, and temperature of a pulsating star as a function of r, we know the solution. Let us fix our attention upon a layer at a distance r_0 from the center of the unperturbed star. The other independent variable is the time, t. The dependent variables are:

$$P(t, r_0), \quad T(t, r_0), \quad r(t, r_0), \quad \rho(t, r_0), \quad M_r, \text{ and } L_r \qquad (5)$$

Here M_r is the mass within a shell of radius r_0. The mass dM_r of this shell is constant in a pulsation if we follow the motion of the material in this layer, thus

$$dM_r = 4\pi r^2 \rho \, dr = 4\pi r_0^2 \rho_0 \, dr_0 \qquad (6)$$

where the subscript 0 refers to the undisturbed values.
Hence

$$\left(\frac{r}{r_0}\right)^2 \frac{\rho}{\rho_0} \frac{\partial r}{\partial r_0} = 1 \qquad (7)$$

We use partial derivatives because both r and t are independent variables. The static relation

$$\frac{dP}{dr} = -\frac{GM_r}{r^2} \rho \qquad (8)$$

must be replaced by the equation of motion for each cm³ of the material. That is, the mass ρ of the unit volume multiplied by its acceleration must equal the forces exerted by the instantaneous pressure gradient $(\partial P/\partial r)$ and the gravitational attraction

$$-\rho \frac{\partial^2 r}{\partial t^2} = \frac{\partial P}{\partial r} + G \frac{M_r}{r^2} \rho \qquad (9)$$

The equation of radiative flow, i.e., the expression involving $d(aT^4)/dr$, remains true, since the flux reacts instantaneously to changes in the temperature gradient. The relation is useful for predicting the light variation. The equation in dL_r/dr cannot remain valid over short intervals of time, since temperature variations occur throughout the star. Energy may be stored up and subsequently released. In a few days the amount of energy that gets out of a shell is small compared with the amount already stored there. Over a period of a thousand years, the dL/dr relation will have to be fulfilled, but it is not valid over a few days.

Further, we shall consider the volume element quite independently of its neighbors. The opacity is so high that little energy will leak in or out of a small element (of diameter of the order of 0.001 that of the star). That is, the energy changes will be practically adiabatic. Hence

$$\frac{P}{P_0} = \left(\frac{\rho}{\rho_0}\right)^\gamma \qquad (10)$$

Also

$$M_r = M_{r_0} \qquad (11)$$

because the mass inside the layer at r_0 remains the same.

The fundamental equations of the problem are not amenable to analytic solution. Therefore we apply the method of micro-pulsations. The first step is to develop the theory as in ordinary acoustics where we work with wave motions that can be superposed linearly to form compound waves. We assume the oscillations are adiabatic and obtain a linear differential equation for the amplitude of the pulsations. In the next step, terms that represent the loss of wave energy by dissipation are included.

The first approximation, wherein the radius variations are much smaller than the radius of the star, gives a good qualitative picture of the motions and also nearly the correct period. We write

$$r = r_0(1 + r_1), \quad P = P_0(1 + P_1), \quad \rho = \rho_0(1 + \rho_1) \qquad (12)$$

Now r_1, ρ_1, P_1 are all small so that we may neglect higher powers of these quantities than the first. Thus, since for small x

$$(1 + x)^n = 1 + nx + \cdots \tag{13}$$

eqn. (7) gives

$$(1 + 2r_1)(1 + \rho_1)\left(1 + r_1 + r_0 \frac{\partial r_1}{\partial r_0}\right) = 1 \tag{14}$$

When we multiply out and neglect the quadratic terms we get

$$0 = 3r_1 + \rho_1 + \frac{\partial r_1}{\partial r_0} r_0 \tag{15}$$

From eqn. (7) we can derive

$$\frac{\partial P}{\partial r} = \frac{\partial P}{\partial r_0}\left(\frac{r}{r_0}\right)^2 \frac{\rho}{\rho_0} = \left[\frac{\partial P_0}{\partial r_0}(1 + P_1) + P_0 \frac{\partial P_1}{\partial r_0}\right]\left(\frac{r}{r_0}\right)^2 \frac{\rho}{\rho_0}$$

$$= \left[\frac{\partial P_0}{\partial r_0}(1 + P_1) + P_0 \frac{\partial P_1}{\partial r_0}\right](1 + 2r_1 + \rho_1) \tag{16}$$

Similarly

$$\frac{GM_r}{r^2}\rho = \frac{GM_{r_0}}{r_0^2}\rho_0(1 - 2r_1 + \rho_1) \tag{17}$$

and

$$\rho \frac{\partial^2 r}{\partial t^2} = \rho_0(1 + \rho_1)r_0 \frac{\partial^2 r_1}{\partial t^2} = \rho_0 r_0 \frac{\partial^2 r_1}{\partial t^2} \tag{18}$$

because ρ_1 and r_1 are small. Therefore $\partial^2 r_1/\partial t^2$ is a quadratic term in small quantities. Note that we must have

$$\frac{dP_0}{dr_0} = -G \frac{M_{r_0}}{r^2}\rho_0 \tag{19}$$

for equilibrium conditions. From eqns. (9), (16), (17), (18), and (19) we get

$$-\frac{GM_{r_0}}{r_0^2}\rho_0(1 + P_1) + P_0 \frac{\partial P_1}{\partial r_0} - G \frac{M_{r_0}}{r_0^2}\rho_0(2r_1 + \rho_1)$$

$$+ \frac{GM_{r_0}}{r_0^2}\rho_0(1 - 2r_1 + \rho_1) + \rho_0 r_0 \frac{\partial^2 r_1}{\partial t^2} = 0 \tag{20}$$

Hence

$$-G \frac{M_{r_0}}{r_0^2}\rho_0 P_1 + P_0 \frac{\partial P_1}{\partial r_0} - G \frac{M_{r_0}}{r_0^2} 4\rho_0 r_1 + \rho_0 r_0 \frac{\partial^2 r_1}{\partial t^2} = 0 \tag{21}$$

and from eqn. (10)

$$P_1 = \gamma \rho_1 \tag{22}$$

Now eqns. (15), (21), and (22) provide us with three equations in three variables. Two of these are differential equations of the first degree which can be transformed to one of the second degree. We retain r_0 and t as the independent variables. Thus we have

$$\frac{\partial^2 r_1}{\partial r_0^2} + \frac{\partial r_1}{\partial r_0}\left[\frac{4}{r_0} - \frac{GM_{r_0}}{r_0^2}\frac{\rho_0}{P_0}\right] + r_1\left[\frac{4 - 3\gamma}{\gamma}\frac{GM_{r_0}}{r_0^2}\frac{\rho_0}{P_0}\frac{1}{r_0}\right] - \frac{\rho_0}{\gamma P_0}\frac{\partial^2 r_1}{\partial t^2} = 0$$

(23)

This is a differential equation whose coefficients depend on the unperturbed values of the density and pressure. These are known from the integration of the stellar model. Eqn. (23) is the acoustical wave equation, but in ordinary acoustics we usually work with plane solutions with constant density and temperature, i.e., without density and temperature gradients. Stellar pulsations are in the nature of big-wave acoustics.

Let us now examine the boundary conditions. At the center the displacement is zero at all times, i.e., $r = 0$ for $r_0 = 0$. All coefficients in eqn. (23) stay finite as r_0 approaches zero, except $4/r_0$ which increases without bound. Hence $\partial r_1/\partial r_0 = 0$ at $r_0 = 0$. Since $\rho/P = \mu/\Re T$, the coefficient of ρ_0/P_0 in eqn. (23) must vanish at the surface when $T = 0$. Hence at the surface

$$-\frac{\partial r_1}{\partial r_0}\frac{GM_{r_0}}{r_0^2} + r_1\frac{4 - 3\gamma}{\gamma}\frac{GM_{r_0}}{r_0^2}\frac{1}{r_0} - \frac{1}{\gamma}\frac{\partial^2 r_1}{\partial t^2} = 0$$

(24)

Eddington sought a "standing wave" solution, i.e., one in which all parts of the star moved in and out in synchronism. The acoustical analogue is an organ pipe closed at one end. Throughout most of its length a standing wave exists, while the constant pressure at the end of the pipe corresponds to the condition of vanishing density at the surface of the star. A running wave solution will not work in the interior of the pipe. In the standing wave the time-instant of greatest displacement is the same everywhere; i.e., the different parts of the wave are in phase. The amplitude a depends on r_0. Furthermore, $a(r_0)$ will be 0 at the bottom of the organ pipe or the center of the star. The appropriate solution will be of the form

$$r_1(r_0\ , \ t) = a(r_0)T(t)$$

(25)

i.e., the variables are "separable" for a standing wave solution. In fact, we find that

$$r_1 = a(r_0) \cos\frac{2\pi}{p}t$$

(26)

will satisfy eqn. (23) provided that $a(r_0)$ is taken as the solution of

$$\frac{d^2a}{dr_0^2} + \frac{da}{dr_0}\left[\frac{4}{r_0} - \frac{GM_{r_0}}{r_0^2}\frac{\rho_0}{P_0}\right]$$

$$+ a\left[\frac{4 - 3\gamma}{\gamma}\frac{GM_{r_0}}{r_0^2}\frac{\rho_0}{P_0}\frac{1}{r_0} + \frac{\rho_0}{\gamma P_0}\left[\frac{2\pi}{p}\right]^2\right] = 0 \qquad (27)$$

with the boundary conditions, $r_0 = 0$, $da/dr_0 = 0$.
and at $r_0 = R$,

$$-\frac{da}{dr_0}\frac{GM_{r_0}}{r_0^2} + a\frac{4 - 3\gamma}{\gamma}\frac{GM_{r_0}}{r_0^3} + \frac{1}{\gamma}\left(\frac{2\pi}{p}\right)^2 a = 0 \qquad (28)$$

Since eqn. (27) is a differential equation of the second order, its general solution contains two free constants. One of these cannot be used to satisfy the boundary conditions, namely, if a is a solution which fulfills the boundary conditions, then $a' = ac$ is also a solution which fulfills the boundary conditions. With the other free constant only one of the boundary conditions can be fulfilled. The second boundary condition must therefore be fulfilled by a proper choice of p. Hence we find p to be the eigenvalue of the problem which is determined by the physical conditions we had to impose on the solution.

This differential equation must be solved by numerical integration to get $a(r_0)$ and the period of oscillation. We start with the unperturbed model of the star, so that the density and pressure are known at each point, and determine $a(r_0)$ in such a way that the boundary conditions are fulfilled. With an assumed trial value of p, one can solve eqn. (27) by a power series expansion near $r = 0$ and $r = R$ (the outer radius of the star) and proceed from these points outward and inward, respectively, by numerical integration. At some point, e.g., halfway to the surface of the star, the outward-progressing and inward-moving solutions must be fitted together. In general they will not fit together, and the value of p must be varied until a fit is obtained. The pulsation of longest period will be the fundamental mode of oscillation of the star.

Although the actual determination of the fundamental period for any given model is laborious, we can easily show by means of a homology transformation that the period p and density ρ are related by the expression

$$p\sqrt{\rho} = \text{constant} \qquad (29)$$

Consider two homologous stars in which the period, displacement function, undisturbed density, and pressure are, respectively,

$$p, a, \rho_0, P_0 \quad \text{and} \quad p', a', \rho_0', P_0'$$

Let us write

$$p = p'f \qquad (30)$$

where f is a constant to be determined. Since the stars are homologous, $a = a'$. Our variables are related by

$$r_0 = \frac{R}{R'} r_0', \qquad M_{r_0} = M_{r_0'} \cdot \frac{M}{M'}$$

$$\rho_0 = \rho_0' \frac{M}{M'} \frac{R'^3}{R^3}, \qquad P = P_0' \frac{M^2}{M'^2} \frac{R'^4}{R^4} \tag{31}$$

Now eqn. (27) will be valid for the primed as well as the unprimed quantities. Thus we have

$$\frac{d^2a'}{dr_0'^2} \frac{R'^2}{R^2} + \frac{da'}{dr_0'} \frac{R'^2}{R^2} \left[\frac{4}{r_0'} - G \frac{M_{r'_0}}{r_0'^2} \frac{\rho_0'}{P_0'} \right]$$

$$+ a' \left[\frac{4 - 3\gamma}{\gamma} \frac{GM_{r_0}}{r_0^2} \frac{\rho_0}{P_0} \frac{1}{r_0} \frac{R'^2}{R^2} + \frac{\rho_0'}{\gamma P_0'} \left(\frac{2\pi}{p'} \right)^2 \frac{M'}{M} \frac{R}{R'} \frac{1}{f^2} \right] = 0 \tag{32}$$

which is identical with eqn. (27) if

$$\frac{R'^2}{R^2} = \frac{M'}{M} \frac{R}{R'} \frac{1}{f^2}$$

that is

$$f^2 = \frac{M'}{M} \frac{R^3}{R'^3} = \frac{\bar{\rho}'}{\bar{\rho}} = \left(\frac{p}{p'} \right)^2 \tag{33}$$

which implies

$$p\sqrt{\bar{\rho}} = p'\sqrt{\bar{\rho}'} = K \tag{34}$$

K is a constant, which should be the same for all stars built on the same model. For a polytropic model, K depends sharply on γ, as the following table computed from integrations by Martin Schwarzschild shows:

γ	1.43	1.54	1.67
$p\sqrt{\rho_c}$	0.46	0.33	0.28 days

where ρ_c is the central density.

That is, if the stars are all built on the same model, $p\sqrt{\bar{\rho}}$ should be the same for all of them. Eddington estimated the dimensions of the classical Cepheids from their absolute magnitudes (obtained from the period–luminosity law) and surface temperatures and guessed their masses from the mass–luminosity law. He found the product $p\sqrt{\bar{\rho}}$ to be very nearly constant along the entire range of classical Cepheids. If the standard model is assumed, the computed period is less than the observed period, which would imply that the value of K and therefore the stellar model is wrong.

If we repeat Eddington's calculation with the revised zero-point of the classical Cepheids and the mass–luminosity law as expressed in eqn. (8) of Chapter *1, we obtain the following results for some typical classical Cepheids.

Star	Period	$\overline{M}_{\text{bol}}$	ρ_c	$p\sqrt{\rho_c}$
SU Cassiopeia	1.950	−2.45	0.054	0.452
RT Aurigae	3.728	−3.06	0.027	0.612
δ Cephei	5.366	−3.57	0.0071	0.452
η Aquilae	7.176	−4.00	0.00346	0.421
ζ Geminorum	10.155	−4.67	0.00115	0.345
X Cygni	16.385	−5.27	0.000463	0.352
Y Ophiuchi	17.121	−5.47	0.000262	0.278
l Carinae	35.528	−6.83	0.000068	0.293

Successive columns give the designation of the star, the period in days, the adopted mean bolometric magnitude, the central density (assuming the standard model), and $p\sqrt{\rho_c}$. The latter is not constant but appears to diminish slightly as the period increases.

If we assume Eddington's model and the mass–luminosity law, the predicted periods seem to be a little too short for their densities. The discrepancy could be removed by assuming the stars to be more homogeneous, but the energy generation requires a dense core with a high central temperature. I. Epstein proposed a model with a dense energy-producing core which had little effect on the pulsation period, the latter being determined by the outer part of the star which might be partly in convective equilibrium.

Furthermore, no bona fide determination of the mass of a Cepheid exists. The extrapolation of mass–luminosity relationship of main-sequence stars to the supergiants is really scarcely justifiable.

A more detailed study of the prototype δ Cephei by Savedoff, in which he refers all calculations to the absolute visual magnitude, temperature, and radius at minimum light, leads to an excellent agreement between the theoretical and "observed" $P\sqrt{\rho}$. He assumed M_{vis} (min) = -3.0 ± 0.3, mass = $1.78 \pm 0.16 \times 10^{34}$ grams from the mass–luminosity law, $T_{\text{min}} = 4950$ °K, and obtained by theory a radius of the star at minimum light of $3.83 \pm 0.4 \times 10^{12}$ cm as compared with a value, 3.70×10^{12} cm from the radial velocity and color.

One other point deserves mention here. To what extent are the mathematical approximations introduced in the theory of small amplitudes justified? This theory gives a sinusoidal velocity curve, whereas

/5576

JUNIOR COLLEGE LIBRARY
YORK, PENNA.

the observed curve shows a distinct skewness. Since the simple theory gives the wrong velocity- and light-curve form, may it not also give the wrong period?

The simple pendulum provides a useful illustration. As long as the oscillation is small, the period is independent of amplitude. For larger amplitudes the period increases. The same conditions might be anticipated for pulsating stars. As the amplitude increases, the velocity curve departs more and more from the sinusoidal form and the period lengthens. The prediction of amplitudes from theory is more difficult than the prediction of periods, just as the prediction of the amplitude of the swing of a pendulum from the elastic constants of the steel spring and a knowledge of the clock escapement would be more trouble-some than the calculation of the period of the swing from the length of the pendulum and the acceleration of gravity.

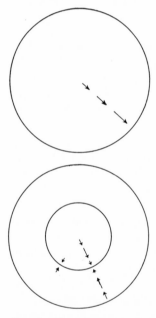

FIG. 6.—FUNDAMENTAL AND OVERTONE OSCILLATIONS

Upper: Fundamental.
Lower: First harmonic.

Rosseland and others have discussed the problem of large (anharmonic) pulsations, and have shown how the shape of the velocity curve may be expected to depend on the amplitude of the pulsations. Bhatnagar and Kothari carried the problem further and gave an exact treatment for $\gamma = \frac{5}{3}$. They concluded that the theory of anharmonic pulsations cannot account for the non-sinusoidal character of the velocity curve of Cepheids. The observed skewness of the curves would demand an amplitude of pulsation of, roughly, the stellar radius, while the observed amplitude is less than a tenth this quantity. Thus, for the observed amplitudes, the increase of period and the degree of skewness of the velocity curves are too small. The theoretical asymmetry and increases of period are consistent with observation, but the amplitude required is much too large. This is the *big* discrepancy of the pulsation theory which can be settled only when the structure of giant stars has been worked out.

Most vibrating systems—strings, drums, or bells, for example, oscillate not only in their fundamental mode, but in overtones as well. In the fundamental mode of oscillation of a gaseous star* all points

*Deformations of an oscillating star where the displacement ξ from an equilibrium position depends on the angular variables, θ and ϕ as well as r, are probably of little importance.

move outward or inward in synchronism. In the first overtone, the points within a nodal sphere of radius, say r_1, will be moving outward, while those outside the nodal sphere will be moving inward. Half a cycle later the material outside the nodal surface will move outward and the material inside will move inward.

For any stellar model one may solve eqn. (27) for higher overtones as well as the fundamental. Schwarzschild has carried out such calculations for the standard model with different values of γ. For $\gamma = 1.54$, the overtone periods p_i, in terms of the fundamental period p_0, turned out to be

overtone	1	2	3	4
p_i/p_0	0.687	0.515	0.412	0.343

Note that the overtones are not simple harmonics of the fundamental; e.g., the ratio of the frequency of the first overtone to the fundamental is 1/0.69 rather than 2/1. The larger the value of γ, however, the closer will be the frequency ratio tend to 2/1. The situation is analogous to that of a drum where the overtones are not simple multiples of the fundamental.

Striking evidence for stars vibrating in an overtone is provided by certain short-period variables observed by Martin Schwarzschild in Messier 3. Color-index–period arrays suggest that these cluster variables vibrate in their first overtone rather than in their fundamental.

Fath concluded that the star δ Scuti has three distinct periods of pulsation, viz., $P_0 = 0^d.193739$, $0^d.157382$, and $0^d.09156$, which possibly represent overtone pulsations. The second period does not appear to be securely established. If it is true, the star must be built on something different from the standard model.

Although the overtones are incommensurable with the fundamental, in some instances one of them may be so nearly commensurable as to produce a beat period long in comparison with the fundamental period. Miss Kluyver suggested that certain peculiarities in the light-curves of the cluster-type Cepheid RR Lyrae could be explained as the effect of resonance between the fundamental and some higher mode. The principal period of this star is $0^d.56685$, but there is also a secondary period of $40^d.6$. Presumably, this is a beat period arising from the fact that the fundamental is nearly commensurable with some higher mode, possibly the second overtone with a period of $0^d.5590$.*

*From the fact that the period–color–amplitude relation for his Type B Cepheids is displaced from that of his Type C by about half a period, Eggen suggests that the Type C objects vibrate in their first overtone.

If the semi-regular or even irregular variables were to be interpreted by the pulsation theory, we might suppose that several overtones were excited at once. The RV Tauri stars and long-period variables often show light-curve changes reminiscent of sporadic phenomena rather than the superposition of overtones, however.

The theory of anharmonic pulsations seems to explain, qualitatively at least, the asymmetry of the light and velocity curves. Possible resonance between different modes of vibration may account for seeming irregularities in the light-curves and the changes thereof. Coupling between different modes also may control the amplitudes of the pulsation. Woltjer suggested that an interaction occurred between the fundamental and some higher mode, in which the damping sufficed to dissipate enough energy to restrict the pulsation amplitude to its observed value.

Savedoff finds that the pulsation theory does not fit the RR Lyrae stars if they obey the mass–luminosity law for Type I main-sequence stars. On the other hand the theory does fit the observations if masses about 1.5 that of the sun are assumed. If we interpret (see Ch. 2) the color-magnitude array for globular clusters as a consequence of the evolutionary development of an ancient main sequence, we cannot expect any stars to be more massive than about 1.5 to 1.7 times the sun. All more massive stars would have burned out long ago. The expected mass of an RR Lyrae star on the basis of the evolutionary developments in globular clusters is just the same as that required by the pulsation theory!

6. Surface Phenomena in Radial Pulsations

Although the standing wave theory fairly successfully predicts the periods of Cepheids, it gives the wrong phase relation between light and velocity. The star ought to be brightest and hottest when most contracted, and coolest and faintest when most expanded. At these phases, the velocities should be zero. Actually the star is brightest and hottest when it is expanding most rapidly and coolest when contracting the fastest.

Martin Schwarzschild has shown us the way out of this difficulty. The trouble with Eddington's treatment was that he assumed the whole star swelled and shrank in phase. On the basis of quite general considerations, Schwarzschild showed that near the surface we must introduce the possibility of a standing wave going over into a running wave, just as in an organ pipe one must consider the transition of a standing wave into a running wave as the edge is approached. The deep interior pulsates adiabatically and in synchronism and there the standing wave theory is valid, but in the outer regions compressional waves appear and run toward the atmosphere. The period remains unchanged since it is fixed by conditions in the main body of the star. In the envelope, the running wave solution gives a different relation between the light variation and the velocity variation than does the standing wave hypothesis. The observed light output and radial velocity depend on the phase of the wave at the surface and bear no direct relation to the phase of the wave in the interior except for the traveltime of the wave from the depths.

We may illustrate the difference between the two kinds of pulsations with the analogy of a one-dimensional wave. In the simplest example, the solution of the wave equation is either a standing wave with a displacement

$$\delta x = g(x)f(t) \tag{35}$$

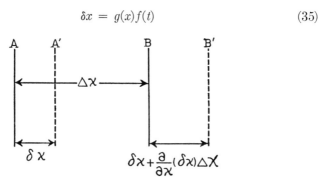

Fig. 7.—Deformation of a Volume Element by a Wave

or a progressive wave with

$$\delta x = f(x - vt) \tag{36}$$

where v is the velocity of the wave. Consider a mass δm of gas contained in the slab of thickness, $AB = \Delta x$, and unit cross-section. A moment later the molecules at A have moved a distance δx to A', while those at B have moved a distance $\delta x'$ to B', Now,

$$A'B' = \Delta x + \left[\delta x + \frac{\partial}{\partial x}(\delta x)\, \Delta x \right] - \delta x \tag{37}$$

The amount of gas in the slab $A'B'$ is the same as the amount of gas in the initial slab AB. Hence,

$$\Delta x\, \rho_0 = \Delta x\, \rho \left[1 + \frac{\partial}{\partial x}(\delta x) \right]$$

or the density obeys the relation

$$\rho \left[1 + \frac{\partial}{\partial x}(\delta x) \right] = \rho_0 \tag{38}$$

For the standing wave, see eqn. (35), we have

$$\frac{\rho_0}{\rho} = 1 + \frac{\partial}{\partial x} g(x) f(t) = 1 + \left[\frac{1}{g(x)} \frac{\partial}{\partial x} g(x) \right] \delta x \qquad (39)$$

while for the running wave,

$$\frac{\rho_0}{\rho} = 1 + \frac{\partial}{\partial x} f(x - vt) = 1 - \frac{1}{v} \frac{\partial}{\partial t} f(x - vt) = 1 - \frac{1}{v} \frac{\partial}{\partial t} \delta x \qquad (40)$$

Thus for the standing wave, the density depends on the displacement δx, while for the running wave, the density depends on the velocity of the material, $\partial/\partial t(\delta x)$. Quoting Schwarzschild:*

Now the law of radiative transfer gives the radiation flux as a function of the absorption coefficient and the temperature gradient; therefore in adiabatic oscillations the radiation flux will depend on the density and pressure gradient, because the temperature can be taken as a function of the density, and the temperature gradient as a function of the pressure gradient. Finally, by the law of motion, the pressure gradient is governed by the acceleration and gravitational forces per unit volume, which again depends on the density. The result is that the radiation flux through a layer is a function not only of the radius and acceleration of the layer but also of the density of the layer. Hence from what is shown above about the density variations in different wave types, it follows that this dependence of the radiation flux on the density does not, in the case of a standing wave, introduce an effect of the velocity of the material upon the light variation, although in the case of a progressive wave it does. Therefore in this progressive wave it seems possible to find an explanation for the observed similarities in form and phase between the light and velocity curves of a Cepheid.

One theoretical point must be mentioned; why must the oscillation run over into a running wave in the upper layers? In a mechanical system with definite boundaries, the wave energy must become dissipated in order for a running wave to be produced. An ocean breaker impinging upon a sloping beach is so strongly dissipated that the reflected wave is too feeble to have any effect upon the incident waves. On the other hand, waves reflected from a vertical wall tend to produce standing waves. In the absence of any dissipation or storing of energy, the surface of a star would act like a reflecting wall, and the waves set up in the star should be of the standing variety. Nevertheless, the phase relation between light and velocity requires the existence of progressive waves and, therefore, the existence of dissipative forces in the outer layers of the star. Eddington and others showed that ordinary conduction, viscosity, and radiation phenomena would be unimportant, but that the hydrogen convective zone near the surface of the star may

*Harvard Observatory Circular, No. 429, 1938.

provide the needed mechanism for storing or dissipating energy. Another possibility, proposed by Pannekoek and Walraven, is that actual shells of material are torn from the surface when the wave reaches it, and the kinetic energy of these shells provides for the dissipation of energy. Years before Schwarzschild suggested the running wave hypothesis, J. A. Aldrich at the University of Michigan found a phase lag between the neutral metallic and hydrogen lines in the spectrum of S Sagittae. The neutral metallic lines reached any particular phase first, the enhanced lines lagged behind, and the hydrogen lines were retarded most of all. Other Cepheids such as η Aquilae also showed conspicuous effects, although δ Cephei showed only small differences.

The pulsation theory attributes this phenomenon to a compressional wave from deep in the star that passes up through the photosphere and successive atmospheric layers. If we integrate the velocity curves for the high-level (hydrogen) and low-level (neutral metal) lines, we find that the radii corresponding to these different heights change in such a way that the maximum compression of the photosphere occurs just after maximum light, when these layers are moving rapidly outward. As the wave approaches the surface, the underlying strata are pushed upward rapidly and compress the upper layers until the outward acceleration stops. The magnitude of the phase lag indicates very extensive atmospheres, quite consistent with the idea of supergiants.

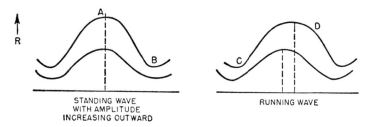

STANDING WAVE
WITH AMPLITUDE
INCREASING OUTWARD

RUNNING WAVE

FIG. 8.—COMPRESSION OF A PHOTOSPHERIC LAYER BY A WAVE

In the standing wave model minimum density occurs when the radius is a maximum A, and maximum density occurs when the radius is a minimum B. In the running wave model maximum density occurs at C, when the velocity is a maximum, and minimum density occurs at D, when the velocity is a minimum.

The phase relation between light and velocity curves depends on the period of the variable, as Joy and McLaughlin found independently. In Cepheids of five-day period, the velocity minimum comes at light minimum. With stars of longer period, the velocity minimum lags more and more behind the light maximum until in SX Herculis the star is brightest when the velocity curve shows it to be smallest!

The larger the star, the longer will be the period and the more extensive will be the atmosphere relative to the size of the star. Thus in stars of longer period, not only is the traveltime of the wave through the atmosphere greater, it is also a larger fraction of the period.

The maximum velocity of approach of the photosphere should always coincide with maximum light, but if the atmosphere is so distended that the atoms effective in producing spectral lines are far above the level of the photosphere, there will be a time lag which will be greater the more extended the atmosphere, i.e., the larger the star. In a classical Cepheid of three- or five-day period, the time lag is small since the atmosphere is close to the photosphere, but as the period and size of the star increase, the lag becomes greater and greater.

With the aid of reasonable assumptions about the temperature and density variations, Schwarzschild attempted to predict the light-curve of δ Cephei from the observed velocity curve. He represented the photospheric density by means of a semi-empirical expression which contained a linear combination of velocity and radius with adjustable constant coefficients. Then he adjusted the constants in such a way as to obtain the best fit with the observations. In particular, he predicted the variation of pressure and density in the surface layers as a function of phase.

Fortunately, such predictions can be tested with the aid of spectroscopic observations, and a number of investigations along these lines have been carried out. The most detailed studies so far published are those of Walraven, who made a careful spectroscopic analysis of high-dispersion plates secured by Pannekoek at Victoria, and of M. and B. Schwarzschild who employed Mount Wilson coudé plates secured by W. S. Adams.

From measures of line intensities at different phases and with relative Nf values derived from the solar spectrum, Walraven derived curves of growth for the different elements. From a mean curve of growth, he found Nf as a function of phase. Then he derived the excitation temperature as a function of phase from the iron lines. With the aid of ionization and excitation theory, plus the assumption that the H^- ions produce the continuous absorption as in the sun, he calculated the ionization and electron pressures. The excitation and ionization temperatures vary in phase with the color temperature, but the excitation temperature shows a smaller amplitude than does the ionization temperature. The electron pressure varies in phase like the radial velocity. The temperature and electron pressure maxima coincide with the light maximum and with the maximum rate of expansion of the star (minimum radial velocity).

Walraven computed the effective surface gravity from the temperature, electron pressure, and the theory of model stellar atmospheres. The effective surface gravity obtained in this way is about 35 times smaller than the gravity computed from the mass and radius. This disparity agrees with the results found from other supergiant stars. Furthermore, the phase variation of the effective gravity resembles that of the velocity of the surface layers, r', and that of the electron pressure.

For the Eddington standing wave model, it follows that the effective surface gravity is given by $g_{eff} = GM/r^2 + r''$. Thus g_{eff} varies in phase during pulsation on account of the changing distance of the radiating layer from the center of the star, and because of the acceleration r''. We may obtain r'' from a differentiation of the radial velocity curve, and r from an integration thereof, as previously noted. The standing wave model predicts only small changes, except near minimum radius where a sharp, high maximum is found. At this same phase the effective surface gravity shows a minimum.

Walraven was able to show that the surface gravity observations could be explained in terms of the running wave hypothesis, if one could suppose that the static surface gravity, g_0, was 1/35 the gravity derived from the mass and radius, and that the velocity of propagation of the outrunning wave was about 2×10^6 cm/sec. The observed pressures, interpreted with the aid of the running wave theory, give phase variations of the effective surface gravity that agree with the observed variations. The pressure variations throughout the cycle appear to be very large, P_{max} is about $10P_{min}$! Hence the velocity of propagation of the outward-moving running wave must nearly equal the amplitude of the velocity of pulsation. This would imply that the regions of pressure maxima are shells of matter separated by nearly empty space. The amplitude of pulsation of a wave must increase until the velocity of the atoms equals or exceeds the velocity of wave propagation, which in turn depends on the thermal velocity of the atoms. Then the pressure wave changes from essentially a sound wave to a shock wave, and a detached shell is thrown off with each pulsation of the star, as Pannekoek had previously suggested. The kinetic energy of the shell is derived from the wave rising from the stellar interior. It thus provides a means of energy dissipation in the photosphere that is required for the production of running rather than standing waves.

In this connection we mention an observation by Struve of peculiar hydrogen lines in the spectrum of RR Lyrae. At the time of median increasing brightness, $H\beta$, $H\gamma$, and $H\delta$ become faint and show a complex structure. Upon a wide, faint, Stark-broadened absorption line there appears a narrow absorption core flanked by narrow emissions. The entire phenomenon lasts not more than half an hour. The hydrogen lines are strong both before and after the peculiar stage, and the higher members of the Balmer series are not affected. The observations suggest that Hβ, Hγ, and Hδ are produced in a shell or extended atmosphere in which emission with central absorption is stimulated during the rapid rise of surface brightness of the star's atmosphere.

Pannekoek suggested that in the classical Cepheids a periodic ejection of shells alternates with times of rest. At minimum the atmosphere is undisturbed. Then an outward-moving layer of higher temperature breaks forth from the depths and determines the spectrum. At maximum the dense, high-temperature shell rising with high velocity is fully displayed. The layers continue to expand, lose their high temperature and velocity until the ejected shell produces an extended atmosphere with a low-density gradient, and the minimum conditions recur. The crest of the outrunning wave may tear itself away from the contracting lower layers and produce a detached shell. As the light decreases, the spectrum changes from the maximum to the minimum type and vice versa. In transition stages we might expect a composite spectrum.

In this connection R. F. Sanford's observations of RR Lyrae are of particular interest. The metallic lines (Fe I, Fe II, Ti I, Ti II, etc.) show a smaller amplitude than do the H and K (Ca II) or Hα lines. Near zero-phase (median increasing brightness), two components of Hα and H and K are observed. Sanford remarks:

If the velocity variations of RR Lyrae are caused by pulsations of its atmosphere, the behavior of the velocities of H and K and Hα would seem to indicate that an atmospheric wave suddenly started outward with the maximum velocity of expansion at the time of maximum light and then slowed down, reaching maximum velocity of contraction at minimum light. Since the wave persists altogether for an interval of 1.060 period for both H and K and Hα, two atmospheric layers may be forming two separate sets of absorption lines simultaneously.*

These observations seem to support the suggestion that the amplitude of the wave gradually increases throughout the upper strata.† Finally, the energy appears to be dissipated in the form of shock waves.

The spectrum and radial velocity changes in the Type II Cepheid-like variable W Virginis as observed by R. F. Sanford give further support to the hypothesis of shock waves and detached shells. Emission lines of hydrogen are visible from minimum to 0.1 $\times$ period after maximum light; the absorption lines are double near maximum light. This doubling of the lines is attributed to the appearance of a new cycle of outrushing gases, before the previously ejected shell has fallen back.

*$Ap.\ J.$ **109**, 210, 1949.
†Detailed studies of the line profiles by R. F. Sanford and M. P. Savedoff strongly support the pulsation theory.

An analysis of the light and color curves, plus the line intensity and velocity measures, has been carried out by H. A. Abt. The layers of gas responsible for the absorption lines are geometrically thin and rise and fall in about twice the period of light variation. The sequence of events appears to be roughly as follows: At light maximum the radius of the photosphere, which is then about 18 million kilometers, begins to expand. Near phase 0.4 or 0.5, when the photosphere reaches a radius of 40 million kilometers, it throws off a shell and begins to con-

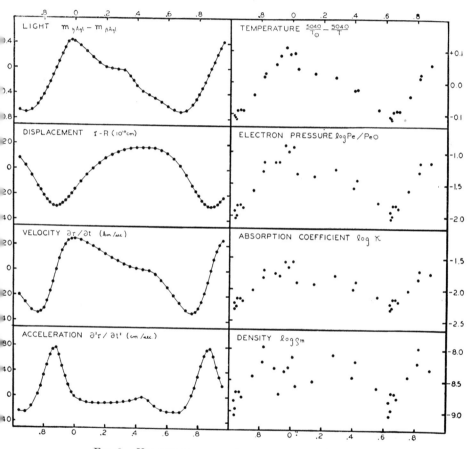

Fig. 9.—Variations in the Atmosphere of η Aquilae

The light and velocity curves are observed directly. The variation in radius or displacement, $r - R$, is found from an integration of the velocity curve; the acceleration is found from a differentiation thereof. The temperature, electron pressure, absorption coefficient, and density are found from an analysis of the line intensities by methods similar to those described in Chapter *8. (Courtesy, M. and B. Schwarzschild and W. S. Adams, *Astrophysical Journal*, University of Chicago Press, **108**, 210, 1948.)

tract. The ejected transparent shell continues to move outward a total of 35 million kilometers in about a period, before it begins to fall inward. Meanwhile, the photosphere has contracted, expanded again, and ejected another shell! An actual physical ejection of shells must take place since shock waves could not account for the 300-fold variation of electron pressure in the course of a cycle.

The Schwarzschild's study of η Aquilae indicates that large-scale convection currents characterized by fast-moving, turbulent elements exist in the photosphere. This large-scale turbulence is indicated by the line profiles (Sec. 15 of Ch. *8) and may be responsible for a mechanical pressure four times as large as the gas kinetic pressure.

From measures of selected iron lines they were able to derive the density variation throughout the cycle. From a comparison of the density with the velocity variation, they found the photospheric pulsations to have neither the character of a standing wave nor that of a simple progressive wave in a uniform atmosphere. The observations can be explained, they suggest, if we suppose that the random velocities increase greatly in the strata above the photosphere and if, in these chromospheric layers rather than in the photosphere, the pulsation consists of a simple progressive wave. The observed pulsations of the photosphere fall in a region between the pure standing wave domain and the pure progressive wave domain but simulate the latter rather than the former.

It should be emphasized that the type of radial velocity changes in which a new set of lines makes its appearance before the old set disappears is characteristic of the Type II Cepheids and never occurs in the Type I Cepheids. This means that the pulsation mechanism in the two kinds of stars is fundamentally different in so far as the surface layers are concerned. Furthermore, classical Cepheids repeat their light and velocity curves faithfully from one cycle to the next, whereas Type II Cepheids may show significant changes between cycles.

7. Atmospheric Pulsations in Long-Period Variables

The fact that each line in the spectrum of a long-period variable cannot be uniquely assigned to a definite stratum renders the interpretation of the long-period variables extremely difficult. The atmospheres are of enormous extent, and the observed radiations represent the composite contributions from layers of vastly different temperature and density.

From an application of the running wave theory to the long-period variables, R. M. Scott concluded that the atmospheric pressure varied over a 70-fold, and the density over a 20-fold, range. Both pressure and density reached their maximum at the time of light maximum.

The outstanding problem is the origin of the emission lines, especially those of hydrogen, whose presence corresponds to a temperature much in excess of what we could expect in an M-type atmosphere.

These emitting gases are observed only during part of the cycle, when they are rising and not during the interval when they are falling. The larger the star and more extensive the atmosphere, the greater the distance between the regions producing the absorption and the emission and the greater the phase lag $(V_a - V_e)$ between the emission and absorption velocity curves, a fact in harmony with Merrill's observation of $V_a - V_e$, although the fluctuations in the correlation near a period of 250 days needs explanation. For Se stars $(V_a - V_e)$ is greater than for Me stars.

The changing relative intensities of the emission lines may arise from the effects of changing depth. In early parts of the cycle, the emission occurs deep in the atmosphere. There $H\gamma$ and $H\beta$ are strongly absorbed by overlying TiO, H by the Ca II H line, while $H\delta$ is unobscured. Later, the weakening of the TiO, possibly by dissociation, plus the fact that the emitting hydrogen is higher in the atmosphere, allows $H\gamma$ and $H\beta$ to strengthen. As the light dims, and the level of excitation falls, the hydrogen layers rise yet higher in the atmosphere, and the dimming of $H\gamma$ by TiO becomes even less.

Scott found the outer envelopes of the Mira stars to be in convective equilibrium and suggested that if a convective exchange extended to a sufficiently deep layer of the star, such currents might bring highly excited atoms up to the photospheric strata. McKellar and Odgers consider the hydrogen convection zone as the source of the bright-line emission. Following Eddington's considerations, the rising columns of gas are regarded as almost completely ionized and the falling columns as almost completely neutral. Recombination occurs in the ascending column so the emission lines are displaced to the violet with respect to the absorption lines. They believe that the optical depth of the top of the convection zone is small and may be visible near maximum light when the continuous absorption in the overlying layers is diminished becaused of the higher temperature. As the variable pulsated, the top of the convection zone would be more hidden at some times than at others, and the bright lines would disappear and reappear during the cycle!

G. J. Odgers has pointed out that the application of the pulsation theory to the long-period variables is complicated by the fact that the theory of small vibrations cannot be applied in even the first approximation. Non-linear oscillations of finite amplitude prevail. Because of the vast extent and low density of the envelope, the gravitational restoring force corresponding to any outward displacement is small and the inertia of small motions cannot be neglected. Furthermore, the

convection currents in the hydrogen-ionization zone contribute significantly to the momentum of the outer layers.   Under these circumstances
the principle of superposition of oscillations will no longer apply.   Each
new vibration is strongly controlled by the initial conditions and since
these vary from one cycle to another there will be no precise, unique
period and amplitude.   The greater the departure from linearity the
more irregular will the oscillations become.   A wave which might have
been smooth and orderly evolves into a shock wave.

Alternatively, it is possible that emission lines may originate as a
consequence of ultraviolet or shock-wave energy released in a vastly
extended atmosphere by mechanisms not unlike those invoked to
explain the solar corona and chromosphere.

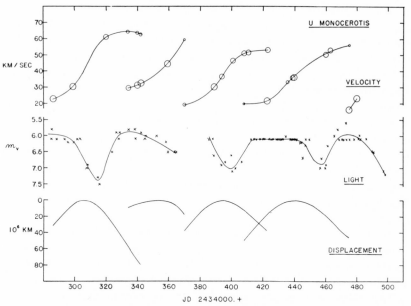

Fig. 10.—Velocity and Light Curves in the RV Tauri Star U Monocerotis

In the top curves, velocity is plotted against time. The size of the circles indicate
roughly the strengths of the spectral lines. The light curve is compiled from observations made by members of the American Association of Variable Star Observers.
Notice the discontinuities in the velocity curves. Just before each light maximum
a weak set of absorption lines appears on the shortward (low velocity) side. The
lines increase in strength as they move redward and gradually fade. Before they
disappear a new set appears and the sequence of events is repeated. A similar phenomenon occurs in the Type II Cepheid W Virginis. The displacements of the layers
where the absorption lines are formed were computed by integrating the velocity
curves. It is assumed that each layer has the same maximum expansion. The largest
displacement (about 80 million kilometers) is associated with the deepest light
minimum. Since the mean radius of the photosphere is about 65 million kilometers
the effective photosphere swells to about twice the radius of the star. (Courtesy,
H. A. Abt.)

McLaughlin and more recently Abt have made spectroscopic studies of the RV Tauri stars. The bright hydrogen lines are strongest during increase of light and fade soon after maximum. Abt finds the spectroscopic behavior of the three low velocity RV Tauri stars, R Scuti, U Monocerotis, and AC Herculis, closely resembles that of Type II Cepheids. See Fig. 10. The RV Tauri stars are less regular; their periods should be chosen as the interval between successive minima rather than twice this quantity as has been done often.

The RV Tauri class comprises a relatively small group of stars; most of the red variables are classified either as long-period, irregular, or semi-regular. Complete photometric, spectroscopic, spectrophotometric, or bolometric observations are available for very few of them. In some instances—e.g., the irregular variable Betelgeuse—actual measurements with the interferometer have revealed fluctuations in the diameter of the star which can be correlated with light variations. For most stars, however, the radius changes can only be inferred from the bolometric observations. There is evidence that most red giant stars fluctuate at least moderately in light. Perhaps stellar pulsations are common among giants.

Joy has made detailed studies of 38 semi-regular variables of spectral classes F, G, and K. From the strengths of the lines of ionized atoms he concludes that many of the stars are bright supergiants. Most of them show bright hydrogen lines with increasing light, while others show titanium oxide bands in a spectrum classified as early as $G4$. The radial velocity variations are so irregular that mean curves cannot be given.

If the stars are grouped according to their radial velocities, Joy finds the fast and slow groups to differ also in mean absolute magnitude, spectral type, distribution in the sky, and strength of the carbon bands. The fast-moving objects appear to belong to population Type II, but the associations of the slower objects with population type are not yet established.

Does the pulsation theory alone suffice to explain the variations of the red giants? An answer cannot be given for most stars partly because of insufficient observations. Even Mira, the best-known, long-period variable, has not been studied adequately. From a spectrophotometric study embracing phases 0 to 0.6, Scott concluded that the entire variation in photographic magnitude resulted from variations in temperature, diameter, and in the absorption by molecular bands and atomic lines. A wave-length region near $\lambda4175$ gave most promise of freedom from band absorption. If we can suppose that it is not affected during the cycle by changes in band or line absorption, these spectrophotometric measures, plus the Pettit and Nicholson radiometric measures, require a temperature variation that shows excellent agreement with the variation deduced from the thermocouple measures by an entirely independent method. In the spectrum of Mira, overlapping TiO bands depress the observed continuum far below that corresponding to a black body; one obtains entirely wrong results if he draws the continuum to pass from band head to band head.

For Mira, at least, it does not appear to be necessary to invoke any cause of variation other than pulsation coupled with the strengthening and weakening of bands as temperature and pressure change. In other stars it is possible that near minima, actual condensation of small solid particles, i.e., smoke formation, does occur. The formation of soot clouds has been invoked to explain the variations of the G-giant carbon star, R Coronae Borealis, whose light occasionally dims abruptly and recovers slowly. Certain Se variables that show less conspicuous band changes than Mira may undergo veiling near minimum, but this problem needs careful examination.

The question of chemical composition and variability is also to be considered. The S stars show ZrO instead of TiO, although in some S variables the TiO bands are present during part or all of the light cycle. In addition, the $\lambda6132$ band of YO sometimes appears in the S spectra. Atomic absorption lines of Sr II, Ba II, Na, and Cr are strong although hydrogen may be absent.* In the Se variables, the hydrogen emission lines appear in the normal order of intensity with Hβ stronger than Hγ and Hδ. Toward maximum light Hδ increases in intensity. When the star fades, the Balmer decrement decreases as though the level of excitation goes down. If the emission lines are produced in the lower layers of this star, they are not affected by the absorption in the overlying layers in any marked selective manner.

From a comparison of the spectra of R Andromedae (Se) and R Leonis ($M8e$) Merrill concluded that Y and Zr are relatively more abundant in the Se star, and that lines of relatively heavy elements are favored in the S-type spectra. These conclusions are substantiated by Keenan and the writer in a study of the infrared spectrum of R Andromedae, and by Keenan's observation of the strengthening of the lines of LaO in the S-type stars.

The R and N stars are characterized by strong bands of carbon, in which the C_{13} isotope appears to be important. The conventional grouping into R and N classes does not form a consistent temperature progression according to Morgan and Keenan. They suggest, among other criteria, the employment of atomic lines and the sodium D lines. In the same subclass the carbon bands vary in intensity in such a way as to imply variations in the abundance of carbon from star to star.

---

*See P. W. Merrill, *The Spectra of the Long Period Variables* (Chicago: University of Chicago Press, 1940), p. 43.

In this connection we may recall McKellar's observation that the C_{12}/C_{13} ratio is not the same in all stars.

A host of special problems connected with the physics of extended atmospheres await solution. The question of the bright emission lines remains outstanding. This problem includes the mystery of the low-excitation lines of metals, which are possibly excited by special chemi-luminescent mechanisms.* Finally, there are the "symbiotic" objects which show an M-type spectrum plus a spectrum of very high excitation.† See Chapter 4.

8. The Origin of the Pulsations

Although pulsating stars may yield important clues to the general problems of stellar structure, particularly to the structure of giant stars, they bring up this outstanding puzzle: How did the pulsations get started and what maintains them with so nearly a constant ampli-tude? Why do they not die out, or increase in amplitude until the star is torn asunder? Evidently a delicate balance must prevail, for there are stars of nearly the same dimensions and luminosities as Cepheids that do not pulsate. For example, Schwarzschild found that in the globular cluster Messier 3, the variables were confined to a small area on the Russell diagram. Stars of almost the same luminosity and color on either side did not pulsate!

Probably a star adjusts its amplitude of oscillation until the dissi-pation of energy, which occurs possibly by interactions between different modes of vibration, precisely balances the power supplied by the driving mechanism of the pulsation. Many years ago Eddington pointed out that a temperature-sensitive energy source could provide mechanical energy for the pulsation. If energy production rose as the star con-tracted and the internal density and temperature increased, the rapid rise of gas pressure and temperature would cause the star to overshoot its equilibrium mark. The star might then simply oscillate between

---

*Near maximum light, emission lines of Fe II and Si I become strong. Also the infrared Ca II, $\lambda 8498$, $\lambda 9542$, and $\lambda 8662$ are bright in Mira near maximum. As the star fades, Fe I $\lambda 4202$, $\lambda 4308$, and Mg I $\lambda 4571$ successively appear, strengthen, and fade away, $\lambda 4571$ remaining until after minimum light. Near minimum phase in late-type Me spectra there also sometimes appears [Fe II]. These lines have not been observed in Mira, where the spectrum of an early-type companion becomes confused with that of the long-period variable at minimum.

†Some long-period variables, e.g., Mira and R Aquarii, and certain irregular variables, have high-temperature companions. The companion to Mira has actually been seen, the existence of the others is inferred from the combination of a high-excitation spectrum showing, e.g., [Ne V] and [Fe VII] with the M spectrum of a red variable. These companions have been blamed for the bright hydrogen lines in the long-period variables, but the difficulty here is to understand why, if these lines are excited by an external source, they appear below the strata of the dark line and TiO absorption. Also many long-period variables do not have observed high-temperature companions.

a state of too rapid energy generation and one of too low energy generation. If the conditions of opacity, turbulent viscosity, etc., were just right, oscillations could be maintained. To calculate the effect of a momentary temperature change upon the energy generation, we must know the particular nuclear transformations involved. With a cyclical process such as the carbon cycle, it is incorrect to suppose that the energy generation varies with the temperature in the same way as for a family of static stars of the same instantaneous temperature and density.

In attacking problems of stellar pulsation it is but natural that the most careful attention has been paid to objects that appear most readily interpretable, i.e., the Cepheids. The general picture of Cepheid variation appears established, but many refinements remain to be worked out. An outstanding problem is the difference between the Type I and Type II Cepheids. We would expect the latter to have masses only slightly in excess of that of the sun. The former might well be very massive stars. The longer-period variables present a far greater complexity because the radiation that reaches us emerges from far separated strata in their atmospheres.

Although actual pulsations can be demonstrated in the case of Mira and the irregular variable Betelgeuse by means of the interferometer, and we seem justified in adopting as a working hypothesis that irregular, semi-regular, and long-period variables owe their fluctuations to pulsations, the road to a satisfactory theory seems long and arduous. It is important to emphasize that most of the variable-star phenomena remain unexplained. We do not know the answer to the very first question: Why are some stars variables, while others are not?

It would appear that the most rapid progress can be made only by carefully planned observational programs. Light-curves of many interesting objects have been obtained, but until these data are supplemented by spectroscopic, velocity, and radiometric observations, they are of little real help. For a selected group of long-period, semi-regular and irregular variables, simultaneous photometric, spectroscopic, spectrophotometric, and radiometric observations should be made. Such observations have been carried out for Mira at different epochs, but since the light-curve changes from cycle to cycle, the results are less informative than those which could be obtained by a systematic study of the star during one cycle.

Spectrophotometric measures would enable us to separate the effects of lines, bands, and continuous spectra in so far as the light variations are concerned. Spectroscopic measures, which usually require large telescopes, are necessary to provide velocity curves throughout the cycle and to find how the lines of different origin are correlated with one another. Observations in the infrared are of particular importance.

REFERENCES

1. General

GAPOSCHKIN, S., and C. H. PAYNE-GAPOSCHKIN. *Variable Stars*. Cambridge: Harvard Observatory Monographs, 1938. See especially chaps. iii, iv, v, vi.

CAMPBELL, L., and L. JACCHIA. *The Story of Variable Stars*. Cambridge: Harvard University Press, 1941. See especially chaps. iv and v, which give detailed accounts of light-curves.

MERRILL, P. W. *The Nature of Variable Stars*. New York: The Macmillan Co., 1938.

McLAUGHLIN, D. B. "The Study of Stellar Variation," *Pop. Astron.* **53**, 131, 1945. Excellent review article with bibliography.

ROSSELAND, S. *The Theory of Stellar Pulsations*. London: Oxford University Press, 1949.

2. Classical Cepheids

The light and color variations of the classical Cepheids have been discussed, for example, by:

PAYNE-GAPOSCHKIN, C. H. *Astron. J.* **52**, 218, 1947.

BECKER, W. *Zeits. f. Ap.* **19**, 289, 1940 (spectrophotometry).

STEBBINS, J. *Ap. J.* **101**, 47, 1945; STEBBINS, J., G. E. KRON, and J. L. SMITH. *Ap. J.* **115**, 292, 1952 (6-color photometry).

EGGEN, O. J. *Ap. J.* **113**, 367, 1951.

The original period–luminosity curve for classical Cepheids was obtained by:

LEAVITT, H. *Harvard Circ.*, 173, 1912.

Improved curves have been obtained by Shapley and his co-workers at Harvard, e.g.:

SHAPLEY, HARLOW. *Galaxies*, 1940. Cambridge: Harvard University Press, 1940, p. 61.

A need for a revision of the zero-point of the classical Cepheid period–luminosity law has been indicated by work at Mount Wilson and Palomar and elsewhere. See, e. g.:

HUBBLE, E. *Proc. Amer. Phil. Soc.* **95**, 464, 1951.

GASCOIGNE, S. C. B., and G. E. KRON. *Publ. Astron. Soc. Pac.* **64**, 196, 1952.

Radial velocity and spectral changes in classical Cepheids have been discussed, for example, by:

JACOBSEN, T. *Lick Obs. Bull.* No. 379, 1926.

WHIPPLE, F. L. *Lick Obs. Bull.* **16**, 1, 1932.

STRUVE, O. *Observatory* **65**, 257, 1944.

CODE, A. *Ap. J.* **106**, 309, 1947.

PANNEKOEK, A. *Physica* **12**, 761, 1946.

RR Lyrae stars have been studied by:

SCHWARZSCHILD, M. *Harvard Circ.*, 437, 1940 (position of variables in Messier 3 on the Russell diagram).

ARP, H. C., W. A. BAUM, and A. R. SANDAGE. *Astron. J.* **57**, 5, 1952 (absolute magnitudes).

STRUVE, O. *Publ. Astron. Soc. Pac.* **59**, 192, 1947 (spectra).

SANFORD, R. F. *Ap. J.* **109**, 210, 1949.

SAVEDOFF, M. P. *Astron. J.* **57**, 25, 1952.

The spectrum and radial velocity changes in W Virginis have been discussed by:

SANFORD, R. F. *Ap. J.* **116**, 331, 1952.

ABT, H. A. *Ap. J. Suppl. No. 3*, 1954.

RV Tauri Stars and Semi-Regular Variables:

McLAUGHLIN, D. B. *Publ. Obs. U. Mich.* **7**, 57, 1938; *Ap. J.* **94**, 94, 1941.
JOY, A. H. *Ap. J.* **115**, 25, 1952.
SAWYER, HELEN B. *J.R.A.S. Canada* **43**, 38, 1949.

Long-Period Variables: Relations between the spectra, absolute magnitudes, and motions of long-period variables are discussed, for example, by:

MERRILL, P. W., and R. E. WILSON. *Ap. J.* **93**, 40, 380, 1941; **94**, 171, 1941; **95**, 248, 1942.

The spectral classification of R and N variables may be found in:

KEENAN, P. C., and W. W. MORGAN. *Ap. J.* **94**, 501, 1941.

The spectroscopic aspects of the long-period variables are summarized in:

MERRILL, P. W. *The Spectra of the Long-Period Variables.* Chicago: University of Chicago Press, 1940.

See also:

MERRILL, P. W. *Ap. J.* **103**, 6, 275, 1946; **105**, 360, 1947; **106**, 274, 1947; **107**, 303, 1948; **116**, 337, 1952.
JOY, A. H. *Ap. J. Suppl. No.* 2, 1954.
SCOTT, R. M. *Ap. J.* **101**, 71, 1945 (spectrophotometry of Mira Ceti).
KEENAN, P. C., and L. H. ALLER. *Ap. J.* **113**, 72, 1951 (infrared of Se variables).

Irregular Variables:

JOY, A. H., and R. E. WILSON. *Ap. J.* **96**, 344, 371, 1942.
KEENAN, P. C. *Ap. J.* **95**, 461, 1942.

Thermocouple measures of irregular and long-period variables were made by:

PETTIT, E., and S. B. NICHOLSON. *Ap. J.* **78**, 320, 1933.

Pulsation Theory. The criterion for pulsations was given by:

BAADE, W. *Astr. Nach.* **228**, 359, 1936.

The classical theory is given in:

EDDINGTON, A. S. *Internal Constitution of the Stars.* Cambridge: Cambridge University Press, 1926, chap. viii.

The running-wave theory was developed by:

SCHWARZSCHILD, M. *Zeits. f. Ap.* **11**, 152, 1936; *Harvard Circ.* 429, 431, 1938.

The effects of large pulsation amplitudes is discussed by:

ROSSELAND, SVEIN. *M.N.* **103**, 233, 1943.
BHATNAGAR, P. L., and D. S. KOTHARI. *M.N.* **104**, 292, 1944.
BHATNAGAR, P. L. *Bull. Calcutta Math. Soc.* **38**, 34, 93, 1946; *Proc. Nat. Inst. of Sciences of India* **11**, 13, 25, 1945.

See also:

PEKERIS, C. L., and P. LEDOUX. *Ap. J.* **94**, 124, 1941.
LEDOUX, P. *Ap. J.* **102**, 143, 1945 (radial pulsations of non-rotating stars).
COWLING, T. G., and R. A. NEWING. *Ap. J.* **109**, 149, 1949 (oscillations of a rotating star).

The effects of atmospheric pulsations in Cepheids upon the spectral changes have been studied by:

WALRAVEN, T. *Publ. Astron. Inst. U. Amsterdam* No. 8, 1948 (δ Cephei).
SCHWARZSCHILD, M. and B., and W. S. ADAMS. *Ap. J.* **108**, 207, 1948 (η Aquilae).
HERBIG, G. H. *Ap. J.* **116**, 369, 1952 (S Sagittae).

Application of the pulsation theory to long-period variables was discussed by:

SCOTT, R. M. *Ap. J.* **95**, 58, 1942.

CHAPTER 4

STARS WITH EXTENDED ENVELOPES, NOVAE, AND SUPERNOVAE

1. Introduction

In preceding chapters we showed how the principal features of the dark-line spectra of stars such as the sun may be explained with a simple model atmosphere in which excitation and ionization may be rather accurately described by the Saha and Boltzmann equations. On the other hand, certain solar phenomena do not fit into this picture; we refer to the chromosphere with its helium lines and particularly to the corona whose bizarre emission lines of [Fe X], [Fe XIV], etc., require an excitation temperature of the order of 700,000°K.

The idiosyncrasies of the familiar sun should prepare us for the seemingly anomalous behavior of other stars. Among the unusual objects to be considered here are those that show emission lines in their spectra. The *Be* stars combine the features of a conventional dark-line spectrum with bright lines that appear to originate in vastly extended atmospheres. If we could examine such a star from nearby in the light of one of its emission lines, e.g., Hα, we would probably perceive a fuzzy, ill-defined object. In the light of the nearby continuum, however, the star would appear as an ordinary main-sequence *B* star.

Except for the T Tauri variables (see Chapter 6), emission-line stars are found almost entirely among objects of high temperature—e.g., *Be*, P Cygni, and W or Wolf-Rayet stars—or among the coolest stars. In the hot stars the bright lines correspond to the same elements in roughly the same stage of excitation as appear in objects of the same temperature that show dark-line spectra. Hence it is tempting to attribute them to a vastly extended envelope. In the cool stars the bright lines do not correspond to the strong lines in the absorption spectrum. We have mentioned the bright hydrogen lines in the spectra of the long-period variables, which require an excitation temperature much in excess of the black-body temperatures of these stars. Even more enigmatic are the "symbiotic" variables which combine bright forbidden lines of high excitation, [Fe VII] or even [Fe X], with an absorption *M*-type spectrum.

In some instances bright lines may arise in an extended envelope from primarily atomic causes such as fluorescence. That is, because of excess energy in some particular frequency, a disproportionate share of atoms may concentrate in the upper level of the transition observed as a bright line. In other objects, e.g., *Be* stars or novae, the atmosphere is so much larger than the main body of the star that the emission in the envelope is not counterbalanced by the absorption that occurs in the region between the observer and the photosphere.

Not all stars with extended envelopes show bright lines. In this category fall certain shell stars whose characteristic spectral features are shallow, rotationally broadened lines upon which are superposed occasional sharp lines, which evidently arise from absorption in a different part of the atmosphere or in a detached shell. Normally, however, such stars show $H\alpha$ in emission.

Following Struve and Merrill, we may classify the stars with extended envelopes in the following groups:

A. Stars with stationary shells
    1. Shells which show primarily absorption lines, e.g., Pleione
    2. Normal *Be* stars; e.g., π Aquarii, κ Draconis

B. Stars with expanding shells (P Cygni type)
    1. Novae and SS Cygni variables
    2. Wolf-Rayet stars
    3. P Cygni stars
        a) Predominately absorption spectra, e.g., 17 Leporis
        b) Both emission and absorption spectra, e.g., P Cygni
        c) Peculiar binaries; e.g., β Lyrae, 29 Canis Majoris

C. Bright-line stars with absorption spectra of late-type
    1. [Fe II], bright hydrogen lines, e.g., WY Geminorum *M3ep*
    2. High-excitation objects with bright He II, [O III], [Ne III]; e.g., Z Andromedae, T Coronae Borealis, RW Hydrae, R Aquarii, BF Cygni, AG Pegasi, UV Aurigae, CI Cygni, AX Persei

In this discussion we shall not include the long-period variables (Ch. 3), nor the T Tauri stars which appear to be dwarf *G* stars associated with extended areas of nebulosity. We shall discuss first the stars with stationary shells; next the objects with seemingly expanding envelopes: P Cygni, and Wolf-Rayet stars, the novae and SS Cygni variables; the bright-line stars with late-type absorption; and finally the catastrophic supernovae. We emphasize that the above classification is based on the spectra of the stars and not on their intrinsic luminosities or dimensions.

2. Stars with Stationary Shells

The existence of tenuous rings or shells around certain stars was inferred long ago from the appearance of hydrogen and other bright lines in their spectra. In some *Be* stars, e.g., ζ Tauri, the emission component is observed only in the earlier members of the series. Hδ and the later lines appear only in absorption. Helium emission occurs rarely, but the metals, particularly Fe II, often show prominent emission lines with a superposed sharp absorption core.

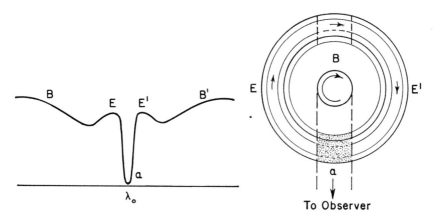

Fig. 1.—Profile of a Hydrogen Line in a *Be* Star

The rapidly rotating *B* star produces the broad shallow absorption line *BB'*. The portions of the shell that are neither occulted by the star nor in front of it produce the two components *EE'* of the emission line, while the sharp, deep absorption line *a* is produced by the atoms in front of the star (indicated by the dotted area).

Figure 1 shows a typical line profile. Upon a broad, shallow absorption line is superposed a narrower emission line, whose center in turn is often crossed by a sharp, narrow line. The broad profiles of the underlying absorptions of Mg II, He I, etc., led Struve to suggest that these lines originate in a rapidly spinning star.* A ring or shell surrounding the star produces the emission line, whereas the part of the shell between the photosphere and the observer gives the sharp central reversal. Since the shell rotates more slowly than the star, the emission line is narrower than the underlying stellar absorption. The narrow central absorption component is produced by atoms of the shell moving at right angles to the line of sight. The sharp metallic lines originate in the same layers as the sharp Balmer lines.

*The great strength of the hydrogen lines arises primarily from the Stark effect.

Some stars lose their emission almost entirely and show an abnormal sharp-line spectrum superposed on a B-type diffuse-line spectrum. Pleione lost all of its emission. Later the emission reappeared, accompanied for the first time by shell lines which strengthened from 1938 to 1941. Since the ionization did not change, the shell must have grown thicker. Thereafter, the level of ionization in the shell gradually fell.

The state of ionization and excitation in the absorption shells is lower than in the reversing layers of the same stars; e.g., the shells of the B stars, ζ Tauri, ϕ Persei, and 48 Librae correspond to Class A. They tend to form around $B3$–$B5$ stars. For a short time, γ Cassiopeiae ($B0n$) had a shell of Type $B1$. The latest is 14 Comae, $A5n$, whose shell is of Type $F2$.

Many Be stars show definite spectral changes. The total emission line intensity may change, and the relative intensities of the two emission components may fluctuate (V/R variation). The latter variations, although not truly periodic, except for ϕ Persei which seems to be a binary, are usually cyclical over a period of a few years. What one component gains the other loses. McLaughlin showed that a qualitative picture of these spectral changes could be obtained if one supposed that the rotating shell alternately expanded and contracted.

From a study of the spectra of stars such as ζ Tauri, ϕ Persei, 48 Librae, ϵ Capricorni, and 17 Leporis, Struve found that shell absorption lines that arise from ordinary atomic levels—from which the atom can cascade to a lower level in a permitted transition—are systematically weaker than lines which arise from metastable levels. The He I lines $\lambda4472$, $\lambda4388$, $\lambda4026$, and $\lambda4009$ are usually broad and diffuse, while $\lambda3965$ is usually sharp and narrow. The broad helium lines originate in the rapidly turning photosphere, $\lambda3965$ (which arises from the 2^1S level) must be produced in the shell. Similarly, stars that show broad strong Mg II $\lambda4481$ in their photospheric spectra often show strong Fe II shell lines but no absorption $\lambda4481$ in their shells. The important fact is that the lower levels of the weakened Si II and Mg II lines are connected to the ground level by strong transitions, whereas the relatively strong sharp lines of Fe II, Ti II, etc., arise from metastable levels. In these envelopes the normal levels are depleted as compared with the metastable levels. An atom which gets to a metastable level will usually remain there until it can absorb a quantum of energy, whereas an atom that enters a normal level will usually cascade to a lower one before it has had a chance to absorb a quantum.

Collisional effects will not modify this picture greatly since in these attenuated envelopes, radiative rather than collisional processes determine the populations of the levels associated with the observed spectral lines.

The atoms in an extended envelope are subject to "dilute" radiation which is often not Planckian in distribution. We define the *dilution factor* as follows:

$$W = \frac{\text{energy density of radiation at point in question}}{\text{energy density at equilibrium with temperature } T} \qquad (1)$$

or, in terms of intensity,

$$W_\nu = \frac{\int I_\nu(\theta, \varphi) \, d\omega}{4\pi B_\nu(T)} \qquad (2)$$

Here $I_\nu(\theta, \varphi)$ is the true intensity of the radiation at the point in question. $B_\nu(T)$ is the intensity of the radiation in an enclosure at some temperature T. Although the frequency distribution of the radiation in the shell may correspond to the temperature T, the intensity would be WB_ν.

Consider, for example, a detached shell of radius r surrounding a star of radius R. The geometrical dilution factor will be the fraction of the sky filled by the star, viz.:

$$W_0 = \frac{\omega}{4\pi} = \frac{1}{2}\left\{1 - \sqrt{1 - \frac{R^2}{r^2}}\right\} \sim \frac{R^2}{4r^2} \qquad (3)$$

For example, in ζ Aurigae for which $r = 1.2R$, $W_0 = 0.22$. In general the true dilution of the radiation in an extended envelope will differ from W_0. The intensity distribution will be modified by absorption and by fluorescence processes in the gas.

To solve for the population of the excited levels, we write down the equations of statistical equilibrium, which state that the number of atoms entering a given level n per unit volume and time equals the number leaving it. We suppose that there are N_n atoms in the nth level and denote the number of transitions from level n to n' per atom per second by $a_{nn'}$. We define

$$a_{nn} = -(a_{n1} + a_{n2} + \cdots + a_{n,n-1} + a_{n,n+1} + \cdots) \qquad (4)$$

The condition for a steady state for each level n is:

$$N_1 a_{1n} + N_2 a_{2n} + \cdots = N_n(a_{n1} + a_{n2} + \cdots) = -N_n a_{nn} \qquad (5)$$

We obtain the system of linear equations:

$$\sum_r N_r a_{rn} = 0 \qquad n = 1, 2, 3, \cdots \qquad (6)$$

A nontrivial solution requires that the determinant of the coefficients vanish.

$$C = \begin{vmatrix} a_{11} & a_{21} & \cdots \\ a_{12} & a_{22} & a_{32} \\ a_{13} & a_{23} & a_{33} \\ \cdots & \cdots & \cdots \end{vmatrix} = 0 \tag{7}$$

That is, the relative populations are proportional to the minors of the determinant C, viz.:

$$N_1 = C_0 \begin{vmatrix} a_{22} & a_{32} & \cdots \\ a_{23} & a_{33} & \cdots \\ \cdots & \cdots & \cdots \end{vmatrix}, \quad N_2 = C_0 \begin{vmatrix} a_{11} & a_{31} & \cdots \\ a_{13} & a_{33} & \cdots \\ \cdots & \cdots & \cdots \end{vmatrix} \tag{8}$$

obtained by striking out the ith row and ith column of C. C_0 is a constant of proportionality.

The explicit expressions for the a's will depend on the physical processes involved. A completely general treatment would take into account collisional as well as radiative processes. In many applications this refinement is not necessary because the densities in the shells are so low that collisions have a relatively small influence on the comparative populations of high metastable and normal levels. For low-lying levels, however, it is often necessary to take the collisional processes into account. For radiative processes,

$$a_{n'n} = B_{n'n} W B_{\nu}, \quad a_{nn'} = A_{nn'} + B_{nn'} W B_{\nu} \tag{9}$$

(cf. Sec. 11 of Ch. *5*).

It is legitimate to neglect the stimulated emissions, and for most purposes we can use the Wien approximation to the Planck law [eqn. (16) of Ch. *5], viz.:

$$B_{\nu}(T) = \frac{2h\nu^3}{c^2} e^{-h\nu/kT} \tag{10}$$

We shall also need the relations [eqns. (63) and (64) of Ch. *5]:

$$g_n B_{nn'} = g_{n'} B_{n'n}$$
$$\frac{g_n}{g_{n'}} A_{nn'} = B_{n'n} \frac{2h\nu^3}{c^2} \tag{11}$$

A qualitative picture of the processes involved may be obtained with the aid of Rosseland's 3-state atom. In order to avoid difficulties with the selection rules, let us identify level (3) with the continuum. For

---

*All references to chapters in the author's *Astrophysics—The Atmospheres of the Sun and Stars* (New York: The Ronald Press Co., 1953) will be designated in this volume by * before the chapter number.

simplicity we shall assume the statistical weights of all levels to be the same. The equations of statistical equilibrium for levels (2) and (3) are, respectively:

$$N_2(A_{21} + B_{23}I_{23}) = N_1B_{12}I_{12} + N_3A_{32} \qquad (12)$$

$$N_3(A_{31} + A_{32}) = N_1B_{13}I_{13} + N_2B_{23}I_{23} \qquad (13)$$

Now $I_\nu = WB_\nu(T)$.

From eqns. (10) and (11) we find

$$B_{ij}I_{ij} = A_{ji}We^{-h\nu_{ji}/kT} \qquad (14)$$

If we eliminate N_3 from eqns. (12) and (13), we find

$$\frac{N_2}{N_1} = We^{-\frac{h\nu_{21}}{kT}} \left\{ \frac{A_{31}e^{-h\nu_{32}/kT} + \dfrac{A_{21}}{A_{32}}(A_{31} + A_{32})}{A_{31}We^{-h\nu_{32}/kT} + \dfrac{A_{21}}{A_{32}}(A_{31} + A_{32})} \right\} \qquad (15)$$

Notice that for $W = 1$ (thermodynamic equilibrium) the brackets approach 1 and the Boltzmann formula is recovered. If the level is metastable, $A_{21} \to 0$, and the population again follows the Boltzmann law. For a permitted level the A's are of the same order of magnitude, and to a fair degree of approximation

$$\frac{N_2}{N_1} = We^{-h\nu_{12}/kT} \qquad (16)$$

i.e., the population is cut down by a factor of W compared with what it would have been in thermal equilibrium. Thus, we may understand the weakening of the Mg II λ4481 line where the lower level connects directly with the ground level via a strong transition, while the Fe II lines, whose lower levels are metastable, remain strong.

Helium provides a fascinating application of some of these considerations. As noted, there are two metastable levels, 2^1S and 2^3S. (See Fig. 4 of Ch. ★2.) In the region of the spectrum normally studied we observe singlet transitions arising from 2^1P and 2^1S, and transitions from 2^3S (λ3889, etc.) and 2^3P (λ4471, 5875, 4026, etc.).* Struve and Wurm found: (1) In the cooler stars, λ3965 ($2^1S - 4^1P$) is the first line to appear in the shell. (2) When the number of atoms is large, the ($2^3P - n^3D$) triplet lines appear in the shell, but λ3965 is stronger than λ4026. (3) In some shells where the excitation is high, the $2^1P - n^1D$ lines appear weakly in absorption. (4) When the shell excitation is very high, the triplet lines become strong and λ4026 is

---

*λ3888 is usually stronger than λ3965 unless obscured by Hζ. The Yerkes plates did not cover the near-ultraviolet.

stronger than λ3965. Although, as in P Cygni, the $2^1P - n^1D$ lines remain weaker than triplets, the difference is smaller than in shells of lower excitation.

To discuss these observations, Struve and Wurm used a 6-state atom, which comprised 1^1S, 2^1S, 2^1P, 2^3S, 2^3P, and the ionized state.

P. Wellmann has given a refined treatment of the problem in which he included the levels $n = 3$ and allows approximately for the contributions of the higher levels. The populations of the excited levels depend not only on the dilution factor W but also on the temperatures of the gas T_ϵ, and of the illuminating star T_s. Table 1 gives the popu-

TABLE 1

Term	$W = 1$	$W = 0.1$	$W = 0.01$
2^1S	100	100	100
2^1P	150	22	2
2^3S	753	6350	12,800
2^3P	608	710	148

lations of the 2^1P, 2^3S, and 2^3P levels in terms of that of metastable 2^1S level as 100, for $T_s = T_\epsilon = 10,000°K$. Notice the striking concentration of atoms in the metastable levels and also the preponderance of the number in triplet states over the number in singlet states. The population of the 2^3S state increases with respect to that of the 2^1S state as the radiation becomes more dilute. This effect arises because an atom in 2^1S level can reach 2^1P by the absorption of an appropriate quantum. From the 2^1P level it returns at once to the ground level. The 2^3S can be depopulated only by transitions involving the continuum, wherein the electron escapes from the atom and is subsequently recaptured in a singlet level. The normal 2^1P term shows a steady population decrease as W decreases in accordance with our expectations. Surprisingly enough, the 2^3P level remains fairly well populated even at appreciable dilutions. Once an atom arrives in this level, it may escape only by a spontaneous transition to 2^3S, but the probability of such a transition is relatively small. Hence atoms tend to collect in 2^3P at the expense of the higher triplet levels.

In the hotter stars the triplets ($2^3P - n^3D$) are reduced even less than indicated in the table above, and they remain stronger than even the favored ($2^1S - n^1D$) singlets.

Leo Goldberg carried out refined calculations for the helium lines in a gaseous nebula, where the radiation field is much more attenuated than in a stellar envelope. Although he formally investigated an

8-level helium atom, his theory was developed in such a form as to allow for the infinite number of discrete levels. His theory predicted a great weakening of the singlet lines with respect to the triplets. In fact, the predicted intensities are of the order of ten times smaller than those observed. Possibly the explanation for this discrepancy lies in the fact that the singlet levels can be populated by direct transitions from the ground level. If the exciting star is rich in resonance radiation, or if sufficient resonance quanta are created in the nebula by photo-ionization and recombination (Zanstra mechanism, Ch. 5), the effective W for the lines will exceed the geometrical W_0. Then there will be more atoms in the permitted levels than we anticipated, and the calculated radius of the shell will be too small.

A clue to the extent of the envelope of an emission B star may be found from the eclipsing variable VV Cephei which consists of an M supergiant with a B companion. The time required for the disappearance and reappearance of the hydrogen emission lines suggests the dimensions of the emitting shell. Goedicke estimated the Hβ shell to be as large as the supergiant Antares and the Hγ shell to be half as large. The B star itself has about one-fifteenth the diameter of its shell.

Detailed examinations of spectrograms give additional information on the physical conditions in extended shells. For example, in ζ Tauri, the Si II lines are appreciably broadened, and even the Fe II lines are not as sharp as He I λ3965 or Ni I λ4067. A stratification of the radiating atoms is suggested. The broad hydrogen and helium lines are produced in the reversing layer of the star; Si II, and sometimes Mg II, occurs in the inner shell; Fe II lies yet higher; and the sharp H, Ni II, and He I λ3965 lines originate in the highest levels. The fact that the emission line widths are not the same for all elements is also an indication of stratification. The lower level of ionization and excitation in the shells is easily understood. The photo-ionization rate for atoms in a thin shell exposed to the dilute temperature radiation of a star of temperature T_1 will resemble that appropriate to an enclosure at a temperature T_1 cut down by the factor W. The recaptures will depend on the electron temperature and density. In thick shells, however, much of the incident continuous radiation is absorbed and re-emitted. In particular, the hydrogen in the shell absorbs all energy beyond the Lyman limit. Hence the level of ionization is cut down below what it would be for a thin shell. In the region of the resonance lines of Mg II and Si II, however, the shells of such stars as 48 Librae are transparent. Hence the excitation of the lower level of λ4481 is determined by direct radiation from the star rather than by re-emission in the envelope.

From an analysis of the equivalent widths of the emission and shell absorption lines in γ Cassiopeiae, P. Wellmann has shown that the line intensities can be interpreted only in terms of a dilute temperature radiation field. Because of the large radial velocity difference between different parts of the shell, little self-reversal occurs. The absorption lines tend to be formed closer to the surface of the star than does the emission which sets in at some distance from the surface and can be regarded as occurring in a separate ring or shell.

G. R. and E. M. Burbridge have estimated the physical character and dimensions of the emitting regions of the outer atmospheres of some *Be* stars from the equivalent widths and profiles of the Balmer emission lines. They suggest that the difference between the Balmer absorption-line profiles in these stars and in normal *B* stars of the same luminosity arises primarily from electron scattering plus differential rotational distortion produced in the outer envelope of the *Be* star.

3. Stars with Expanding Shells

In addition to the *Be* stars where the shell and stellar lines give the same radial velocity, there exists a class of objects in which the absorption lines give velocities of approach and the emission lines are widened about the normal position with the violet edge cut off by absorption. This second group includes such objects as P Cygni, the Wolf-Rayet stars, and the novae. The formation of a line profile in a nova is illustrated in Fig. 2. Atoms in the cross-hatched area *a* produce an ab-

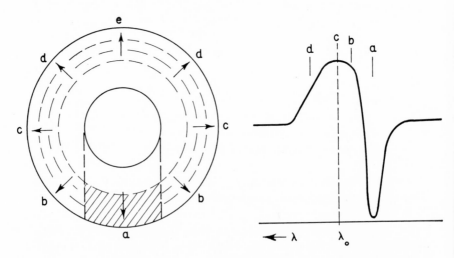

Fig. 2.—Interpretation of a Line Profile Produced by an Expanding Shell

The expanding shell of gas about the star produces a broadened emission line upon whose violet edge occurs an absorption component due to the atoms in the line of sight (in the cross-hatched area *a*) between the star and the observer.

sorption line displaced to the violet edge of the emission line which arises from the parts of the shell b, c, and d. Since the receding atoms at e are occulted, the profile tends to be truncated on the red side. The emission profile shows a relatively steep slope on the violet side.

The relative prominence of the emission and absorption features in P Cygni-type spectra varies from star to star. In P Cygni itself, emission and absorption are both strong. The reversing layer of the star is concealed beneath the thick envelope. Several lines of evidence indicate marked stratification effects. Atoms with such widely different ionization potentials as Si I (16 ev) and He II (54.2 ev) are observed in the same spectrum. Among the lines of an element like silicon, which exists in several stages of ionization, the intensity of the emission component is greater the lower the level of ionization (see Table 2). Evidently the atoms of lower ionization potential are found in larger shells than those of high ionization potential. Likewise, as Table 2 also illustrates, the velocity of the absorption component increases with decreasing ionization potential. A part of this effect may be due to an acceleration of the outward-going atoms and part to the influence of the emission-line profile.

TABLE 2

INTENSITIES AND VELOCITIES OF LINES OBSERVED IN P CYGNI*

Atom	I.P.	Mean		Mean V(abs)
		I(em)	I(abs)	
Si II	16.3	65	5	−289
C II	24.3	7	4	−154
N II	29.5	18	20	−92
Si III	33.3	9	27	−80
Si IV	45.0	–	19	−33
C III	47.7	1	1	−28

*After C. S. Beals, *J.R.A.S.C.* **34**, 169, 1940.

The Wolf-Rayet stars and novae exhibit some of the P Cygni characteristics on an exaggerated scale.

In some P Cygni stars, such as *HD* 190,073 or *BD* + 47° 3487, the broad hydrogen lines of normal main-sequence objects may be recognized beneath the expanding shell. In other instances, as 17 Leporis, the lines occasionally double; a lower stratum of the shell appears to be actually stable. Other expanding shells seem to be associated with supergiants, e.g., α Cygni and β Orionis show P Cygni-type Hα lines. Beals has pointed out that a few stars combine the characteristics of both *Be* and P Cygni stars, e.g., *HD* 108, *HD* 190,073, 17 Leporis, 29 Canis Majoris, and 9 Sagittae. Struve identifies three layers in a typical shell star: (1) a fixed main-sequence reversing layer, (2) an inner shell which remains stationary, and (3) an outer shell which produces P Cygni-type profiles. These three layers grade continuously into one another. In some stars such as *HD* 49,510, all three layers are observed, but in others only two are found. In 1946 the shell of Pleione appeared to consist of an inner portion rotating with a velocity of 140 km/sec, and an outer part contracting with a velocity of 12 km/sec. Miss Underhill found the density to be about 0.001 that of the solar atmosphere but because of its large optical thickness the shell was close to thermal equilibrium at 8000°K.

4. The Problem of Shell Formation

A shell may change from one type to another. For example, a thin *Be* shell may thicken and produce strong absorption lines, e.g., γ Cassiopeiae and Pleione. Normal *B* stars develop shells and become *Be* stars and vice versa. Also peculiar *Be* stars have been observed to develop P Cygni shells and vice versa. The P Cygni lines of supergiants may disappear or show marked intensity and structural fluctuations.

How do these shells come into being and how are they maintained? Why do the V/R ratios and other parameters show periodic or irregular variations; why do some shells expand whereas others do not, and why do some stars produce shells while closely similar objects do not?

The fact that all *Be* stars have large rotational velocities (of the order of 250 km/sec) suggests that rotation assists in shell formation. The centrifugal acceleration at the equator of a *B* star of ten solar radii and rotational speed of 250 km/sec amounts to 10^3 cm/sec^2 as compared with a gravitational acceleration of 10^3–10^4 cm/sec^2.

The influence of radiation pressure has been considered by Gerasimovic, Ambarzumian, Chandrasekhar, Struve, Menzel, and others. As in a gaseous nebula, Lyman quanta would tend to be degraded into Lyman α, whose intensity would be built up toward its equilibrium value. Under these circumstances the selective Lyman α radiation pressure may become so great as to produce a differential expansion—the outer parts of the shell would be pushed outward while in the central portions the net force exerted by the Lyman α quanta would tend to zero. Chandrasekhar suggests that the division of the shell into effectively three layers may be accounted for in this manner. Also, since the radiation pressure is sensitive to the velocity of expansion, slight changes in the latter may effect the shell profoundly. In a rapidly rotating shell the pressure due to Lyman α would become unimportant, and electron scattering and continuous absorption would become significant. S. Miyamoto has treated this problem for the P Cygni stars.

The blackness of the centers of the absorption lines indicates that the shells hide the photospheres completely. It is not clear, however, why the stationary and expanding shells should differ so markedly from star to star. Whenever the optical thickness of the whole shell (stationary plus expanding portion) is small, there appears to be little expansion. We observe the fixed shell and the underlying spectrum of the rotating star. When the optical thickness of the shell is large, it often may expand (P Cygni) or remain stationary with perhaps small pulsations (α Cygni).

Although rotation may trigger the ejection of shells in B stars, it does not appear to be involved in the mechanics of the P Cygni stars. Whereas the Be stars are main-sequence objects, the brighter P Cygni stars, such as the prototype itself, have high luminosities. This characteristic may favor the ejection process.

Shells are often associated with close spectroscopic binaries, e.g., β Lyrae, 29 Canis Majoris, and RY Scuti, where possibly the combined effects of the gravitational fields of the two stars plus radiation pressure conspire to facilitate the formation of shells.

Sometimes, as in SX Cassiopeiae, the emission lines, although variable in intensity, remain visible throughout the entire cycle, whereas in stars like RW Tauri the lines are visible only at minimum.

The velocity of the ring or shell varies inversely as the cube root of the binary period, which is shorter for the earlier spectral classes and the more massive stars. Struve estimates the masses of these rings to be about 10^{-8} times that of the star and suggests that they are formed by prominence action, only to dissipate and subsequently reappear. He calls attention to the peculiar circumstances that the level of ionization in the shell of the Be star ($T = 20,000°$K) is closely comparable with that in the envelope of a binary the temperature of whose components is $10,000°$K. We would expect a much lower ionization level in the latter object.

5. Fluorescence Effects in Extended Envelopes

So far we have been primarily concerned with the effects of a geometrical dilution of the radiation. From a study of line intensities in P Cygni, Struve and Swings found that the usual effects of geometrical dilution cannot explain the observed intensity anomalies. In this and other stars, the emission lines show a peculiar selectivity.

The usual permitted lines may appear with anomalous intensities; one multiplet may be in absorption while another multiplet of the same ion appears in emission. Such intensity anomalies are believed to be due to fluorescence, not unlike the type noted by Bowen for the planetary nebulae.

As an example in point we shall mention the peculiar O star 9 Sagittae, which was studied by Plaskett and more recently by Struve and Swings and by J. B. Oke. Apparently, the star has a shell which gives rise to both emission and absorption lines. Hα has a P Cygni-type of profile, and Balmer lines in absorption may be followed up to H24. The Inglis-Teller formula gives log N_ϵ = 12.90. The He II Pickering series is also observed in absorption. The He II λ4686 line seems to consist of a strong absorption line upon which is superposed a strong emission produced in the shell. On the other hand, λ3203 appears in absorption with no trace of emission. Bowen explained this behavior as follows: The Lyman α hydrogen line coincides in frequency with the second Balmer line of He II (see Fig. 3). Hence He II ions can be raised to the

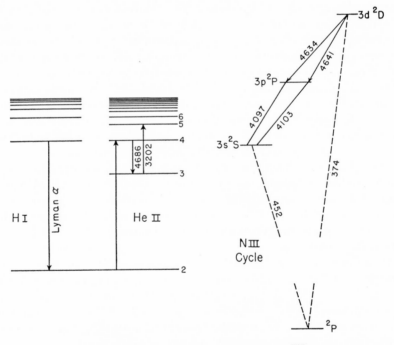

FIG. 3.—FLUORESCENCE IN HE II AND N III

Left: The hydrogen Lyman α line excites Hβ of He II. These He II atoms may return to the third level with the emission of λ4686 which tends to be filled in with emission in many early-type stars, while λ3202 remains a predominantly absorption feature.

Right: In fields of dilute temperature radiation, atoms tend to reach the N III $3p^2P$ term by absorption of λ374 followed by cascade with the emission of λ4634 and λ4641 more often than by the successive absorption of λ452 and λ4097 or λ4103.

$n = 4$ level from $n = 2$ by the absorption of this $\lambda 912$ line. From the $n = 4$ level the atom can return to $n = 3$, with the emission of a quantum of $\lambda 4686$. Hence the $\lambda 4686$ line will tend to be filled in with emission. Since $\lambda 3203$ has no such source of energy, it will appear only as a strong absorption line in the spectrum.

N III also shows a selective fluorescence. All the lines of this ion which appear in absorption evidently originate in the atmosphere of the star itself, except for $\lambda 4634$ and $\lambda 4641$ which appear in emission. In pure absorption O stars, $\lambda 4097$ and $\lambda 4103$ are stronger than $\lambda 4634$ and even the high-level transition $\lambda 4379$ $(4f^2F - 5g^2G)$ is nearly as strong as $\lambda 4634$. Apparently, $3d^2D$ is excited predominantly by the resonance $\lambda 374$ transition. More atoms cascade to ^2P and emit $\lambda 4634$ and $\lambda 4641$ than rise from ^2P to ^2D with the absorption of these same lines. On the other hand, the excitation of $3s^2S$ by $\lambda 452$ is sufficiently vigorous to maintain a large enough population for the $^2S - {}^2P$ absorptions to prevail over emission. The dilution factor in the shell is about 0.1 and the $^2D - {}^2P - {}^2S$ cycle is favored over the reverse sequence. The energy distribution of the radiation to which the atom is exposed corresponds to the stellar temperature, which is high, while the energy density is appropriate to a much lower temperature. Under these circumstances the atom tends to absorb the high-frequency quantum first and emit successive quanta of lower frequency by cascade rather than vice versa. (See Problem 3.) Recombination may also play a role in some objects, although it can be excluded for 9 Sagittae because transitions higher than $3d^2D$ appear in absorption.

One further difficulty arises. If the N III absorption lines are strong in the underlying star, radiation in $\lambda 374.20$ and $\lambda 374.44$ ought to be somewhat depleted. The gases in the shell are in motion relative to the reversing layer. Because of the Doppler effect, the atoms in the shell may absorb energy from the nearby continuum rather than from the center of the line.

Further illustrations of fluorescent effects are given by Struve and Swings, who have considered the excitation of the bright lines of He I, C III, N II, N III, N IV, Si III, and Fe II in hot stars. The effects are complicated by cyclical processes and Doppler shifts in an expanding extended envelope. Even if the incident photospheric radiation were Planckian, subsequent radiative transformations in the shell would produce marked changes.

The fluorescent mechanism will become important when the mean interval of time between two collisions is greater than the average lifetime of the atom in the levels considered. For example, if the lifetime of a level is 10^{-7} sec, but collisions excite the atom to it only once every 10^{-4} sec, fluorescent effects can become important. The maximum electron density in Be or P Cygni shells, as inferred from the Inglis-Teller formula, is 10^{12}–10^{13} electrons/cm^3. At $T = 25{,}000°$K, an electron density of 10^{15} would be required in order that the interval between collisional excitations to the upper level be less than 10^{-7} sec. Therefore, at the densities prevailing in the shell stars, fluorescent effects are to be expected.

The transfer of radiation in the outer envelopes of an extended atmosphere, where the curvature of the layers must be taken into account, has been discussed by Kosirev and also by Chandrasekhar, who derived a general method for the solution of the transfer equation when the product $k\rho$ depends only on the radius r. One often assumes $k\rho$ proportional to $r^{-n}(n > 1)$. If the source of opacity is electron scattering, k will be constant and the density ρ may be expected to vary as r^{-2} for an atmosphere expanding with a constant velocity. With the aid of tables given by Chandrasekhar, one can evaluate the appropriate integrals and solve for the intensity distribution in the continuum.

The mathematical problem of absorption-line formation in an expanding atmosphere is one of extreme complexity. In an envelope in large-scale motion, radiation scattered in different directions will have different frequencies because of the Doppler effect, the volumes of the transparent radiating gases are large, and the effects of temperature are important. Since the envelope is exposed to dilute temperature radiation, fluorescent processes are more important than in normal atmospheres.

6. The Wolf-Rayet Stars

Among the least understood of all the objects in the heavens are the rare Wolf-Rayet stars, whose spectacular spectra are characterized by broad emission lines of atomic origin, sometimes 50–100A wide, sometimes with absorption components on their violet edges.

R. E. Wilson's proper motion studies indicate these stars have a mean absolute magnitude of about -3.4. Hence they are comparable with normal O stars of the same temperature. The strong interstellar lines in their spectra show that they lie at a considerable distance. The upper limit to the luminosities of the Wolf-Rayet stars is obtained from the Magellanic Clouds, but the best data are those obtained by Miss Roman for the group in Cygnus.

Our most extensive information on the Wolf-Rayet stars comes from the eclipsing binary HD 193576 (BD $+38°$ 4010 or V444 Cygni), which Olin Wilson first noted as a spectroscopic binary and which S. Gaposchkin found to be an eclipsing system. A Wolf-Rayet star of about 12 solar masses is attended by a brighter $O6$ companion which has a diameter 10 times and a mass 28 times that of the sun. This binary belongs to the well-known cluster of early-type stars in Cygnus which lies at a distance of the order of 1000 parsecs. From the intensities of the interstellar lines and the color excesses of nearby stars, the distance appears to be about 1200 parsecs. The visual absolute magnitudes would be -3.08 and -4.83 for the Wolf-Rayet and O components, respectively.

Although the spectroscopic observations showed the stars to move in nearly circular orbits, the precise light-curve obtained by G. E. Kron and Mrs. Katherine Gordon Kron revealed that the primary minimum (when the Wolf-Rayet star was in front) was more than twice as wide as the secondary minimum. This means that the effective diameter of the Wolf-Rayet star when it blocks the light is greater than when it itself is eclipsed. These facts suggest that the Wolf-Rayet component has an extended semi-transparent envelope which dims the light of the O star at primary minimum, although its own luminosity is so low that when the O star passes before it, no light loss occurs. Z. Kopal and Mrs. M. Shapley, on the basis of an analysis of the light-curve near the primary minimum, suggested that the opacity in the extended envelope arose almost entirely from electron scattering. At heights where extinction just begins to be noticeable, the electron density is about 10^9 electrons/cm^3, whereas at the lowest levels it is estimated to be 2×10^{12} electrons/cm^3. It is of interest that the electron density inferred from purely spectroscopic data appears to be 10^{11}–10^{12} electrons/cm^3.*

More recently, the Krons have measured the light-curve at $\lambda 7200$ to supplement their earlier determinations for $\lambda 4500$. The solution indicates that the Wolf-Rayet component consists of a small opaque core of about two solar radii with an effective temperature of 80,000°K. This is surrounded by a luminous, semi-transparent envelope of about seven solar diameters whose brightness depends on the wave length. Finally, the observations suggest a detached shell of about 16 solar radii in which the opacity is produced by electron scattering.

Photometric measures of the asymmetrical emission lines in the Wolf-Rayet spectrum by Wilson and by Beals showed that the profiles varied with phase, possibly because of the tidal attraction of the O

---

*The electron density of the shell that produces the observed lines can be estimated from the intensities of the emission lines if we know the distance and size of the star. Under the assumption that most of the electrons are supplied by helium, one may employ the intensity of $\lambda 4686$ to estimate $N_i N_e$ in much the same way as the electron density of a planetary nebula can be estimated from the intensity of Hβ. In this way an electron density of 10^{11}–10^{12} electrons/cm^3 was found for the layers responsible for the emission lines in $BD + 38°\ 4010$. If the densities were much lower than this value, the [O III] lines should be observed.

star upon the vastly extended atmosphere, where the radiations are believed to originate. Wilson's spectrophotometry of the λ4686 He II line indicated that there was little, if any, eclipse of this radiation. The Kron model suggests that the emission lines might originate in the envelope around the inner core, in which event eclipse effects should be observed. If, however, the λ4686 radiation is asymmetrically distributed, interpretation of the results is complicated.

The broad Wolf-Rayet emission lines recall those observed in novae shortly after maximum (Fig. 4). Hydrogen and helium, carbon, nitrogen, oxygen, and silicon in various stages of ionization are represented in their spectra. The hydrogen lines are usually weak and blended with He II. Spectroscopically, the stars tend to fall in two groups; one of which is characterized by lines of helium, carbon, and oxygen in various ionization stages, whereas the other contains predominantly helium, some nitrogen, a small amount of carbon, and no trace of any oxygen. In addition to the letter W to denote all Wolf-Rayet stars, C and N are affixed to distinguish stars of the carbon and nitrogen sequences. Finally a number based on the line ratios, λ5411 (He II)/λ5875(He I) denotes the level of ionization (temperature). Thus, designations such as WC6, 7, 8, or WN5, 6, 7, 9 are employed.

The simultaneous appearance of He I (I.P. = 24ev) and N V (97ev) in the same spectrum suggests that radiation reaches us from many different layers. Marked differences occur in the widths of lines of ions of different ionization potential in the sense that the lines of lowest excitation show the largest breadth. If the widths of the lines arise from the Doppler effect in an expanding shell, as Beals and Menzel suggested, this would mean that the ions of highest ionization potential (which show the narrowest lines) have the smallest outward velocities and are supposedly found in the lowest layers. Correspondingly, the ions of lower ionization potential are in the upper stratum. Presumably they suffer an acceleration as they move outward. The radiation seems to come from a stratified atmosphere whose transparency is rather high. The photospheres of these stars are concealed; indeed, we cannot be sure they even possess photospheres in the ordinary understanding of the term.

The "temperature" of a Wolf-Rayet star depends on how it is defined, since few objects show greater deviations from thermal equilibrium.

Color temperatures have been measured by Gerasimovic (1929) and recently by W. Petrie, who found the interstellar reddening so patchy as to make a determination of the true color temperature impossible. Kosirev has shown that the color temperature of a star with an extended envelope is lower than its effective temperature.

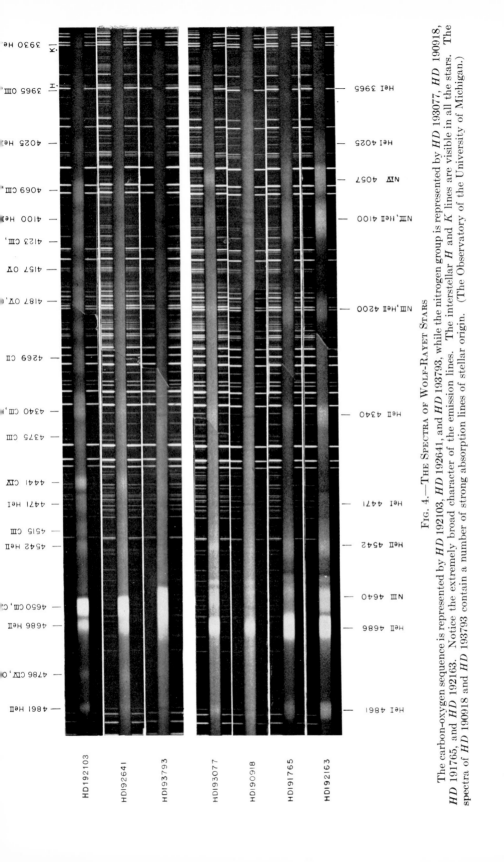

FIG. 4.—THE SPECTRA OF WOLF-RAYET STARS

The carbon-oxygen sequence is represented by HD 192103, HD 192641, and HD 192163, while the nitrogen group is represented by HD 193077, HD 190918, HD 191765, and HD 192163. Notice the extremely broad character of the emission lines. The interstellar H and K lines are visible in all the stars. The spectra of HD 190918 and HD 193793 contain a number of strong absorption lines of stellar origin. (The Observatory of the University of Michigan.)

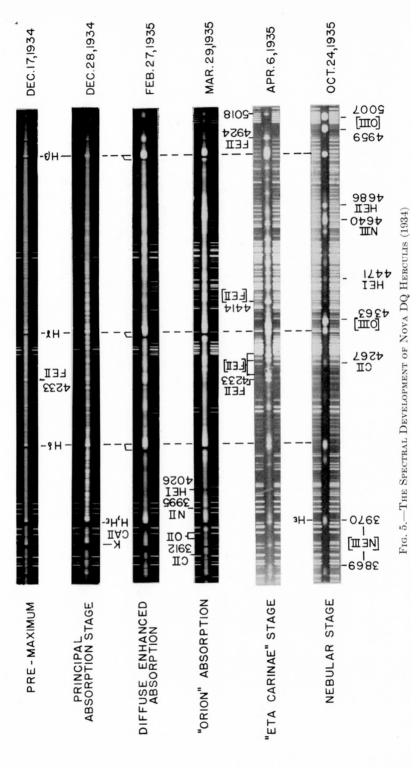

FIG. 5.—THE SPECTRAL DEVELOPMENT OF NOVA DQ HERCULIS (1934)

The successive stages in the development of a nova, described in McLaughlin's nomenclature, are well illustrated in this slow nova (see text).
(The Observatory of the University of Michigan.)

Effective temperatures could be estimated if the actual sizes of the Wolf-Rayet components of eclipsing binaries were known. The value of 13,000°K derived by Gaposchkin for V444 Cygni is probably much too low.

The excitation temperatures are derived from the relative numbers of atoms in different energy levels with the aid of the Boltzmann formula. If self-reversal is negligible, the populations of two levels of excitation potential χ_r and χ_s may be estimated from the relative intensities of lines arising from these levels. Since

$$I_1 \propto N_r A_{rr'} h\nu_{rr'} \quad \text{and} \quad I_2 \propto N_s A_{ss'} h\nu_{ss'}, \tag{17}$$

we have

$$\log \frac{I_1}{I_2} = \log \frac{N_r A_{rr'} \nu_{rr'}}{N_s A_{ss'} \nu_{ss'}}$$

$$= \log \frac{g_r}{g_s} - \frac{5040}{T}(\chi_r - \chi_s) + \log \frac{A_{rr'} \nu_{rr'}}{A_{ss'} \nu_{ss'}} \tag{18}$$

For each line the Einstein coefficient A may be estimated from atomic theory.

The results obtained are what might be expected for a stratified atmosphere. The more highly ionized atoms give the higher temperatures, the ions of low ionization potential give the lowest temperatures. Strictly, we cannot speak of the "temperature" of such a star; we have to refer to a particular layer, or stage of ionization. It is important to clearly understand what is meant by "excitation" temperature. We compare the relative populations of two levels. From this ratio a temperature is found by means of the Boltzmann formula which is used as an interpolation device. This temperature has only a formal significance that is concerned with the distribution of atoms among the higher levels. It is probably correlated with the electron temperature at the layer where the lines are formed. In some respects we are entitled to regard it as a sort of local temperature appropriate to the stratum in question. The high-level lines of N III, for example, give the temperature appropriate to the level where much of the nitrogen exists as N IV, and the N III lines largely arise from recombination.

R. N. Thomas has concluded, however, that a homogeneous atmosphere in which the electron temperature exceeds the radiation temperature may explain the observations just as well as a stratified model. He suggests that the atmosphere is supported by anisotropic, macroscopic motions equal to those inferred from the emission-band width. The ionization increases outward in at least the lower part of the atmosphere. Weenen also suggested a homogeneous, unstratified atmosphere.

Beals assumed that the envelope of a Wolf-Rayet star could be regarded as a small planetary nebula, so that the Zanstra theory of nebular luminosity could be applied. In this theory it is postulated that all the emission lines arise exclusively from recombination followed by cascade to lower levels.

The physical significance of temperatures derived in this way is not clear. The He I absorption lines give very little evidence of dilution of radiation. If the envelopes are much larger than the central stars, this observation suggests that the upper levels are excited by strong-line radiation from the lower layers. Furthermore, the stronger emission lines show evidence of self-reversal, which indicates that the upper levels are, to some extent at least, excited by line radiation, and not exclusively by recombination. Therefore, an application of the Zanstra method is open to serious question.

The splitting of the spectral sequence into a carbon and nitrogen branch suggests differences of chemical composition. The stratification of the atmosphere, as well as our ignorance of the mode of excitation of the line spectrum, makes the estimation of the relative abundances of the elements difficult. Different atoms behave in different ways with depth in the star. The emission-line intensities of O III, for example, give an estimate of the number of O IV ions multiplied by the electron density in the layer relevant to the production of O III lines. Similarly, the O V line intensities are proportionate to $N(\text{O VI})N_e$ in the presumably much deeper layers responsible for the O V lines. It is easier to compare carbon and oxygen, which can exist in several stages of ionization, than to compare oxygen and helium, since helium appears mostly as He II. In the stars of the carbon sequence we find that the observed features of the spectrum can be explained with a helium/oxygen ratio of about 50, and a carbon/oxygen ratio of about 3. The spectra of the stars of the nitrogen sequence are consistent with a nitrogen abundance of about one-twentieth that of helium, whereas carbon may be 0.05 to 0.1 as prevalent as nitrogen. At best these results can be regarded as little better than order-of-magnitude estimates. The Wolf-Rayet star *HD* 45166 shows lines of both carbon and nitrogen with comparable strength, as though an atmosphere of the same composition as τ Scorpii or 10 Lacertae were excited to emit the Wolf-Rayet–type of spectrum. Spectra of this intermediate type are present among the nuclei of planetary nebulae.

Bidelman's hydrogen deficient star *HD* 160641 shows strong lines of carbon, nitrogen, and helium. A comparison of the composition of its atmosphere with that of the Wolf-Rayet stars (cf. page 84) shows the C/N ratio to more closely resemble that found in "normal" stars.

Although the hypothesis of an expanding shell has been invoked to explain the great widths of the lines in the Wolf-Rayet stars, it encounters some important difficulties. In his study of the eclipsing binary V444 Cygni, Olin Wilson pointed out that if the expanding shell is large, the ejected layers whose velocities are measured spectroscopically should be left behind in the orbit as the star moves. Hence there should exist a phase shift between the eclipses predicted from the spectroscopic orbit and those actually observed. Such a phase difference must be small; hence the envelope cannot be large. In the latter event a pronounced violet shift and asymmetry of emission lines should be observed, but these effects are not found either! Perhaps the great widths of the emission lines are due to electron scattering, and the change of width with stage of ionization is to be accounted for by the variation of temperature with depth in the star. Until the causes of line broadening in Wolf-Rayet stars is clarified, it seems unsafe to lay any stress on the velocities of expansion derived by Beals and others.*

7. Light-Curves of Novae

The novae are variable stars of initial visual absolute magnitude about +4, which rise abruptly to absolute magnitudes −6 or −7 and then decline in brightness, sometimes speedily, sometimes slowly, to return to their initial luminosity after a period of several years. They are not to be confused with the supernovae which have roughly similar-looking light-curves, but which attain luminosities about 10^8 that of the sun. The distinction between supernovae and the classical novae appears to lie in the nature of the processes involved as well as the brightnesses attained.

Without exception novae brighten more rapidly than they fade. The rate of decline varies from star to star. The slow nova DQ Herculis required 100 days to decline 3 magnitudes, whereas the fast Nova Puppis 1942 faded that far in one week. McLaughlin has identified several distinct stages in the light variations of a typical nova (see Fig. 6): (1) *Pre-outburst stage.* Most of the few novae caught before outburst were fainter than the 14th magnitude. They are either constant in brightness or fluctuate through a small range. (2) *The initial rise* is defined as that portion of the light-curve in which the brightness increases from minimum to 2 magnitudes below maximum. This increase is of the order of 9 magnitudes on the average and takes place in a couple of days, irrespective of the speed of later development of the star, except for objects such as RT Serpentis, FU Orionis, etc., which

*Recently, G. Münch has made a detailed study of the spectroscopic and radial velocity changes in *HD* 193576. He favors an interpretation of some of the observed changes with the aid of an envelope in which the material is decelerated as it moves outward. The kinetic energy is partly dissipated as heat and is partly used up against the gravitational potential.

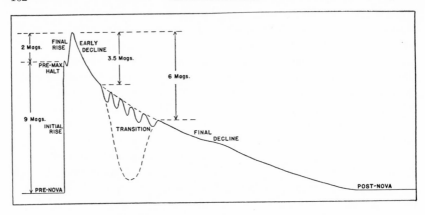

Fig. 6.—Schematic Light–Curve of a Nova

The time scale is not uniform throughout; it has been magnified in the early stages. (After D. B. McLaughlin.)

are slower. (3) *Pre-maximum halt.* Often the brightening star halts in its rise about 2 magnitudes below the maximum, a phenomenon which serves to differentiate the fast and slow novae. In most fast novae the *still-stand* is blurred over, although in Nova Aquilae 1918 the halt was marked. This stage is usually short, e.g., 1.5 days for Nova (DQ) Herculis, although it lasted 40 days for Nova Pictoris 1925. (4) *Final rise.* The increase to maximum proceeds much more slowly than the initial rise. A fast nova requires about as long to brighten through the last 2 magnitudes as it needs for its initial rise, while a slow nova may take much longer, e.g., 7 days for DQ Herculis. (5) *Maximum* is of brief duration, a matter of hours for fast novae and not more than a few days for slow ones, except for those of long duration such as RT Serpentis. It may be followed by a lesser secondary maximum as the star declines. (6) *The early decline* is defined as extending from maximum light to 3 or 4 magnitudes below the maximum. All rapid novae, e.g., Nova Persei 1901 and Nova Lacertae 1936, show a smooth decline, whereas with slow novae fluctuations of the order of 1 to 2 magnitudes are common (e.g., Nova Herculis and Nova Pictoris). (7) *The transition stage* sets in at about 3.5 magnitudes below the light maximum. The transition may take one of three forms: (a) A series of strong oscillations as in Nova Persei 1901 or Nova Aquilae 1918. In each instance the onset involved an abrupt fading of the star below the smooth extrapolation of the early decline (McLaughlin emphasizes this point to compare the behavior with the deep minimum of DQ Herculis). After a couple of months, when the star was 6 magnitudes fainter than maximum, the oscillations ceased. (b) A single minimum of some weeks' duration followed by a brightening. Nova Herculis was a spectacular example of this behavior. (c) A temporary steepening of the decline followed by a smooth fading at a slower rate than the initial decline, e.g., Nova Lacertae 1936. Regardless of the type of transition, the nova leaves this part of the light-curve about 6 magnitudes below the maximum. (8) *Final decline.* After the transition period, the nova fades uneventfully and smoothly into its final decline. The duration of this decline is greater than all the preceding history of the outburst. Even the fast novae take about seven years to reach the final stage (Nova Persei 1901 required 15 years). The slow novae DQ Herculis and Nova Pictoris 1925 have not yet reached minimum. T Aurigae 1891, however, has reached minimum. (9) *Post-outburst stage.* The star finally declines to its pre-outburst luminosity and may be of constant brightness or it may vary in an irregular manner through a fraction of a magnitude. Nova Persei, however, was observed to vary more than one magnitude. The initial and final magnitudes of novae appear to be the same.

For an understanding of the nova process it is necessary to correlate the light changes with the spectroscopic changes.

8. The Intrinsic Luminosities of Novae

The novae appear to belong to the Type II population and show a pronounced concentration to the central bulge of the galaxy. They appear at about the same rate (25–30 per year) in the Andromeda spiral Messier 31 as in our system. Direct trigonometric parallaxes are valueless; secular parallaxes and parallaxes based on the intensities and displacements of the interstellar lines (see Ch. 6) have been employed to give statistical distance estimates, but far better statistical results can be derived from the novae concentrated to the central bulge of our galaxy. Similarly, the novae observed in the Andromeda Spiral Messier 31 have been used to derive absolute magnitudes, sometimes by the judicious extrapolation of fragmentary light-curves.

A much better procedure, when it can be used, involves the comparison of angular rates of expansion of the nebular shells, observed around novae some years after the outburst, with the velocity of expansion in km/sec as deduced from the displacements of the emission lines in the nebulae. Such shells have been observed in a number of objects, e.g., Nova Aquilae and Nova Herculis. The nebulosity around Nova Herculis was observed by Baade 5.77 years after the outburst to be $3''.50 \times 2''.71$. That is, the average angular rate of expansion per year is $S_a = 0''.303$ along the major axis and $S_b = 0''.235$ along the minor axis. The radial velocity of expansion is 289.4 km/sec (Struve, Swings, and Humason). Since a speed of one astronomical unit a year corresponds to 4.75 km/sec, the velocity of expansion v (km/sec) $= S'' \times$ D (parsecs) $\times$ 4.75 where D is the distance of the nova. Hence

$$D = 0.2112 \frac{v}{S} \tag{19}$$

With an adopted mean value of $S = 0''.27$ Baade found $D = 226$ parsecs. The apparent magnitude at maximum was 1.4; therefore, $M = -5.4$.

Lundmark, who employed these and other less reliable methods, concluded that $M_{max} = -7.0$ for all novae, a result in good agreement with that of McLaughlin (1942). Cecchini and Gratton found $M_{max} = -7.3 \pm 0.2$. McLaughlin finds evidence from the most reliable distance determinations that a life–luminosity relation for novae exists in the sense that brightest novae fade most rapidly. The relation holds for objects between Nova Aquilae 1918 ($M = -9$) and RT Serpentis ($M = -3.6$) but not for supernovae, nor for objects such as η Carinae.

TABLE 3

RELATION BETWEEN BRIGHTNESS AND RATE OF DECLINE OF NOVAE

Class	M	t
Very fast	-8.2	10
Fast	-7.2	30
Average	-6.5	60
Slow	-5.4	200
RT Serpentis	-3.6	1000

In Table 3, t denotes the number of days required for the star to fade 3 magnitudes. Notice that the novae cover a considerable range in maximum luminosity.

9. Spectroscopic Changes in Novae

The light-curves give little hint of the spectacular spectral changes of a nova. We observe the metamorphosis of a supergiant F spectrum at maximum light to a forbidden-line spectrum characteristic of a planetary nebula. In the course of the development of the star, the initial continuous spectrum fades, there appear numerous broad bright lines with absorption components on their violet edges. The multiplicity, displacement, and intensities of these dark lines show remarkable changes with time. As the star declines, the bright-line spectrum changes. The emission lines of permanent gases replace those of metals and forbidden lines replace permitted ones. In the last stages even these disappear, leaving only the weak continuum of a hot star.

The observations suggest that the star ejects its photospheric layers with a high velocity. As long as the shell is dense enough for its optical thickness to be greater than about unity, it will radiate a continuous spectrum with the usual dark lines. The spectrum will resemble that of a supergiant. As the density falls, the continuous absorption declines and the optical thickness of the shell falls. As the radiating envelope becomes increasingly transparent, the spectrum becomes predominantly one of emission. Vapors in the outer parts of the shell, on its nearer side, absorb light of both the star and the inner emitting layers, producing absorption lines with violet displacements. The emissivity of the shell gradually ebbs away until finally the object reverts to its initial state, a blue, relatively faint star.

Let us now turn to a more detailed account of the spectral changes. The following account is due to McLaughlin.

Generally, spectroscopic observers have distinguished four different sets of absorption lines, apparently associated with as many different ejections from the central star and characterized by differing displacements from their normal position. In DQ Herculis a *pre-maximum* set of lines appeared just before maximum light and lasted for a day or two after maximum. Most novae are caught after maximum, and these lines are not observed. In the terminology of McLaughlin, the three important systems of absorption lines are the *principal absorption*, the *diffuse enhanced absorption*, and the *"Orion" absorption*.

Corresponding to each of these absorption systems there is an emission spectrum. In each instance the lines are broadened with their centers in the normal position. The absorption line of the associated spectrum falls upon the violet edge of the emission line; the red edge of the emission line has a displacement numerically equal to the displacement of the absorption line. Novae show two additional emission spectra—the *nebular emission*, which is derived from the greatly expanded principal shell, and the post-outburst stellar spectrum, which is observed after the dimming shell has disappeared.

We shall illustrate these changes with the aid of spectrograms of DQ Herculis (see Fig. 5). The plate, taken on December 17, shows a P Cygni-type profile with diffuse absorption with a large violet displacement (-176 km/sec). After maximum this absorption component is replaced by the principal absorption whose velocity is -316 km/sec. The plate of December 28 shows the principal absorption, which resembles a supergiant A or F except for the strong O I and C I lines. Lines such as $\lambda 4481$ and those of O I whose lower levels are connected with the ground level by allowed transitions fade rapidly, whereas the Ca II, Ti II, and Fe II lines that arise from ground or metastable levels remain strong for a long time in accordance with expectations for dilute radiation in shells.

While the principal spectrum is yet strong, a set of diffuse strong lines of about twice the displacement appears. The diffuse enhanced Balmer lines are indicated by arrows on the spectrum of February 27, when the displacement was -760 km/sec. In addition to hydrogen, Ca II, Mg II, and sometimes Fe II, appear. The number of atoms absorbing these lines is probably smaller than the number responsible for the principal spectrum. Their great strength may arise from a curve of growth—turbulence effect. Although the diffuse enhanced absorption may disappear rapidly in fast novae, its lifetime may be considerable in slower objects where $\lambda 4481$ disappears first; Ti II, Ca II, and Fe II endure longer; hydrogen is the last to go.

The "Orion" absorption spectrum exhibited in the March 29 plate derives it's name from the diffuse lines of O II, N II $\lambda 3995$, and He I $\lambda 4026$, $\lambda 4471$, so prominent in the Orion stars. These lines appear when the diffuse enhanced absorption is yet strong and they show velocity shifts which are probably correlated with the magnitude of the star. They show a larger displacement than the preceding absorptions. Hydrogen and He I disappear first, O II lasts much longer, while N II absorption usually becomes replaced by N III as the excitation of the spectrum slowly rises. Gradually these features fade and the nova shows no more absorption lines.

In addition to these lines there sometimes appear undisplaced absorption features which, in the case of the H and K and the D lines, are to be assigned to the interstellar medium. Other lines have been attributed to atoms in a nearby cloud or shell-like nebula which became excited as the nova brightened.

An emission component extends longward from each absorption component; hence an observed emission line will consist of superposed radiations from several outbursts. McLaughlin finds that the differing widths of these emission structures, their sometimes different profiles, and their times of appearance and disappearance permit their assignment to groups corresponding to different absorption systems. In fact, some of the emissions associated with the later absorptions may escape observation because of their extreme diffuseness. The principal emission usually dominates the spectrum during the entire development, even though the corresponding absorptions fade. Some lines, e.g., N III $\lambda 4640$, may appear in two or more emission systems.

In studies of emission spectra it is important to distinguish between relative and absolute line intensities. Measures of absolute intensity variations such as Popper's study of Nova Lacertae shows the permitted lines to fade rapidly, the forbidden lines slowly. Hence, on account of lengthened exposure, one easily obtains the illusion that the forbidden lines strengthen appreciably as the nova fades. Actually, [O III] showed only a slight initial rise as the nova faded.

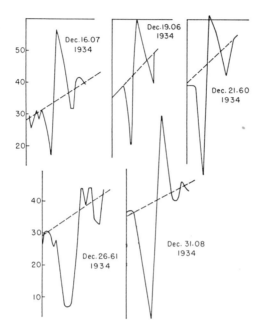

FIG. 7.—LINE PROFILE CHANGES IN CA II K ($\lambda3933$)

Tracings of spectrograms of DQ Herculis are reduced to a true intensity scale. Note the increase of absorption with time. The dotted line indicates the estimated position of the continuum. (From observations obtained at the Lick Observatory.)

DQ Herculis showed a prominent pre-maximum emission spectrum of diffuse lines of He I, C II, and N II that became replaced by bright lines of Fe II, Ca II, and Mg II. These faded away just after maximum to become supplanted by the broader, sharply defined lines of the principal emission, Ca II, Fe II, H, Na, and weaker lines of Ti II and Cr II. The diffuse enhanced emission is about twice as broad as the principal emission and is observed in H, Ca II, Fe II, Na, and O I $\lambda6155$. Notice that on February 27, when the diffuse enhanced spectrum had appeared, the hydrogen emission lines were appreciably broader than the pure principal emission of December 28. Soon after maximum, forbidden [O I] $\lambda6300$, $\lambda6363$, and $\lambda5577$ appear and later [N II] $\lambda5755$. To these were added He I $\lambda4472$, $\lambda4026$, and the [O III] lines. Still later, [O I] and [N II] $\lambda5755$ faded. The Orion emission refers to the

broadened radiations which do not share in the structure of lines of
the principal spectrum and which are associated with the Orion absorption spectrum. The "4640" line, which is due primarily to N III,
frequently shows superposed components of both the "principal" and
"Orion" emissions. The lines of this system—N II, N III, and N IV—
show fuzzy edges even in slow novae like DQ Herculis.

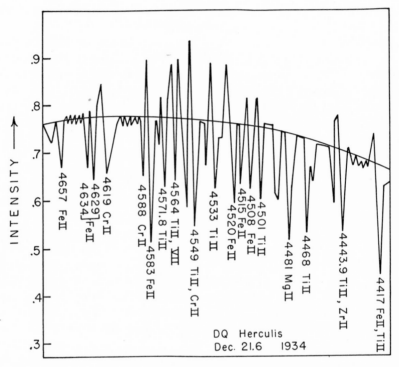

Fig. 8.—Trace of a Portion of the Spectrum of DQ Herculis Near Maximum
(December 21.6, 1934)

Note the complex mixture of absorption and emission features even in the predominantly absorption spectrum. The tracing is reduced to a true intensity scale.
(From observations obtained at the Lick Observatory.)

In certain slow novae, e.g., DQ Herculis and Nova Pictoris, strong
[Fe II] lines appeared when the nova was 3–5 magnitudes below maximum. These emissions correspond to a definite excitation stage in
the layers responsible for the principal emission. As these layers
decrease in density and increase in excitation, lines of N II λ5680,
N III λ4634, λ4641; He II λ4686; and C II λ4267 appear. These radiations also arise in strata responsible for the "Orion" spectrum, and the
observed emission lines are the superposed contributions of the two

systems. The spectrum of April 8 shows the [Fe II] stage or "η Carinae" phase of DQ Herculis.

The final nebular emission spectrum evolves from the principal emission. The strongest lines are those typical of planetary nebulae: [O III]; [Ne III] λ3869, λ3968; and [N II] λ6584, λ6548. Presumably, the physical conditions in the two kinds of objects are similar. At this stage the nova is often surrounded by a small nebula consisting of the gases that have been ejected from the central star. When the slit of the spectrograph is placed across the diameter of the nebula, each spectral line has a bow shape due to the Doppler shifts of the expanding gaseous shell. The amount of the splitting corresponds to the widths of the broadened lines observed in the integrated light of the nova. At this stage the shell expands uniformly and the size of the nebula gradually increases. Nova DQ Herculis showed an excellent example of such a shell.

Finally, the nebular emission disappears and all that is left is the continuous spectrum of the central star. Humason found that several of these old novae showed emission-line spectra of the Wolf-Rayet type with lines of He II λ4686, and C III λ4650 much narrower than those of the principal emission, e.g., 6A wide versus 70A for Nova Aquilae. During the last one or two magnitudes of decline, a decrease of excitation is indicated by the fading of He II relative to hydrogen. Other novae show purely continuous spectra with no absorption or emission features. In this respect they are similar to the nuclei of certain planetary nebulae. We cannot, however, conclude that all novae eventually lose their emission lines. No correlation between "age" and presence or absence of bright lines is evident among the objects Humason observed.

In slow novae, such as DQ Herculis, the bright lines are narrow and numerous; in fast novae the weaker lines are washed out against the continuous spectrum, and the strongest of the broadened emission lines are recognizable. McLaughlin concluded that the spectral stage depended only on the magnitude decline from maximum and that the rate of decline was inversely proportional to the square of the velocity of the principal spectrum.

The relation of absorption line displacement to light and spectral changes is also significant. The principal spectrum usually shows no response to sporadic light variations, but continuously increases in displacement. The diffuse enhanced absorption, however, shows fluctuations of position in the early stages, probably due mainly to variable blending of components with diverse displacements, whereas the Orion spectrum is strongly affected by brightness changes in the star.

Studies of the color temperatures, photo-ionization, or "Zanstra" temperatures (Ch. 5), and excitation temperatures show that as the nova rises to a maximum the color and excitation temperature fall, while the reverse is true as the nova declines. The pre-outburst nova appears to be a subdwarf with a temperature of about 50,000°K. As it rises to maximum, the color and excitation temperature of the distended photosphere falls to 6000–8000°K. As the star fades, both the color and excitation temperatures rise until the star is about two magnitudes above its minimum. Thereafter there is a slight decline in excitation. If there are oscillations, the color temperature is higher at light minima than at maxima. The star finally reverts to something similar to its pre-outburst status.

10. The Profiles of Emission Lines in Novae

Some information on the ejection process should be obtainable from the profiles of the emission lines. The simplest form of line shapes are those that are computed on the assumption that all atoms are expelled with the same velocity, and that the radiation from each atom contributes equally to the widened emission lines. Beals derived an expression for the line profile in the following way: Let a sphere of radius r surround a star whose relative radius R is negligible. Suppose that n atoms pass through each cm^2 of the shell in each second with a velocity v. Consider the atoms passing through a zone of angular width $d\theta$ symmetric with respect to the line drawn from the star to the observer. The radius of the zone is $r \sin \theta$, where θ is the angle between the line drawn from the center of the star to the observer and the line drawn to the zone. The area of the zone is $2\pi r^2 \sin \theta \, d\theta$. Hence the number of atoms passing through the zone in each second is $dN = 2\pi n r^2 \sin \theta \, d\theta$, and the contribution to the intensity will be $dE = K \, dN$. The velocity component in the line of sight will be $u = -v \cos \theta$. By differentiation we obtain

$$d\theta = \frac{du}{v \sin \theta}$$

from which $dE = C_1 \, du/v$ where C_1 is a constant. If we put the formula in terms of wave-length units, the equation is

$$dE = \frac{\text{constant}}{v} d\lambda \qquad (20)$$

where $\delta\lambda = v\lambda/c$. This equation means that a flat-topped profile should be observed. In practice the observed profiles frequently are saddle-shaped and often their structures are complicated. Two modifications are immediately suggested: (1) Self-reversal sometimes must be taken into account since the shell is not always transparent to its own radiation. In later stages when permitted and forbidden lines show the same profiles, self-reversal in not important. (2) A spread of velocities may occur. If the frequency curve of velocity is divided into a series of strips of constant width, and if the velocity in each strip is taken as constant and equal to the mean value over the interval concerned, the contributions of each strip may be summed and the resultant profile obtained. Beals concluded that if appropriate assumptions are made concerning the frequency distribution of the ejected atoms almost any observed symmetrically broadened line profile can be represented. Conversely, from the line profile, the process can be inverted to get the velocity distribution of the radiating atoms. If the frequency distribution of velocities is narrower than the half-width of the line, so that there are no velocities near zero, the profile will have a flat top. Although Beals found some flat-topped profiles in Nova Aquilae, most novae show very complicated line profiles.

J. A. Rottenberg has investigated the profiles of lines in steady-state expanding envelopes, taking into account the scattering of the radiation in the envelope and the effects of recombination. He finds that the characteristic features of many complex profiles may result from the coupling of the Doppler displacements (resulting from the radial expansion) with the conditions imposed by the geometry (relative sizes of the star and scattering and "recombination" shells). Spherically symmetrical shells expanding at constant velocities may yield asymmetrical profiles with central "reversals." These results show that caution must be applied in the interpretation of asymmetrical profiles in terms of non-symmetric ejections and accelerated motions.

Nevertheless, there is abundant evidence, both from the complicated forms of the emission lines and from the character of the nebulosity surrounding old novae that many of these stars do eject their envelopes in a patchy manner. In other words, the shells are not uniform structures, and material may be ejected preferentially in certain zones or areas of the surface. Different "shells" are ejected at different times, and perhaps from different parts of the surface, so that clouds of gas that find themselves side by side may be moving with different velocities.

In DQ Herculis part of the material appears to have been ejected in two large jets tangentially to the line of sight. These were later seen by G. P. Kuiper at Yerkes, and they gave the nova the appearance of a double star. In Baade's photograph in 1942, emission in $H\beta$, N_1, and N_2 extended uniformly over the whole nebula, while the emission in the red due to [N II] $\lambda6548$, $\lambda6584$ was restricted to two pairs of condensations, each symmetrical with respect to the center. Those along the minor axis were much the stronger and showed remarkable changes

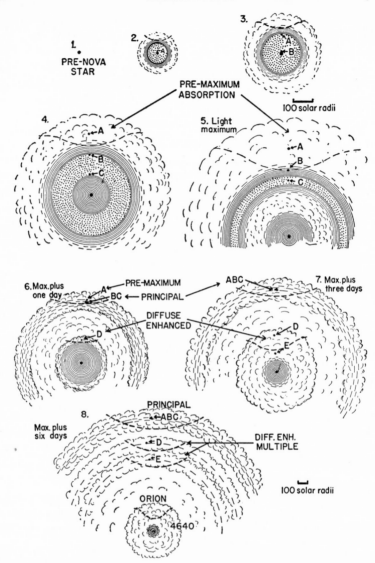

FIG. 9.—MODEL OF A NOVA OUTBURST

(1–5) Cross-sections of an active nova during the increase to maximum. The observer is above the top of the figure. The large black dot is the main body of the star. Stippled area represents the densest part of the ejected material, in which the opacity is great. Concentric circles represent the optically thinner photospheric layers, which merge into the cloudy forms that represent the true atmosphere, highly transparent except in the line frequencies. In each section, a heavy dashed line outlines the region effective in producing the absorption spectrum. Successively ejected atoms A, B, and C are shown. Note that with expansion the layer containing A, and later that containing B, become transparent. By light maximum (sketch 5), with time. According to Swings and Struve, the velocities of expansion ranged from 338 km/sec for [O II], to 256 km/sec for [O III]. Hence a mechanical stratification of the material may have occurred. The work of Baade suggests that in Nova Aquilae the material was ejected in zones symmetrical with the equator, but differing from one another in velocity.

11. Physical Picture of a Nova Outburst

Any attempted model of a nova's behavior must account for the complicated spectral, velocity, and temperature changes mentioned in Sec. 9. Concerning this problem, McLaughlin remarks:* "If we are to understand the physical processes in novae, we must differentiate features from one another not only in terms of excitation, but also in terms of the locality of their origin. Neither physics nor geometry alone will 'explain' a nova. Perhaps the judicious use of both, each in its proper place, or together, will do so. Similarity of structure is the proper guide to use in unravelling complexities of the nova emission spectrum."

The pre-outburst star is a subdwarf. The near equality of pre- and post-outburst luminosities suggests that the main body of the star is relatively undisturbed, and the eruptive activity all occurs in a thin superficial layer. A large amount of energy presumably is released a short distance below the surface of the star. The region becomes heated, and the overlying layers are blown away by the increased gas and radiation pressure. Thus a relatively small layer of material, much less than the mass of the star, becomes detached and ejected with a high velocity. Estimates of the "stellar" radius, based on the luminosity and temperature, really refer only to the dimensions of the greatly expanded photosphere, as measured down to a point where the optical

---

Fig. 9—(*Continued*)
C has begun to overtake B. The atmosphere is of great depth and the pre-maximum spectrum is correspondingly strong. At this time the ejection has abruptly diminished, and the shell, still opaque and acting as an expanding atmosphere, has become detached. Ejection from the star continues, however.

(6–8) Cross-sections of an active nova during the early decline. The density in the rapidly growing shell falls steadily. In sketch 6 the shell has just become transparent. Atoms B and C, owing to increased velocity of the inner layers of the shell, have overtaken A. The resultant shell is the "principal" shell, the pre-maximum spectrum having disappeared with the engulfment of the outer layers (A) in the accelerated inner ones (B) and (C). Atom D, in the atmosphere about the inner ejected cloud, is contributing to the "diffuse enhanced" spectrum. In sketch 7 the inner cloud has become more extensive and the diffuse enhanced spectrum is correspondingly stronger. Atom E is emerging into the absorption region. In sketch 8 the gas ejected in the diffuse enhanced stage is in the form of two detached shells overtaking the principal shell, while the inner cloud has developed into the "Orion" and λ4640 spectral stages. (After D. B. McLaughlin.)

*Publ. Univ. of Mich. Obs., **8**, 166, 1943.*

depth is about one. There is probably an initial burst followed by the continuous ejection of matter at a declining rate. Whipple and Mrs. Gaposchkin showed that, in Nova Herculis, the ejected matter was expelled continuously over a long period of time.

As the envelope expands, the inner portion remains dense enough to stay opaque for a time, but the outer part becomes less dense and more transparent, so the absorption lines intensify as the number of atoms above the effective photosphere increases. The outburst cannot supply energy at a sufficient rate to prevent the expanding photosphere from cooling. Hence the color and excitation temperatures fall, and the spectral class becomes later. At maximum light the expanded photosphere and surrounding atmosphere simulate, in so far as radiative processes are concerned, a supergiant F star of a hundred solar radii.

As the shell continues to expand and the ejection of material from the star fails to keep pace, the density falls to the point where the envelope becomes transparent, except in line frequencies. This portion of the shell produces the principal absorption. Emission is observed from all parts of the cloud except the denser gases near the star, which may still radiate a continuous spectrum. The dilution of the radiation becomes pronounced. Lines such as Mg II $\lambda 4481$ weaken rapidly, whereas lines which arise from metastable levels fade more slowly. The forbidden lines appear when the intensity of the continuum has declined sufficiently.

Even after the main outburst, the star still ejects material with a velocity greater than that of the principal shell. These gases produce the diffuse enhanced spectrum which initially imitates that of P Cygni (with an optical thickness of about one). Gradually the mass rate of ejection declines and, as the outer layers thin out, the hotter regions close to the star increasingly become exposed to view, and the excitation gradually rises. The "Orion" emission spectrum appears when the effective radius of the photosphere is about ten times that of the sun.

Finally ejection ceases, and the star settles back to some semblance of normalcy. The material thrown out in the original outburst is now spread over a radius of tens of thousands of astronomical units. The gases have become so attenuated that the nebular spectrum disappears, and the spectrum of the star alone is left.

One important difference between fast and slow novae must be mentioned. In fast novae the main shell is ejected between the premaximum halt and the maximum itself. In slow novae ejection appears to last as long as 100 days. Thus, ten days after discovery, DQ Herculis reached a maximum of $1^{m}.3$ on December 23, 1934. Thereafter it declined slowly with irregular fluctuations of 2.5 magnitudes and reached $4^{m}.5$ at the end of March, 1935. The fluctuating decrease in the intensity of the continuous spectrum and the increase in the prominence of the emission lines implies a fluctuating decline in the mass rate of ejection of material. The photospheric zone drew closer to the stellar core, while the shell responsible for the bright lines extended to ever increasing distances from the nucleus. In April the star went to a deep minimum of $13^{m}\!.1$ after which it slowly recovered to a magnitude of $6^{m}\!.7$ near the end of August. During the minimum and subsequent brightening, the object showed the characteristic radiations of a planetary nebula. Presumably, the ejection from the star ceased at the end of March, and the surrounding nebula was suddenly exposed to the radiation of the high-temperature core.

Grotrian postulated that the brightening of the object subsequent to the deep minimum arose, not from changes in the temperature and dimensions of the central star, but from the establishment of radiative equilibrium in a gaseous mass suddenly exposed to high-temperature radiation. The nebula consists mostly of hydrogen, presumed largely initially neutral. The atoms become photo-ionized and emit the observed Balmer lines when the ions and electrons recombine. As in the planetaries (Ch. 5), most of the quanta absorbed in the shell will photo-eject an electron. That is, Q, the total number of quanta absorbed in the nebula per second (essentially the number of quanta emitted by the star beyond the Lyman limit), will equal the number of freed electrons. Under equilibrium conditions, Q will equal the number of recombinations per second; i.e., $\chi n_i n_\epsilon$ or χn_i^2 where χ is the recombination coefficient and $n_i = n_\epsilon$ is the total number of ions in the nebula. The intensity of the emitted radiation is assumed proportional to the total number of recombinations, i.e.,

$$I = A\chi n_i^2 \tag{21}$$

where A is a constant which depends on the transition probabilities, etc.

The rate of change of the number of ions will equal the number of photo-ionizations minus the number of recombinations, viz.:

$$\frac{dn_i}{dt} = Q - \chi n_i^2 \tag{22}$$

If $n_i = 0$ at $t = 0$, we find

$$n_i = \sqrt{\frac{Q}{\chi}} \frac{1 - e^{-t/\tau}}{1 + e^{-t/\tau}} \tag{23}$$

where

$$\tau = \frac{1}{2\sqrt{\chi Q}} \tag{24}$$

is the time constant of the recombination process. After a very long time (assuming the star to remain constant after it has ceased ejecting material), I approaches the limiting value, $I_0 = AQ$, and we find

$$I = I_0 \left[\frac{1 - e^{-t/\tau}}{1 + e^{-t/\tau}} \right]^2 \qquad (25)$$

as the equation representing the time variation of the intensity. With $\tau = 36$ days, Grotrian found a good representation of the light-curve after the deep minimum and showed that the required photo-ionization rate Q was of the right order of magnitude.

Grotrian's explanation of the deep minimum appears essentially sound. A quantitative explanation of the rapid initial decline of the star would be of great interest in rounding out the picture, however.

12. Mass and Energy of the Ejected Layers

To determine the mass and composition of the ejected layers, it is necessary to have quantitative information on the line intensities and how they change with time. Sayer and Popper have made such studies for Nova Ophiuchi 1933 and Nova Lacertae 1936, respectively. From the line intensities (expressed in ergs/cm^2/sec) and the distance of the nova, it is possible to calculate the total number of radiating atoms producing the observed lines. To determine the ionic density and the total mass of the shell, it is necessary to know the radiating volume $V(t)$ as a function of the time. Sayer estimated $V(t)$ from the rate of expansion of the shell and derived the ionic density on the assumption (a) the combined Boltzmann-Saha equation could be applied, and (b) the spectrum is produced by pure recombination followed by cascading. He found the mass of the shell to be of the order of 10^{-28} gm, i.e., about 10^{-5} of the probable mass of the star itself.

The mass of the shell ejected by Nova Herculis has been estimated from the line intensities in the *absorption* spectrum near maximum light, when the temperature was about 6000°K and $M = -5.5$. Thus the radius was computed to be approximately 100 solar radii or 7×10^{12} cm. The equivalent widths of absorption lines of Ti II and Fe II were measured on Lick plates at four days near maximum light, December 20, 21, 22, 23, 1934. On the basis of the character of the spectrum (near $F5$) the curve of growth for the supergiant, α Persei, was employed to compare the relative numbers of atoms above the solar photosphere and in the nova shell. The absorption-line intensities in the nova are consistent with the suggestion that there is about five times as much material per unit area above the level of the "photosphere" of the nova as above that of the sun. Since each cm^2 of the nova shell contains at least 10 grams, the total mass of the shell must be at least 6×10^{27} grams.

From a spectrophotometric study of five bright novae, the Gaposchkins found ionic densities to vary from 10^9 to 10^4 ions/cm^3 during the nebular stage, and the total mass of the ejected material to be 10^{27} to 10^{28} grams.

The total amount of energy radiated in a nova outburst may be computed from the light-curve of the star. Thus Nova Aquilae radiated 1.2×10^{45} ergs, Nova Herculis 9×10^{44} ergs, Nova Pictoris 4.3×10^{45}, and Nova Persei 7.2×10^{44} ergs. We might expect the energy of the ejected mass of material to be related to the original outburst of radiation. Sayer has tested this suggestion for Nova Ophiuchi 1933.

The ejected shell of material has three kinds of energy: (a) kinetic energy, (b) potential energy, and (c) energy of ionization. The kinetic energy of a shell of mass 10^{28} grams traveling with a velocity of 2000 km/sec is $mv^2/2 = 2 \times 10^{44}$ ergs. The potential energy is

$$GMm \int_{r_0}^{\infty} \frac{dr}{r^2} = \frac{GMm}{r_0} \tag{26}$$

where m is the mass of the shell, and M and r_0 are the initial mass and radius of the central star. If we assume for M and r_0 the corresponding solar values, we obtain a potential energy of $7 \times 10^{-8} \times 10^{28} \times 2 \times 10^{33}/7 \times 10^{10} = 2 \times 10^{43}$ ergs. If the radius is 1/10 that of the sun, the potential energy would be comparable with the kinetic energy. The energy required to ionize 10^{28} grams (or 10^{52} atoms) is about 10^{41} ergs, since the ionization energy per atom is 2×10^{-11} ergs. Notice that this energy is much less than that needed to eject the whole shell, or the total energy emitted, which is 10^{44}–10^{45} ergs.

13. Origin of the Nova Phenomenon

The masses of the ejected shells show that only the superficial layers of the atmosphere are disturbed. The evidence from the light-curves is harmonious with the suggestion that the objects observed before the outburst are identical with those found after the star has completed its variation. Quiescent novae appear to be faint blue stars of visual absolute magnitude about +4. If the temperature is 50,000°K, the bolometric correction is -4.3 magnitudes; hence $M_{bol} = -0.3$. The corresponding radius is 0.15 that of the sun. Hence the normal star is definitely a subdwarf but not a white dwarf. The most nearly comparable objects are certain blue and white stars found in some globular clusters and the nuclei of planetary nebulae, but it is certain that ordinary novae cannot be the parents of existing planetaries. Apparently only a special species of stars can show nova activity, and these objects may actually repeat their outbursts as does T Coronae (Sec. 14). Stars such as Nova Aquilae, on the other hand, are expected to repeat only at intervals of many milennia.

With these facts in mind, Biermann attempted a theoretical interpretation of novae. Recall that just below the photospheric layers of the sun there exists a layer in which the energy transport is by convection. In the sun the difference between the radiative and convective gradients is large, and the layer always remains in adiabatic equilibrium. Biermann supposed that novae were built primarily of elements heavier than hydrogen and helium. Then the temperature gradient for adiabatic equilibrium would be very close to that for radiative equilibrium. Normally the layer is in radiative equilibrium, but occasionally the temperature gradient changes toward the adiabatic gradient, the layer becomes unstable, and an outburst occurs. Biermann suggested that it might be triggered by the Helmholz contraction of the star. After the outburst the star would settle back to its initial condition, and the cycle would be repeated.

Although attractive as a start, the Biermann theory encounters a number of difficulties. The total energy radiated in the outburst is to be equated to the ionization energy of the ejected material. Since the ionization energy is of the order of 10^{14} ergs/gram for a mixture of heavier elements, an ejected mass of at least 10^{30} grams is required—about a hundred times as much material as appears to exist in the envelopes of DQ Herculis or Nova Ophiuchi 1933. Since only one-tenth of this energy may be available for the process Biermann suggested, the mass of the critical layers may be as much as 0.01 that of the sun. Furthermore, the theory requires a low hydrogen and helium content in the critical layers involved in the ejection. The spectroscopic evidence, however, suggests that there is much hydrogen and helium in these layers; their composition may even be "normal."

The novae may represent Type II population stars that are nearing the end of their evolutionary developments. Possibly they are contracting steadily and are in a state of secular instability (Chapter 2, Sec. 6) such that the outermost layers are thrown out violently at certain intervals. That is, the star readjusts itself by spasmodic eruptions rather than by a smooth variation of internal density and temperature.

The determination of the compositions of the envelopes of novae is an unusually difficult task. Few stellar spectra are produced under conditions deviating more wildly from equilibrium, and the range in density and temperature of the radiating strata must be tremendous.

Theoretical methods developed for the study of the planetary nebulae by Menzel and his colleagues at Harvard may be applied to the novae. The results indicate that, on the average, the novae have compositions similar to that of the sun, although some differences appear to be real. Nova Pictoris showed strong forbidden sulfur and later [Fe VII] lines, whereas Nova Persei demonstrated strong neon lines.

Although existing data on several bright novae have given us the broad outlines of nova phenomenology, many questions remain unanswered. What is the cause of nova outbursts? This is partly a question for theory and partly one for observation. Projected objective prism surveys with large Schmidt cameras may provide pre-outburst spectra of a number of novae. If the pre- and post-outburst phases are the same, continuing studies of the spectra and color temperatures of old novae would be of interest. Do the stellar emission lines disappear in old novae to become replaced by a continuous spectrum or even an absorption spectrum before the next outburst?

Masses of novae are entirely unknown. Various estimates based on applications of the mass–luminosity relation or the supposed deceleration of expanding shells are of doubtful validity.

Better data on the masses of the envelopes may come from quantitative measures on the emission line intensities and their changes with time.

The irregularities in line displacements and intensities exhibited by novae in their decline are probably connected with spasmodic outbursts from the central star. There appears to be no hope of explaining these phenomena quantitatively, but perhaps we may obtain eventually a reliable qualitative picture of what actually occurs.

Of considerable interest is the star, RT Serpentis, which took several years to go through the usual spectral changes of a nova. From 1919 to 1921 it exhibited the conventional pre-maximum features. It remained at maximum near magnitude 10.6 from 1918 to 1923 and then declined slowly to the 13th magnitude. By 1928 the continuous spectrum had disappeared and [Fe II] and hydrogen were conspicuous. By 1931, [O III] and [A IV] had become prominent, and the lines of H, He I, He II, [Fe II] had all but disappeared. In 1942 the [Fe V] and [Fe VII] lines appeared, showing that the electron density in the shell remained high.

Perhaps the best-known example of a slow nova is η Carinae (Sec. 15). P Cygni has also sometimes been classed with the novae, although its lack of change would seem to disqualify it from this group. Slow novae are of interest in connection with the suggestion that they may be the parents of planetary nebulae (Ch. 5). It seems well established that the planetary nebulae cannot originate from the envelopes ejected by fast novae.

14. Recurrent Novae and Stars with Combination Spectra

The hypothesis that novae represent repeated outbursts from the same star seems strengthened by the behavior of objects such as RS Ophiuchi, T Pyxidis, and T Coronae Borealis. The latter exhibited a typical nova-like outburst in 1866 and an exactly similar one in 1946. The spectrum, while generally resembling that of an ordinary nova with bright lines of H, Fe II, Ca II, etc., in its post-maximum decline, contained also the coronal lines of [Fe X], [Fe XI], [Fe XIV], and [A X]!* The relative intensities of these lines indicated a lower level of excitation than in the solar corona (see Table 5 of Ch. *9). The coronal lines gradually disappeared as the star declined in brightness. The spectrum now consists of an M-type absorption spectrum upon which are superposed bright lines of H and He.

Other objects in which a long-period or irregular M-type variable is associated with a high-temperature, sometimes nova-like, source include: Z Andromedae, R Aquarii, CI and BF Cygni, AX Persei, RW Hydrae, and AG Pegasi. In 1923-26, H. H. Plaskett found the spectrum of Z Andromedae to consist of bright lines of H, He I, He II, Ti II, Si II, and radiations subsequently identified as those of [Fe II], [Fe III], [O III], and [Ne III]. Underneath these radiations Merrill subsequently noted titanium oxide bands whose relative intensities increased as the star faded. In 1939 the star suffered a nova-like outburst, displaying a P Cygni and then an A-type spectrum. Subsequently the star has reverted to a state similar to that found by Plaskett, with [Fe II], [Fe V], and [Fe VII], but not [Fe III], present. The absence of the intermediate phases in excitation suggests marked stratification effects.

AX Persei, RW Hydrae, and CI Cygni exhibit somewhat similar spectra, but there are no marked nova-like outbursts.

As a tentative model to explain some of these phenomena, we may envisage a cool, M-type (perhaps variable) giant or subgiant star that is associated with a small, hot, nova-like object. This binary is surrounded by a nebulous envelope perhaps a thousand astronomical units or more in radius. The M star produces the low-excitation absorption lines. The hot star ionizes the surrounding nebulosity in which are produced the recombination lines of H and He and the forbidden lines by the same mechanism as they are produced in the planetary nebulae. The nebulosity may consist of material ejected from the hot star, and possibly to some extent from the M giant as well.

An alternative hypothesis is that there exists only a single star and the high-excitation bright lines are excited perhaps by the dissipation

*McLaughlin finds that the red coronal line of [Fe X] appeared in a number of "ordinary" novae. Blending with nearby lines is often serious.

of shock waves much as the solar coronal lines are excited in Schwarzschild's theory.

Radial velocity measures, particularly by Merrill, show the velocities of the radiating gases to vary with time and from one element to another. Even the He I singlets show different velocities than do the He I triplets. Merrill suggests that the observations are to be understood in terms of pulsations in which the spectroscopic effects are stratified, the nebular lines being produced in the outer zones.

BF Cygni shows a rich emission-line spectrum of [Fe II], [Fe III], H and He, and occasionally an underlying gM spectrum. Most remarkable of the spectral features, however, is the behavior of the [O III] lines whose intensities fluctuate from night to night. Evidently, the oxygen in the nebular shell is usually in the O II state, but often becomes ionized to the O III state and then recombines as the source of high-temperature radiation is cut off. From the time required for the disappearance of the [O III] lines we may estimate the lower limit to the electron density in the nebular shell to be about 10^6 electrons/cm^3, considerably greater than the electron density in the planetary or diffuse gaseous nebulae.

Measures of the intensities of the H and He II ($\lambda4686$) lines may be utilized to obtain Zanstra temperatures T_s of the hot source, whereas the electron temperatures T_ϵ of the nebular shells are estimated from the relative intensities of $\lambda4363$ and the [O III] 5007, 4959 lines on the assumption that the electron density is so great that the populations of the levels are controlled by collisions. The results secured for BF Cygni, Z Andromedae, and CI Cygni (1950) are as follows:

	BF Cygni	Z Andromedae	CI Cygni
T_s (hydrogen)	23,000–34,000°K	28,000°K	60,000°K
T_s (He II)	–	90,000	130,000
T_ϵ	7500°–11,500	8500–10,500	18,000

The Zanstra temperatures are consistently higher for He II than for H.

The "symbiotic" character of the spectra of these objects poses a difficult problem. A single bizarre star may be responsible. On the other hand there are systems in which a hot star is observed for certainty in association with a cool star. One such system is Antares, where an M supergiant is accompanied by a B companion of about 20,000°K. The latter is surrounded by a nebula of radius 5″ which shows [Fe II] and presumably originates from the tenuous envelope of the M supergiant, since such lines are not seen in similar B stars. Puzzling, however, is the absence of hydrogen, which one would expect to be excited by the high-temperature star. Another example is VV Cephei where extended clouds surrounding an M supergiant appear to be excited by radiation from a hot blue star. The hot companion to the celebrated variable Mira Ceti has been actually observed!

Before we can understand the processes operative in these stellar envelopes we must measure the emission-line intensity variations on an absolute scale, so as to distinguish between relative changes and intrinsic changes. These observations then must be combined with the kinematical data to obtain a complete picture.

15. The Problem of η Carinae and the [Fe II] Lines

Among the most dramatic of slow novae is η Carinae, which remained at maximum for twenty years and slowly faded away. More than 60 years after the star brightened, the first spectra were obtained (1890) and showed an absorption F spectrum with strong emission. Eventually, a pure emission spectrum, mostly of narrow lines of [Fe II], replaced it. When such a spectrum is radiated by a slow nova we refer to it as the "η Carinae" stage. DQ Herculis exhibited this phase in April, 1935 (see Fig. 5).

Frequently, both permitted Fe II and forbidden [Fe II] lines are observed. In objects such as Z Andromedae, permitted Fe II is the stronger, whereas the opposite is true for WY Geminorum and Boss 1985. Both of these stars show composite spectra apparently due to the superposition of a strong ultraviolet continuum with a Balmer absorption appropriate to a temperature of about 15,000°K, and a cool star about 3000°-4000°K whose spectrum shows Ti O, Ca I, and Fe I. The emission lines arising from higher levels are weak, and one is tempted to suppose that the lines are excited by collision. Wurm has pointed out that, with decreasing electron density, the populations of the metastable levels would fall off more slowly than the populations of normal levels, until the density became so low that every atom that was excited by collisions to either kind of level would escape to a lower level by radiation. Since the target areas for collisional excitation are about the same for both normal and metastable levels, both Fe II and [Fe II] would appear with comparable strength. The lower the electron temperature, the greater the relative strength of the [Fe II] lines, since the metastable terms are closer to the ground term than are the non-metastable levels. The energy from the hot source determines the degree of ionization of the envelope, but the actual excitation of lines must depend on electron collision. In the ordinary Be stars, the Fe II lines are present with normal relative intensities; [Fe II] is absent.

There appears to be a general tendency for Fe II to appear in emission, while Ti II tends to appear in absorption. When the principal absorption in DQ Herculis faded, the lines of Fe II disappeared before those of Ti II despite the fact that the iron lines arise in absorption from metastable levels.

Whether our criterion be light-curves or spectral properties, transition types between novae and conventional stars are plentiful. It is difficult to know where to distinguish between conventional novae and objects such as η Carinae, whose slow development and high luminosity set them in a class apart. Objects like Z Andromedae, C I Cygni, and BF Cygni may represent yet other categories.

16. SS Cygni Variables

The light-curves of stars like SS Cygni or U Geminorum suggest nova-like outbursts. They remain nearly constant at minima for periods of 20–150 days, rise to maxima in a couple of days, and fade more slowly than they rose. The entire outburst lasts only a few weeks. SS Cygni and U Geminorum have amplitudes of 4.2 and 5 magnitudes, respectively, and their variations are semi-periodic.

Strand finds the absolute magnitude of SS Cygni to be 9.9 and 5.7 at minimum and maximum, respectively. The average energy radiated per cycle appears to be about 6.0×10^{38} ergs as compared with the output of a normal nova of 2×10^{45} ergs!

At minimum the spectra of these stars tend to be dwarf G with bright lines of H, He I, and Ca II. At maximum the spectrum is continuous with vague absorption lines of hydrogen and helium. As the star fades, broad emission lines of hydrogen and helium appear, but they have no absorptions on their violet edges. The stars tend to be "cool" at minimum and "hot" at maximum, just opposite to the behavior of conventional novae. Their spectra have not been explained as yet.

It is of interest to note, however, that Kukarin and Parenago found the SS Cygni stars and the two recurrent novae T Pyxidis and RS Ophiuchi to obey an amplitude–period relation of the form

$$\overline{A} = 0.80 + 1.667 \log \overline{P}$$

where A is the amplitude in magnitude and P is the period. The formula fails, however, when applied to the major outbursts of Z Andromedae. If applied to bona fide novae, it gives periods of the order of 10^5–10^6 years. On the basis of this result Baade estimates the numbers of "old" novae in the central bulge of our galaxy to be comparable with the number of RR Lyrae stars, i.e., about 100,000, as compared with perhaps 500 planetaries. In the Russell diagram for the Type II population the old novae fall below the extreme blue end of the horizontal zero-absolute-magnitude branch of blue-white stars. The location of the SS Cygni stars and T Coronae Borealis is not known. Presumably they fall in the same general part of the diagram.

17. Light-Curves and Spectra of Supernovae

Unlike the ordinary novae, dozens of which probably flare up in our own galaxy every year, the spectacular supernovae appear in a given galaxy on the average of once every 400 years. Systematic surveys of external galaxies, particularly by Zwicky, have shown that they appear in systems of all types, elliptical as well as spiral nebulae.

On the basis of their spectra Minkowski found that the supernovae could be divided into two groups, while Baade found that the maximum luminosities and light-curves also suggested two types of objects. Type I supernovae attain a luminosity of the order of a hundred million that of the sun. The brightest one, which appeared in IC 4182, attained a maximum luminosity of about 600,000,000 suns and faded rapidly. The light-curves are similar to those of ordinary novae. According to Baade, these objects stay near maximum for about one week, then decline at the rate of 0.10 magnitude a day for 20 or 30 days, and thereafter they fade away at the rate of 0.02 magnitude a day. The Type II objects attain a maximum luminosity of about ten million suns. The outburst in the spiral NGC 4725, in 1940, is a typical example. This star attained a luminosity of 30 million suns or one-seventh the luminosity of the nebula. It faded slowly at first and then more rapidly until it reached the normal light-curve; thereafter it faded in a normal way.

No identifiable emission or absorption lines appear in the spectra of these stars at any time.* Minkowski reports that in Type I, no continuum appeared other than a faint trace suspected at maximum. Diffuse features of the order of 400A wide narrowed to a width of the order of 100A within a month after maximum. The spectra are remarkably uniform from object to object, the same fuzzy structures appear at the same phases as the star fades. Evidence of various sorts indicates the effective temperature to be near 10,000°K (a surprisingly low value) near maximum. The continuum fades and the temperature rises within 200 days after maximum light. Changes in the appearance of the spectrum suggest marked changes in ionization and excitation.

At maximum, Type II objects show the continuous spectrum of a hot star. Broad emission structures, similar to those observed in

*The only exceptions are two narrow red lines of [O I] at λ6300 and λ6364, which appear five or six months after maximum.

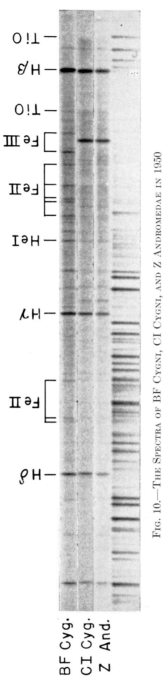

FIG. 10.—THE SPECTRA OF BF CYGNI, CI CYGNI, AND Z ANDROMEDAE IN 1950

Notice the strong emission lines of the ionized metals, especially in BF Cygni (July 15). In CI Cygni (July 16) and Z Andromedae (August 22), λ4686 of He II (the strongest line between Hβ and Hγ) attains great strength, and the heads of the titanium oxide bands are conspicuous. The iron comparison spectrum is shown at the bottom. (The Observatory of the University of Michigan.)

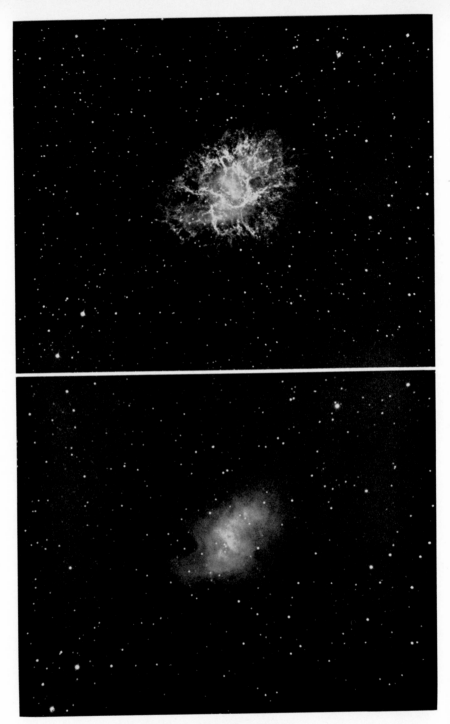

Fig. 11.—The Crab Nebula

The photograph covering the region λ6400–λ6700 shows the filaments in the light of the [N II] lines and Hα. The plate taken in the near infrared, λ7200–λ8400, shows the amorphous mass. (Courtesy, Walter Baade, Mount Wilson and Palomar Observatories.)

ordinary novae, appear four or five days after maximum and suggest a velocity of 4000 km/sec.

Whipple and Mrs. Payne-Gaposchkin attempted to explain these features with the aid of synthetic spectra. They assumed that the spectra of supernovae consisted principally of the superposition of greatly broadened emission lines of astrophysically common elements upon a continuous background. They supposed the lines to be broadened by a Doppler shift corresponding to a relative expansion of 12,000 km/sec (measured along the line of sight). With the aid of Einstein A values supplied by theory and experiment, they made theoretical determinations of the relative intensities of permitted lines of H, He, C, N, O, Ca, and Fe in various stages of ionization. By combining the theoretical patterns for various temperature levels (ionization), they found it possible to construct synthetic spectra that duplicated many features of the supernova spectra as observed by Minkowski. One important result of their investigation is that hydrogen appears to be less abundant than in ordinary stars or novae, whereas iron and helium seem to be more prominent. Could it be that supernovae are stars that have converted all their hydrogen into helium by the carbon cycle and have entered upon an unstable phase wherein the entire star undergoes a catastrophic rearrangement? At maximum a supernova radiates as much energy in one day as the sun radiates in 100,000 or 1,000,000 years. Estimates of the energy released during an outburst, from an integration of the observed light-curve, suggest it to be comparable with the total thermal energy of the star. Thus, at least for Type I supernovae, the outburst may represent a collapse of the star from a normal configuration to a state of high density.

18. The Crab Nebula

Perhaps the most important clues to the nature of the supernovae are provided by the "Crab" Nebula, a remarkable gaseous nebula unlike any other object in the sky. Baade's remarkable photographs (see Fig. 11) show striking differences in the appearance of the nebula in different spectral regions. In the $\lambda7200$–$\lambda8400$ range (where there are no strong emission lines), the nebula appears as an amorphous mass without any sharp structural details. The photograph covering the $\lambda6300$–$\lambda6700$ range (which includes Hα and the red [N II] lines) shows a striking filamentary structure with the amorphous background no longer prominent.

Minkowski's spectrograms show that the amorphous mass, which contributes more than 80 per cent of the light of the system, produces a continuous spectrum with no indication of bright lines. In contrast the filaments give a bright-line spectrum in which strong red radiations of

[N II] are present. The usual [O II], [O III], Ne III, hydrogen, and helium lines characteristic of a planetary nebula or of a nova in the nebular stage are present. The [S II] lines are much stronger than in the planetary nebulae, and the hydrogen lines are much weaker with respect to helium, even when allowance is made for a higher electron temperature in the Crab Nebula.

Baade finds that the system of filaments is elliptical in outline with only a minor distortion (major axis = 178″, minor axis = 120″). The amorphous mass is much less regular in outline than the filamentary envelope and is more flattened. The filaments appear to occur mostly in the outer part of the nebula; the inner regions appear as the amorphous mass.

Photographs taken a number of years apart show the nebula to be slowly expanding. From measures of the rate of expansion, Duncan concluded that the material originated from the outburst of some star about 800 years ago. In July, 1054, the Chinese recorded the appearance of a "guest" star in the constellation of Taurus in the present position of the Crab Nebula. It became brighter than any other object in the sky and remained visible in broad daylight for 23 days. It slowly faded; 650 days after the outburst it was no longer visible to the unaided eye. According to the discussion by Oort and Mayall, the maximum apparent magnitude attained by this star was -5, somewhat brighter than Venus (-3.3).

The decision as to whether this object was an unusually bright nova or a supernova requires a knowledge of its distance. Fortunately, additional information is available. Observations by V. M. Slipher and, subsequently, Mayall's spectrograms taken with the Crossley Reflector at Lick Observatory show the lines to be split because of the expansion of the nebula. By combining Duncan's measures of the rate of angular expansion, $0.''21/\text{year}$, with the rate of radial expansion measured from his spectra, 1300 km/sec, Mayall estimated a distance of 1250 parsecs. The corresponding absolute magnitude, $M = m - 10.5$, is then -16.5 for the absolute photographic magnitude at maximum, if we suppose that -5 was its apparent magnitude at maximum and that space absorption (estimated from the colors of distant B stars and counts of distant galaxies in this region) amounted to 1 magnitude. Hence the Chinese guest star was comparable in brightness to the supernova in IC 4182 which attained the highest known luminosity, -16.6. Therefore it was quite definitely a Type I supernova. The discrepancy between the date found by Duncan, A.D. 1172 for the outburst and the observed outbreak in A.D. 1054 can be explained by supposing that the outward-moving material was accelerated or that there are small systematic errors in the earlier measures.

Now the integrated photographic magnitude of the Crab Nebula is 9.0, while that of the central star is 15.9. The amorphous mass, which contributes more than 80 per cent of the total light, therefore radiates 450 times as much visible light as the star. Approaching and receding filaments have about the same intensity; hence the nebula is transparent in photographic light. The star cannot be dimmed by the nebula, and the amorphous mass cannot shine by reflected light. The emission of the nebula may be excited by a high-temperature star.

Minkowski measured the energy distribution in the continuum. For wave lengths between $\lambda 4000$ and $\lambda 5000$, $T_{color} = 8400°K$, while for the $\lambda 5500$–$\lambda 6500$ interval, $T_{color} = 6700°K$. This decrease of color temperature toward the red is exactly the opposite from what would be produced by space reddening, and may be taken as direct observational evidence that the continuous spectrum is produced by free-free and bound-free transitions of electrons. Minkowski examined the mechanisms involved and showed that the color and intensity of the continuous spectrum can be explained if the electron temperature is near $50,000°K$. The amount of material in the line of sight is of the order of 5×10^{-5} gm/cm^2, and the opacity of the material due to bound-free transitions in the observable part of the spectrum is negligible. The opacity in the far ultraviolet is high. It is probably due to bound-free transitions (photo-ionizations) of highly ionized, heavy atoms, since hydrogen (which furthermore may not be abundant) is all ionized. Since the rate of emission in free-free transitions goes as Z^2 and in recaptures as Z^4, the heavy, highly ionized atoms can play an important role despite a low abundance.

In spite of the uncertainty in the electron temperature and the hydrogen abundance, Minkowski found that the values of the electron density and the mass of the nebulosity seem to be uniquely determined. The electron density appears to be of the order of 10^3/cm^3, i.e., comparable with the densities of planetaries. Since the outer radius of the nebula is 0.64 parsec, the total mass will be 15 times that of the sun as compared with about 0.1 for typical bright planetary nebulae.

Since there is evidence that the mass of the central star is of the order of that of the sun, the supernova before the outburst must have had a mass of about 16. The present spectrum of the central star is continuous without any absorption lines. The color cannot be earlier than that of a late B, and the spectrum does not extend into the ultraviolet. Nevertheless, the color of the star does not require it to be a low-temperature object. Certain Wolf-Rayet stars, which we know to be very hot objects, have low-color temperatures. Let us *assume* that all of the energy radiated by the nebula is derived from the star. The energy content of the nebula equals the sum of the kinetic energy of the electrons and ions plus the ionization energy (about 5×10^{47} ergs). If left to itself, the nebula would radiate this amount of energy away in 20 years! The absolute photographic magnitude of the nebula is -2.2, and its color is similar to that of the sun. This means an energy output of at least 1.3×10^{36} ergs/sec. Then, if T_e is the effective temperature of the star and R is its radius, the luminosity of the star is $L_s = 4\pi\sigma R^2 T_e^4$. If the star radiates as a black body, Minkowski finds that with $M_{ptg} = 4.8$, and $L_s > 1.3 \times 10^{36}$

$$T > 120,000°K \quad R < 0.042R_\circ \quad \rho > 19,000\rho_\circ$$

if the nebula is in a steady state. These represent extreme limits since the total amount of energy radiated in the continuum is much greater than that observed. Further, all the radiation emitted by the star may not be transformed by the nebula.

The star certainly does not radiate like a black body in the ordinary spectral region, and it is probably unsafe to use this assumption. Therefore, Minkowski considered the emission processes in the nebulae. With the electron temperature and density derived from the color and energy output of the nebula at λ4250, he derived a lower limit to the total luminosity of the nebula, taking into account the radiation over the entire spectral range. From these calculations he concluded that the central star is probably characterized by the following parameters:

$$L/L_\circ = 30,000 \quad T = 500,000°K \quad R/R_\circ = 0.020 \quad \rho = 180,000\rho_\circ$$

At a temperature of $500,000°K$, the black-body distribution of the star would have a maximum at a frequency of 3×10^{16} sec^{-1} which corresponds to 120 ev. Hence the C, O, N, or Ne atoms would be in the fifth and higher stages of ionization and incapable of emitting radiation in the visible frequencies. The absence of even He II λ4686 in the amorphous mass indicates a level of ionization and a temperature much greater than in a planetary nebula. If the level of ionization is greater than 125 volts, [Ne V] and [Fe VII] would not appear. If it was lower than 233 volts, it would not suffice to produce [Fe X]. Since neither [Ne V], [Fe VII], nor [Fe X] appear, it seems that a stellar temperature of $500,000°K$ would be appropriate.

The Crab Nebula is a strong source of radio-frequency emission (see Sec. 9 of Chapter 6). The dependence of the energy distribution on frequency is different from that of other radio sources. Greenstein and Minkowsky recently have shown that this radio emission cannot be explained as thermal emission like that from the quiet sun (see Ch. *9, p. 389). It must have a nonthermal origin, perhaps similar to that emitted by solar flares. They suggest that the temperature of the amorphous mass may be as high as two million degrees. Under such circumstances, the energy content of the nebula would be large. Furthermore, the degradation of only 1 or 2 per cent of the kinetic energy of expansion could supply the observed emission for a millenium. No central star is needed to supply energy under these conditions. It is possible that neither of the stars seen projected upon the nebula is associated with it.

The filaments, on the other hand, show a level of excitation comparable with that of an ordinary planetary nebula. They are in the outer parts of the nebula, shielded from the high-frequency radiation of the central star by the amorphous mass which degrades the quanta to lower frequencies by processes similar to those occurring in planetary nebulae (except that the role of hydrogen is here played by helium and heavier elements). A similar process is seen in the stratification of planetary nebulae wherein the high-excitation lines are produced close to the nucleus and the low-excitation lines [O II], etc., appear in the outermost ansae and envelopes.

From these observations, Minkowski was able to draw important conclusions concerning the physical nature of supernovae. The analysis suggests that before the outburst, supernovae are massive stars of low hydrogen content. A possible example of this type of star is v Sagittarii which has been studied by Greenstein and Merrill.

Minkowski suggests that the filaments are probably to be identified with the outer mass of the ejected envelope in which the relatively narrow [O I] $\lambda 6300$, $\lambda 6364$ lines appear, whereas the amorphous mass is to be correlated with the portion of the envelope that gives the principal spectrum. The difficulty with this proposal is that the emission features of the main spectrum are broader than the [O I] lines, yet the smaller volume of the amorphous mass would require a smaller expansion velocity than the filaments.

Chandrasekhar advanced the hypothesis that supernovae develop from stars that are too massive to contract to white dwarfs. If the mass exceeds the critical value, $\mathfrak{M} = 5.7/\mu^2$, where μ is the molecular weight of the material, the star cannot develop a degenerate core. Only by shedding the excess mass could the star evolve into a conventional white dwarf.

Evry Schatzman and recently L. Mestel have suggested radically different mechanisms whereby white dwarfs may evolve into supernovae, but this subject must be regarded as speculative at present. The strong radio-frequency radiation of the Crab Nebula may be an important clue to the true nature of supernovae.

An apparent example of a Type II object is provided by Tycho's nova of 1572 which flared up in Cassiopeia, rivaled Venus, and remained visible for eighteen months. Then it faded away to something less than a hundred-millionth of its maximum brightness. A radio source of moderate intensity, however, has been found exactly in the position of Tycho's supernova, although nothing unusual has been found by optical telescopes. If any nebula surrounds the Tycho object, it must be many times fainter than that surrounding the 1054 object.

The light-curve of Kepler's nova of 1604, which has been discussed by Baade, shows this object to have been a Type I supernova which reached an apparent magnitude of -2.2. A search for the remnant of the supernova led to the discovery of a small patch of emission nebulosity, which is undoubtedly a part of the masses ejected during the outburst. Since it lies behind heavy obscuration, its distance and luminosity cannot be determined. Minkowski found the spectrum of this nebulosity to be similar to that of the filaments of the Crab Nebula, and the evidence is strong that it is actually a remnant of Kepler's nova.

The low abundance of hydrogen in the Crab Nebula, as well as the indirect evidence from the synthetic spectra of Type II objects, fits into the suggestion that supernovae represent stars that have exhausted their hydrogen fuel and are readjusting to the white-dwarf status. This hypothesis brings up many questions that must go unanswered until another supernova appears in our own galaxy.

Although both novae and supernovae are recognized as transient catastrophic phenomena, the Wolf-Rayet and P Cygni stars appear to have quasi-permanent status. If the ejection hypothesis is correct, and N_e is about 10^{11}–10^{12} atoms/cm^3, an envelope such as that of V444 Cygni would represent a dissipation of ten solar masses in a million years; hence the Wolf-Rayet stage* would be a temporary phase in the life of certain massive stars.

The interpretation of stars which show the P Cygni-type spectrum may differ from object to object. P Cygni-type profiles are exhibited by supergiants such as α Cygni as well as by the envelopes of recognized dwarf stars. In many instances the material must certainly return to the star and remain in circulation in the atmosphere. The rapidly spinning Be stars and such objects as β Lyrae appear to shed material from their equatorial regions to form extended chromospheres.

In ordinary novae only the surface layers seem to be disturbed. Nova-like objects such as Z Andromedae, which may be associated with late-type stars, exhibit more complex phenomena. For example, why do the [O III] lines in BF Cygni show rapid, almost day-to-day

*It has been suggested that the Wolf-Rayet stars are massive stars that have exhausted their hydrogen fuel and are continuously ejecting their atmospheres into space. From this view the Wolf-Rayet process would represent an alternative evolutionary path whereby a massive star might eject its outer layers and ultimately settle down as a white dwarf.

fluctuations? Probably both velocity and absolute line intensity measures will be needed to give a complete kinematical and physical interpretation of the data.

PROBLEMS

1. In 48 Librae, Merrill and Sanford (*Mt. Wilson Contr.* 690, 1944) observed Balmer lines up to $n_{max} = 41$. Compute the electron density in the shell. (See Ch. *8, pp. 312, 317.)

2. Prove that in the three-state atom, discussed in Sec. 2, the number of transitions $1 \to 3 \to 2 \to 1$ is greater than the number $1 \to 2 \to 3 \to 1$ when the radiation field is dilute (Rosseland's theorem).

3. Consider a four-state atom wherein level 3 is metastable, level 2 is normal, but both have the same excitation potential. Let the dilution factor of $1 \to 2$ radiation be W', that of $1 \to 4$, $2 \to 4$, and $3 \to 4$ be W. Let $A_{42} = A_{43}$, $A_{21} = yA_{41}$, and $A_{42} = A_{41}$. Then prove

$$\frac{n_2}{n_3} = \frac{2W'y + W\rho_{24}}{y + W'y + W\rho_{24}}, \quad \rho_{ik} = e^{\frac{-h\nu_{ik}}{kT}}$$

4. A nova ejects a thin shell in which the density distribution is $\rho = \rho_0 \cos^2 \theta$, where θ is the angle between the axis of the nova and the vector drawn to a point in the shell. If the emission is proportional to ρ, the velocity of the shell is 300 km/sec, and if we can neglect the self-reversal, calculate the observed profile, assuming the angle between the axis of the nova and the line to the observer to be 45°.

REFERENCES

1. *Extended Envelopes*

STRUVE, O., and K. WURM. *Ap. J.* **88**, 84, 1938;
STRUVE, O. *P.N.A.S.* **26**, 117, 1940; *Proc. Amer. Phil. Soc.* **81**, 211, 1938; *Ap. J.* **95**, 134, 1942 (shell stars).
WURM, K. *Zeits. f. Ap.* **14**, 321, 1937.
CHANDRASEKHAR, S. *M.N.* **94**, 444, 1934; *Ap. J.* 101, **93**, 1945; *Rev. Mod. Phys.* **17**, 138, 1945; *M.N.* **94**, 522, 1934 (line profiles).
MIYAMOTO, S. *Publ. Astron. Soc. Japan*, **4**, 1, 28, 38, 1952; *Ap. J.* **113**, 181, 1951.
KOSIREV, N. A. *M.N.* **94**, 430, 1934.
ROTTENBERG, J. A. *M.N.* **112**, 125, 1952.
GAPOSCHKIN, S. *Ap. J.* **101**, 56, 1945.

For studies of Be stars see, e.g.:

UNDERHILL, A. *Ap. J.* **110**, 166, 1949 (shell spectrum of Pleione).
HYNEK, J. A. *Perkins Obs. Contr.* 14, 1940 (ϕ Persei).
BALDWIN, R. *Ap. J.* **92**, 82, 1940 (γ Cassiopeiae).
DODSON, H. *Ap. J.* **84**, 180, 1936.
GERASIMOVIC, B. P. *M.N.* **94**, 737, 1934.
STRUVE, O. *Ap. J.* **98**, 98, 1943;
HILTNER, W. A. *Ap. J.* **99**, 103, 1944 (48 Librae).
MERRILL, P. W., and R. F. SANFORD. *Ap. J.* **100**, 14, 1944 (48 Librae).

WELLMANN, P. *Zeits. f. Ap.* **30**, 71, 88, 96, 1952.
BURBRIDGE, G. R. and E. M. *Ap. J.* **117**, 407, 1953.

2. *Peculiar Stars*

MERRILL, P. W. *Ap. J.* **98**, 334, 1943; **99**, 15, 1944; **105**, 120, 1947; **107**, 317, 1948;
    111, 484, 1950.
SWINGS, P., and O. STRUVE. *Ap. J.* **91**, 546, 1940; **94**, 291, 1941; **95**, 152, 1942;
    96, 254, 1942; **97**, 194, 1943; **98**, 91, 1943; **99**, 205, 1944; **101**, 224, 1945.
BOWEN, I. S., and P. SWINGS. *Ap. J.* **105**, 92, 1947.
GAPOSCHKIN, C. H. P. *Ap. J.* **104**, 362, 1946.

3. *Wolf-Rayet Stars*

For a discussion of $BD + 38°$ 4010 see:
WILSON, O. C. *Ap. J.* **91**, 379, 1940; **95**, 402, 1942.
GAPOSCHKIN, S. *Ap. J.* **93**, 202, 1941.
KRON, G. E., and K. GORDON. *Ap. J.* **97**, 311, 1943; **111**, 454, 1950.
KOPAL, Z. *Ap. J.* **100**, 204, 1944.
KOPAL, Z., and M. S. SHAPLEY. *Ap. J.* **104**, 160, 1946.
RUSSELL, H. N. *Ap. J.* **100**, 213, 1944.
BEALS, C. S. *M.N.* **104**, 205, 1944.
MÜNCH, G. *Ap. J.* **112**, 266, 1950.

Spectra and Interpretation:
SWINGS, P. *Ap. J.* **95**, 112, 1942.
ALLER, L. H. *Ap. J.* **97**, 135, 1943.
BEALS, C. S. *J.R.A.S. Canada* **34**, 169, 1940; *Publ. Dom. Ap. Obs.* **4**, 273, 1930; **6**,
    95, 1934.
GAMOW, G. *Ap. J.* **98**, 498, 1943.
THOMAS, R. N. *Ap. J.* **109**, 500, 1949.
PETRIE, W. *Publ. Dom. Ap. Obs.* **7**, 383, 1947.
ZANSTRA, H., and J. WEENEN. *B.A.N.* **11**, 165, 1950.
WEENEN, J. *B.A.N.* **11**, 176, 1950.

The most recent discussion of absolute magnitudes of Wolf-Rayet and related
stars is by
ROMAN, NANCY. *Ap. J.* **114**, 492, 1951.

4. *Novae*

GAPOSCHKIN, S. and C. H. P. *Variable Stars.* Cambridge: Harvard University
    Press, 1938, chaps. vii, viii, and ix.
CAMPBELL, L. and L. JACCHIA. *Story of Variable Stars.* Cambridge: Harvard
    University Press, 1941, chap. vi.
Novae and White Dwarfs. Conference Papers, No. 901. Paris: Herman et Cie,
    1941.

See also various articles in *Vistas in Astronomy*, edited by Arthur Beer; London:
Pergamon Press, Ltd., 1954.

(a) Representative Novae:
McLAUGHLIN, D. B. N. Persei 1901. *Publ. Mich. Obs.* **9**, 13, 1949.
WYSE, A. B. N. Aquilae 1918. *Lick Publ.* **14**, No. 3, 1939.
PAYNE-GAPOSCHKIN, C., and D. H. MENZEL. N. Pictoris. *Harvard Circ.* 428, 1938.
SAYER, A. N. RS Ophiuchi. *Harvard Ann.* **105**, 21, 1948.
WHIPPLE, F., and C. PAYNE-GAPOSCHKIN. N. DQ Herculis. *Harvard Circ.*, 412,
    413, 414, 1936-37;
McLAUGHLIN, D. B. DQ Herculis. *Mich. Publ.* **6**, 107, 1937.

POPPER, D. M.   N. Lacertae. 1936.   *Ap. J.* **92**, 262, 1940.
WEAVER, H. F.   N. Puppis. 1942.   *Ap. J.* **99**, 280, 1944.

Spectrophotometric study of 5 novae:
GAPOSCHKIN, S. and C. H. P.   *Harvard Circ.* 445, 1942.

(b) Nebular Stage:
HUMASON, M. L.   *Publ. Astron. Soc. Pac.* **55**, 74, 1943.
SWINGS, P. and O. STRUVE.   *Ap. J.* **92**, 295, 1940.

For expanding shells see also:
BAADE, *Publ. Astron. Soc. Pac.* **54**, 244, 1942; *Mount Wilson Report*, 1942-43.

(c) Old Novae and Novae at Minimum:
HUMASON, M. L.   *Ap. J.* **88**, 228, 1938.
MCLAUGHLIN, D. B.   *Ap. J.*   **117**, 279, 1953.

(d) Light-Curves:
MCLAUGHLIN, D. B.   *Pop. Astron.* **47**, 410, 481, 538, 1939.
PARENAGO, P. R., and B. W. KUKARIN.   *Verein Freunde der Phys. Astr.*, Nishni-Novgorod, p. 251, 1934.

(e) Luminosities:
MCLAUGHLIN, D. B.   *Publ. Astron. Soc. Pac.* **57**, 69, 1945.

(f) Spectral Development:
MCLAUGHLIN, D. B.   *Ap. J.* **95**, 428, 1942; *Publ. Mich. Obs.* **8**, 149, 1943; *Ap. J.* **91**, 369, 1940.

(g) Analysis of Emission Line Profiles:
WILSON, O. C.   *Ap. J.* **80**, 259, 1934.
BEALS, C. S.   *Victoria Dom. Ap. Obs. Publs.* **6**, 9, 1934.

(h) Relative Dimensions of Shells:
TAI.   DQ Herculis.   *M.N.* **100**, 435, 1940.

(i) Theory of Nova Outbursts:
BIERMANN, L.   *Zeits. f. Ap.* **18**, 344, 1939.

(j) Interpretation of the Deep Minimum in the Light-Curve of DQ Herculis:
GROTRIAN, W.   *Zeits. f. Ap.* **13**, 215, 1937.

5. *Supernovae*

(a) Survey:
ZWICKY, F.   *Ap. J.* **88**, 529, 1938.

(b) Spectra:
MINKOWSKI, R.   *Ap. J.* **89**, 143, 1939.
HUMASON, M. L.   *Publ. Astron. Soc. Pac.* **48**, 110, 1936.
HUMASON, M. L., and R. MINKOWSKI.   *Publ. Astron. Soc. Pac.* **52**, 146, 1940.
POPPER, D. M.   *Publ. Astron. Soc. Pac.* **49**, 283, 1937.

(c) Spectral Synthesis:
WHIPPLE, F. L., and C. PAYNE-GAPOSCHKIN.   *Proc. Amer. Phil. Soc.* **84**, April, 1941.

(d) Crab Nebula:
MAYALL, N. U.   *Publ. Astron. Soc. Pac.* **49**, 104, 1937.
MAYALL, N. U., and J. Oort.   *Publ. Astron. Soc. Pac.* **54**, 95, 1942.
BAADE, W.   *Ap. J.* **96**, 188, 1942.
MINKOWSKI, R.   *Ap. J.* **96**, 199, 1942.
GREENSTEIN, J., and R. MINKOWSKI, *Ap. J.*   **118**, 1, 1953.

(e) Kepler's Nova:

BAADE, W. *Ap. J.* **97**, 119, 1943.

MINKOWSKI, R. *Ap. J.* **97**, 128, 1943.

See also "Symposium on Progress in Astrophysics," *Proc. Amer. Phil. Soc.* **81**, No. 2, 1939, for papers by F. L. Whipple, on physical characteristics and origin of the supernovae, p. 253, and D. Hoffleit on light-curves of supernovae, p. 265.

(d) Theory:

SCHATZMAN, E. *Ann. d. Ap.* **9**, 199, 1946.

MESTEL, L. *Observatory* **72**, 184, 1952.

Additional bibliography will be found in the references cited.

CHAPTER 5

THE PLANETARY NEBULAE

1. Introduction

The gaseous nebulae associated with the Type II population are the *planetary nebulae*—so called because they often appear as faint, greenish disks, not unlike the images of Uranus and Neptune. Their bright-line spectra consist not only of the familiar radiations of hydrogen and helium, but also of the forbidden lines of oxygen, neon, nitrogen, and other elements. There is also a continuous spectrum which is often fairly strong in nebulae of high surface brightness.

The energy radiated by the planetary nebulae is degraded from the far ultraviolet radiation of central stars that are usually so hot that but a small fraction of their energy is emitted in the visual region. Hence the nebulae often appear brighter than their central stars. The high-excitation object *NGC* 7027 provides an extreme example. Its central star remains invisible even on long exposures with special filters that block out the principal nebular lines. For a fixed bolometric magnitude, the hotter the central star, the fainter it will be photographically (since the far ultraviolet radiation is cut out by the earth's atmosphere), and the greater the magnitude difference between star and nebula. Hubble found that bright central stars tend to be associated either with small nebulae of high surface brightness or with large nebulae of low surface brightness.

The planetary nebulae are rare, remote, Type II objects. Their distances cannot be determined by conventional trigonometric or by statistical parallax methods. They move presumably in highly elliptical orbits, and methods based on galactic rotation appear inadmissible. For illustrative calculations we shall use distances published by L. Berman, who employed mean parallaxes based on proper motions, angular diameters, and radial velocities used in conjunction with the theory of galactic rotation. He also used apparent nebular and central star magnitudes, m_n and m_s, interpreted in connection with a physical theory of nebular luminosity. Berman supposed the diameters were not affected by galactic absorption, and that large faint objects and condensed bright ones were statistically comparable in diameter and absolute magnitude.

The spatial distribution of the planetaries appears to be that of an extreme Type II population similar to the RR Lyrae stars. One is found in a globular cluster, and the central bulge of our galaxy, which is a Type II population, contains a very large number. Many must be hidden behind obscuring clouds.

Large, and apparently nearby, objects appear in all longitudes and in high galactic latitudes, whereas the fainter, condensed objects show a strong concentration to the galactic center, as we would expect if all types of planetaries were evenly mixed throughout the galaxy with a distribution similar to that of the RR Lyrae stars. The shapes of the nebulae do not appear to be correlated with apparent diameter if allowance is made for the effects of observational selection. Minkowski's survey has added 212 new planetaries bringing the total to 371. Some of them appear to be as remote as the galactic center and in this direction the mean apparent diameter is about 6 seconds of arc. Many can be observed only in the light of Hα, since reddening is so great as to extinguish lines in the blue and violet. Karl Henize has extended the survey to include the southern hemisphere.

To summarize, the planetaries belong to the Type II population and are strongly concentrated toward the galactic center. Their sizes and surface brightnesses show a considerable range—from small objects indistinguishable from stars (*IC* 4997) to giant ringlike structures like *NGC* 7293 in Aquarius (Fig. 1). A typical bright planetary has a radius of about ten or twenty thousand astronomical units, and a mass probably less than a fifth that of the sun. The densities of typical planetaries probably fall between those of diffuse galactic nebulae on the one hand and the expanding shells around novae in the "early nebular" stage. The densities range from 10^{+2} ions/cm^3 or less for the fainter objects to 10^3–10^4 ions/cm^3 for the brighter ones. The tenuity of the gases is comparable to that of a few tablespoonfuls of air expanded to the size of Pike's Peak.

2. Structure and Spectra

The best-known example of the planetary nebulae is the celebrated Ring Nebula in Lyra, *NGC* 6720. Even telescopes of moderate aperture show this object to have an extremely complex structure. Other objects such as *NGC* 3242 or *NGC* 2392 have double rings. The probable shell-like character of many of the "ring" planetaries was recognized a century ago. Concerning *NGC* 3587, the "Owl Nebula," Sir John Herschel wrote in 1849,* "We might be induced to conclude its real constitution to be either that of a hollow spherical shell or a flat disk,

*The Outlines of Astronomy, p. 508.

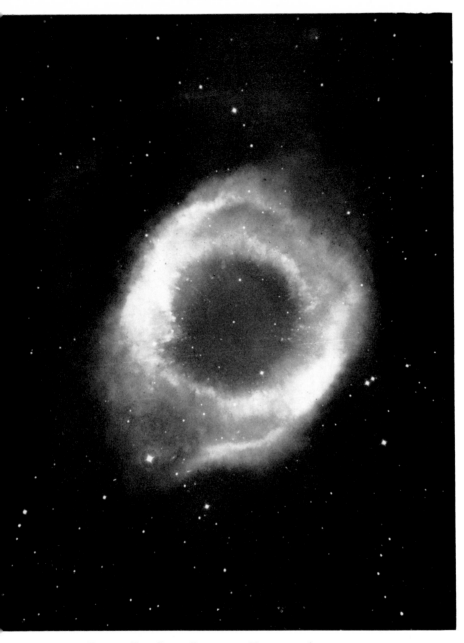

Fig. 1.—The Great Planetary Nebula in Aquarius

The dimensions are approximately 12′ × 15′. Intrinsically, it is probably one of the largest planetaries. (Photographed by Walter Baade at the Mount Wilson Observatory.)

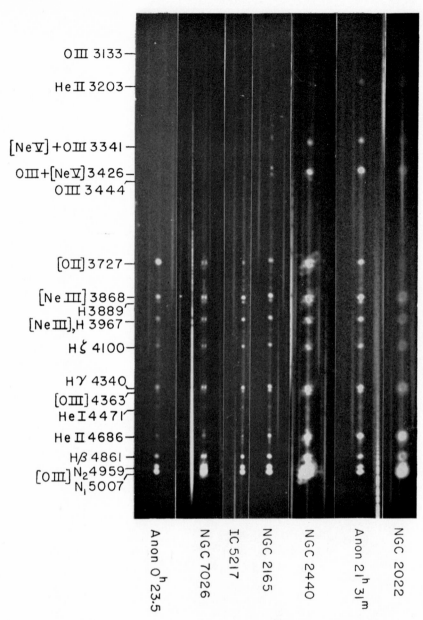

FIG. 2.—SLITLESS SPECTRA OF SOME PLANETARY NEBULAE OF MODERATE TO HIGH
EXCITATION

The nebulae are arranged in order of decreasing excitation from *NGC* 2022 and
Anon 21ʰ31ᵐ, where [Ne V] and He II are prominent, to Anon 0ʰ23ᵐ5 where He II is
weak. Notice the great strength of He II λ4686 and the absence of [O II] λ3727 in
NGC 2022, and the binuclear structure of *NFC* 2440 and *NGC* 7026. (Photographed
at the Lick Observatory with the Crossley reflector and quartz slitless spectrograph.)

presented to us, by a highly improbable coincidence, in a plane precisely perpendicular to the visual ray."

The extreme complexities and bizarre irregularities of the planetary nebulae are well exhibited in the beautiful direct photographs secured by Minkowski at Palomar. The ring "structures" are far from simple and most of them cannot be regarded as thin uniform shells in even the first approximation. Truly amorphous forms appear to be rare. Fine wisps and condensations are frequent, although some objects such as the Owl Nebula have a perfectly smooth structure, even under conditions of the very best seeing. The fine structure must have a dimension less than $0\rlap{.}''5$. Many planetaries are stellar in appearance, e.g., IC 4634. Conventional blue and yellow direct photographs are not too useful, since they cover a long wave-length range and record images corresponding to different spectral lines. The use of plate-filter combinations that isolate a narrow wave-length range often enable photographs to be taken in nearly monochromatic radiation; but if we wish to separate emissions that are close together in the spectrum, e.g., $H\alpha$ and the [N II] lines, it is necessary to employ a slitless spectrograph. An image of the nebula in each of its monochromatic emissions is thereby recorded. (See Fig. 2.) Observations of this type were first obtained at the Lick Observatory and showed that the [O II] radiation tended to concentrate in outlying ansae and condensations and that the nebular image of this line was always largest. On the other hand, the He II $\lambda4686$ radiation appeared only in the central regions, while the $\lambda3426$ image of [Ne V] was smallest of all. Furthermore, certain nebular lines vary together in intensity; i.e., their relative intensities seem to be about the same. Examples are $\lambda4959$ and $\lambda5007$ of [O III], $\lambda6548$ and $\lambda6584$ of [N II], $\lambda3869$ and $\lambda3967$ of [Ne III], the [O II] $\lambda3727$ pair, and $\lambda3426$, and $\lambda3346$ of [Ne V]. Forbidden lines of either [O III], [O II], or [N II] are usually the strongest, followed by the hydrogen and helium lines. Then follow weaker forbidden lines of other light elements and the metals and, occasionally, permitted lines of oxygen and carbon. Bowen and Wyse at Lick Observatory made the most complete study of nebular spectra with the aid of Bowen's *image slicer*.* Their first report on *NGC* 7027, 7662, and 6572 is supplemented by an account of the spectra of seven additional objects observed by Wyse. He lists the following ions: H I, He I, He II, C II, C III, C IV, N I, N II, N III, N V(?), O I, O II, O III, F II(?), F IV, Ne III, Ne V, Mg I(?), Si II, Si III(?), S II, S III, Cl III, Cl IV, A III, A IV,

---

*This is an optical device in which the image of a source larger than the slit of the spectrograph is reflected to a series of narrow mirrors mounted in such a way that the light is reflected through the slit so that a series of spectra of successive strips of the source are formed side by side. See *Ap. J.* **88**, 113, 1938.

A V, K IV, K V(?), K VI, Ca V, Fe II, Fe III, Fe VI, Ni VIII(?). Further analyses of atomic spectra in high stages of ionization should provide further identifications.

The first quantitative information on the energy distribution within the monochromatic nebular images was obtained by Berman from the laborious procedure of making successive tracings across monochromatic images and fitting the strips together to get isophotal contours of the spectral lines. He observed *NGC* 7009, 6543, 6572, and 6826, with the quartz slitless spectrograph on the Crossley Reflector at the Lick Observatory. Fig. 3 shows the isophotal contours of [O II] λ3727 in *NGC* 6720 measured on more recent plates taken with the same instrument. Notice the concentration of intensity at opposite ends of the minor axis. Unfortunately, the evidence of the intricate network of filaments is lost in the process of reduction which tends to smooth out the irregularities.

Fɪɢ. 3.—Iꜱᴏᴘʜᴏᴛᴀʟ Cᴏɴ-
ᴛᴏᴜʀꜱ ᴏꜰ λ3727 [O II] ɪɴ
ᴛʜᴇ Rɪɴɢ Nᴇʙᴜʟᴀ ɪɴ
Lʏʀᴀ *NGC* 6720

Contours are drawn for steps of 0.10 in log *I*. Because of the small scale of the original plate, the irregularities are smoothed over so that only the large-scale features of the intensity distribution are shown. Compare with Fig. 10. (From a plate taken at Lick Observatory.)

Isophotic contours
of NGC 6720
λ3727 [OɪɪI]

If the nebula is large, the effect of overlapping images on the slitless spectrograms is often troublesome. On the other hand, with small nebulae, a single plate may give a rather complete record of the energy distribution in the monochromatic images. To observe the weaker lines and to separate those that fall close together, slit spectrograms are necessary.

Thornton Page has obtained spectra of a number of planetary nebulae with a wide slit to study the continuous energy distribution and the relative intensities of the stronger lines. His method eliminates some of the worst disadvantages of the slitless spectrograph.

Recently, Olin Wilson has secured slitless spectra of the brighter planetaries with the coudé spectrograph at the 100-inch reflector of the Mount Wilson Observatory. In his method the spectrograph slit is removed so that there is recorded upon the plate not the usual slit spectrogram, but a series of monochromatic images, each a picture of the nebula in the light of one of its characteristic radiations. With the high dispersion of the coudé there is usually little overlapping of images. The large-scale and excellent quality of his plates reveal many structural details missed in previous investigations with smaller telescopes. The lack of uniformity in the ring structures is clearly shown, and the small diffuse-appearing nebula *NGC* 6572 is resolved as a ring surrounded by an amorphous structure. Fig. 4 shows the contours of an amorphous nebula.

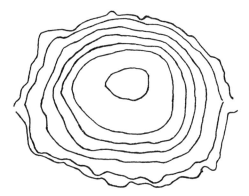

Fig. 4.— Isophotal Contour of λ4959 [O III] in the Amorphous Nebula
NGC 6210

Steps of 0.3 in log I are represented except for the central contour, which differs by 0.15 from the next contour. Notice the steep sides of the nebular image. The slitless spectrogram was obtained by Olin Wilson and traced with the Hiltner-Williams isophotometer.

Isophotic contours may be derived either from direct photographs or slitless spectrograms. If the nebula has large internal motions, the the slitless images are to a small extent blurred by the radial motion of the emitting gases. This circumstance is not entirely disadvantageous because, by comparing a direct and slitless image, the radial velocities of fine condensations sometimes may be found. This technique was used by Wilson and Minkowski to study the internal motions in *NGC* 2392.

Various devices may be used to get isophotic contours. The Hiltner-Williams isophotometer* has been successfully employed to get line contours in nebulae as complex as *NGC* 2392.

The complete quantitative description of the monochromatic emissions involves not only the measurement of the contours but also the

*Publ. Mich. Obs. **8**, 45, 103, 1940.

determination of the surface brightness at some point in the contour or its average over the image in terms of appropriate units, e.g., ergs/cm^2/sec. Usually the relative intensities of the lines are measured on slit spectrograms taken at some point in the nebula, while the total amount of energy from the brightest images (usually the images of the green nebular lines) may be established by photoelectric photometry. Minkowski and the writer have made detailed spectrophotometric studies of typical planetary nebulae, while Liller has measured a number of the brighter planetaries by photoelectric methods. For a number of representative objects it will be possible to give fairly precise measures of the intensities of the nebular radiations. Fig. 7 shows the spectrum and tracing of the bright nebula, *NGC* 7027.

Before further discussion of the observational material, it will be profitable to review some of the physical processes occurring within the nebula and to describe how estimates of temperatures and densities have been made.

3. The Excitation of the Hydrogen Lines

In our analysis of the physical state of a planetary nebula, we shall consider first of all the excitation of the hydrogen lines. As a first approximation we take a thin shell surrounding a hot star which is presumed to radiate as a black body at temperature T_1. For the moment we suppose the shell to be composed of pure hydrogen. Later we shall see the effects of "impurities" in the form of oxygen, neon, etc.

The intensity of the radiation reaching the inner surface of the shell will be

$$I_\nu = W_0 \frac{2h\nu^3}{c^2} \frac{1}{e^{h\nu/kT_1} - 1} \tag{1}$$

where

$$W_0 = \frac{R_0^2}{4r^2} \tag{2}$$

is the geometrical dilution factor. It is the fraction of the total surface of the sky that is filled by the star as seen from a point in the nebula. Numerically, W_0 is of the order of 10^{-15}. Here R_0 denotes the radius of the star, r that of the shell.

Since the star is hot (often 50,000°K or more), most of its energy will be radiated in the far ultraviolet. Hence the nebula is exposed to radiation which corresponds in frequency distribution to a high temperature, but in energy density to a low one. Essentially all of the neutral hydrogen atoms in the nebula reside in their lowest level. Excitations by radiation are cut down by the factor $1/W$ as compared with thermal equilibrium. On the other hand, atoms cascade downward from excited levels at a rate determined only by the Einstein A values. Therefore virtually all ionizations must take place from the ground level as a consequence of absorption of quanta beyond the Lyman limit. The recaptures, however, may take place on any of the excited levels, as well as on the ground level. See Fig. 5. If the free electron is recaptured in the ground level, an ultraviolet quantum similar to the original is reborn, and this quantum may ionize yet another hydrogen atom. If it is recaptured on the second level, a quantum will be emitted in the Balmer continuum, while a recapture on the third level will give a quantum of the Paschen continuum. If an atom jumps from the third to the second level, it will emit an Hα quantum. This process of photoelectric ejection of electrons plus subsequent recapture and cascade is called the *primary mechanism* of excitation. The lines of neutral and ionized helium are also produced by this primary mechanism.

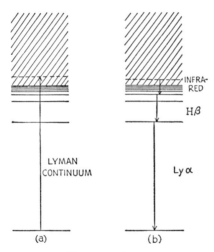

FIG. 5.—THE ORIGIN OF THE HYDROGEN LINES IN THE PLANETARY NEBULAE

(a) A hydrogen atom in the ground level is photo-ionized by a quantum in the Lyman continuum. (b) In the example depicted, the electron is recaptured in the fourth level with the emission of a quantum in the Brackett continuum. Then it cascades to the second level with the emission of Hβ and finally to the ground level with the emission of Lyman α. Hβ and the Brackett quantum escape from the nebula; Lyman α is scattered from atom to atom. (Courtesy, Goldberg and Aller, *Atoms, Stars, and Nebulae*, Cambridge: Harvard University Press, 1943.)

We shall refer to all quanta beyond the Lyman limit as *ultraviolet quanta*. Following Zanstra we now ask what happens when this stellar ultraviolet radiation is completely absorbed in the nebula. If an electron is recaptured on the second level, the resulting quantum of the Balmer continuum will simply escape from the nebula. Then the atom will return to the ground level with the emission of Lyman α (Lyα) which can be absorbed and re-emitted over and over again, i.e., simply scattered. If recapture occurs on the third level, the atom may cascade to the second level (emitting Hα), or it may jump directly to the ground level with the emission of Lyβ. When Lyβ is reabsorbed, there is a finite probability that the atom will emit Hα + Lyα. In general, quanta corresponding to subordinate lines cannot be reabsorbed in the nebula and must escape directly. The degradation of energy is irreversible; i.e., a cycle such as Lyγ → Hβ + Lyα is not compensated for by the reverse process. Similarly, Lyδ will be broken into Lyα + Hγ, Lyα + Hβ + Brα, etc. Zanstra and Menzel independently arrived at the important result that *in a thick nebula, every quantum of ultraviolet energy will be ultimately broken down into a Lyα quantum plus a quantum of the Balmer series or continuum.* Other quanta of the Paschen or Brackett series will also be produced, but these are usually not observed.

For a nebula sufficiently thick to absorb all the ultraviolet quanta, we can write that the number of ultraviolet quanta equals the number of quanta of the Balmer series plus the number of quanta in the Balmer continuum, or in Zanstra's notation,

$$N_{\mathrm{ul}} = \mathrm{Bac} + \mathrm{Ba} \tag{3}$$

This relationship forms the basis of an important method for getting the temperature of the central star (cf. Sec. 12).

The state of ionization of hydrogen in a nebula may be calculated with the aid of the theory developed by Strömgren for the ionization of the interstellar medium in the neighborhood of an O or B star (see Sec. 5 of Ch. 6). The theory may be modified to take the density variations in the nebula into account. Near the center of a thick nebula the hydrogen is essentially all ionized and remains so until numbers of neutral atoms begin to appear. The level of ionization drops rapidly to zero, the emission per unit volume declines abruptly, and the luminous nebulosity has a sharp edge. Long-exposure photographs of some planetary nebulae show irregular faint outer rings which presumably define the outer edge of the actual material. The main luminous portion of the nebula is the zone of ionized hydrogen. The filamentary structure of the nebula permits some radiation to leak through and produce a small amount of ionization (and recombination) right to the edge of the nebula!

In the brighter, more compact nebulae what we probably see is the hydrogen-ionization zone; in those of low surface brightness the luminous portion may often encompass the entire nebula itself. Detailed application of the Strömgren ionization theory has been made to *IC* 418, whose edge is less steep than the Strömgren theory would require—possibly the effect of filamentary structure.

4. The Balmer Decrement

If the considerations of the preceding section are sound, it should be possible to calculate, for a given electron temperature and density, the rate at which electrons are recaptured by hydrogen ions in various excited levels, and the rate at which the atoms cascade to lower-energy levels. If line radiation from the central star or from the degradation of Lyman line and continuum quanta is present in a known amount, its effect on populating the higher levels can be evaluated. In other words, for a specified set of physical conditions and a steady state, it is possible to calculate the relative populations of all the excited levels. Since the transition probabilities are known, the relative intensities of the hydrogen lines—in particular the Balmer lines—can be found and compared with observations.

The detailed calculations, based on the fact that a steady state exists, and that all ionizations occur from the ground level, involve formulae of the type developed in Chapter *5.* The computations are straightforward but lengthy.

Menzel and Baker first calculated the Balmer decrements for a nebula with a nuclear star that radiates no energy in the Lyman lines. Their model A corresponds to an optically thin nebula in which all the Lyman line radiation produced by photo-ionization and recombination escapes without further absorption. B represents an optically thick nebula from which no Lyman radiation save Lyα escapes. Menzel and his colleagues later considered a model C, an optically thin nebula (similar to A) but with a central star which radiates as a black body in the Lyman lines. The addition of the stellar line radiation markedly steepens the decrement. C, however, corresponds to a nebula of very low surface brightness.

Comparison of theory with an extensive series of observations obtained with the Crossley Reflector at the Lick Observatory in 1943-45 shows that after the observed decrements have been corrected for the effects of space absorption (Ch. 6) the agreement is best with B, the optically thick nebula in which every quantum of ultraviolet energy is ultimately degraded into a Balmer quantum and a Lyman α quantum which escapes from the nebula. The accompanying table tells the story. Successive columns give the wave lengths of the Balmer lines, the mean intensity from 41 nebulae (corrected for space absorption

*All references to chapters in the author's *Astrophysics—The Atmospheres of the Sun and Stars* (New York: The Ronald Press Co., 1953) will be designated in this volume by * before the chapter number.

and referred to Hβ as 10), and the theoretical values A, B, and C, referred to an electron temperature of 10,000°K. The Balmer decrement will be nearly the same at higher electron temperatures.

THE BALMER DECREMENT

λ	Observed Intensity	Theoretical Intensity		
		A	B	C
4861	10.0	10.0	10.0	10.0
4340	5.58	5.76	5.1	3.47
4101	3.13	3.74	3.1	1.62
3969	2.03	2.55	2.06	0.89
3889	1.42	1.82	1.43	0.55
3835	0.98	1.36	1.05	0.36
3797	0.75	1.05	0.79	0.25
3770	0.54	0.81	0.59	0.18
3750	0.43	0.65	0.46	0.14

This result is in accordance with expectations since all the nebulae are optically thick, as their surface brightnesses would otherwise be too low to have permitted their observation.

A more accurate theoretical treatment of the Balmer decrement would require a solution of the equation of radiative transfer. Henyey has given a formal solution for the static nebula, and his work should be extended to take account of processes involving the continuum and the expansion of the nebulae. Boundary conditions become complicated for an expanding symmetrical shell and, in an actual nebula, are likely to be so intricate as to make any exact calculation impossible.

5. The Electron Density

The continuous emission at the head of the Balmer series arises from the direct capture of electrons in the second level. If we know the volume of the emitting gases and have some idea of the electron temperature, we can find the electron density from the intensity of this Balmer recombination spectrum.

From eqn. (106) of Chapter ⋆5 we have that the emission in ergs/cm³/sec in a frequency interval $d\nu$ at a frequency ν in the Balmer continuum is given by

$$E_{\kappa 2}\, d\nu = 2.70 \times 10^{-33}\, \frac{N_i N_\epsilon}{T_\epsilon^{3/2}}\, g e^{-h(\nu - \nu_2)/kT_\epsilon}\, d\nu \qquad (4)$$

where T_ϵ is the electron temperature, ν_2 is the frequency of the Balmer limit, N_i is the density of hydrogen ions, and N_ϵ is the electron density.

In practice it is convenient to measure the intensity in a finite interval (e.g., 20A of the continuum). If we use eqn. (105) of Chapter *5, adopt $g = 0.876$, and note that $\Delta \nu = 2.254 \times 10^{11} \, \Delta\lambda$, at the Balmer limit, we find for a 20A interval at the beginning of the continuum

$$E_{\kappa 2} \, \Delta\nu = 10.66 \times 10^{-21} \frac{N_i N_\epsilon}{T_\epsilon^{3/2}} \tag{5}$$

The total emission of a homogeneous shell of thickness d and outer radius A will be

$$L_0 = \frac{4\pi}{3} E_{\kappa 2} (3A^2 d - 3Ad^2 + d^3) \, \Delta\nu \tag{6}$$

Since the surface through which this energy must flow is $4\pi A^2$, the average surface brightness in ergs/cm^2/sec per 20A in the recombination continuum at the Balmer limit is

$$S_n = \frac{L_0}{4\pi A^2} = 3.55 \times 10^{-21} N_i N_\epsilon D T_\epsilon^{-3/2} \tag{7}$$

where

$$D = 3d\left(1 - \frac{d}{A} + \frac{d^2}{3A^2}\right) \tag{8}$$

If we assume the proportions of helium and other elements to be negligible in comparison, $N_i = N_\epsilon$, and from equation (7) we find

$$N_\epsilon = 1.68 \times 10^{10} S_n^{1/2} D^{-1/2} T_\epsilon^{3/4} \tag{9}$$

An estimate of D may be made if we know the angular diameter of the nebula, the thickness of the shell, and the distance. Estimates of d and A may be taken from the descriptions published long ago by H. D. Curtis. For illustrative calculations we shall adopt the distances estimated by Berman.

The electron temperature is uncertain. It appears to range from about 8000°K to perhaps more than 20,000°K in the various objects studied. Assignment of precise values for each nebula must await the accumulation of more accurate observational data on the line and continuous spectra. For the purposes of the illustrative calculation we shall take $T_\epsilon = 10{,}000°$K; hence the actual values of N_ϵ will be $(T_\epsilon/10{,}000)^{3/4}$ times the tabulated values.

The intensity of the 20A interval of the Balmer continuum may be compared with emission lines in the spectrum by methods of photographic photometry. It is necessary to allow for, and subtract off, the contribution of the underlying continuum which includes not only the Paschen and Brackett continua, but also a continuum due to other processes as well. Although the relative intensities of the emission lines are known, this information is of little value until the mean surface brightness in c.g.s. units of at least one of the lines is known.

If a nebula emits or reflects a continuous spectrum of about the same color as the sun, its surface brightness, expressed in magnitudes per square minutes of arc, may be easily converted into ergs/cm^2/sec (see Sec. 1 of Ch. *5). The planetaries, however, radiate emission-line spectra, and photographic magnitudes determined in the usual way are not easy to interpret unless very detailed information is available on the plate sensitivity and filter plus telescope transmission.

The best work on the photometry of the planetaries has been done photoelectrically, and we shall employ here some of the results obtained by W. Liller. He used narrow band-pass interference filters, two transmitting in regions near $\lambda5500$ and $\lambda4200$, where most planetaries have no strong lines, and one including the green nebular lines which are the strongest visible radiations in most planetaries. With these three-color observations he was able to separate the line contribution from that of the nebular continuum plus central star. For comparison stars he used $G2$ dwarfs whose magnitudes and colors were carefully compared with primary standards of accurately known magnitudes. Liller's measures give essentially the surface brightness of the green nebular lines, and since these have been measured with respect to other lines, including Hβ, the surface brightness in the Balmer continuum can be expressed at once in terms of ergs/cm^2/sec.

Very recently, the intensities of the green [O III] and Hβ lines in a number of planetaries have been measured photoelectrically by MacRae and Stock at Case Institute and by Liller and the writer. The surface brightnesses measured in this way are in excellent agreement with those found by the filter method. The intensity ratios [O III]/Hβ found by the two teams are in excellent agreement with one another

TABLE 1

THE ELECTRON DENSITIES OF SOME PLANETARY NEBULAE

Nebula	A''	$\dfrac{d}{A}$	r (parsecs)	$D \times 10^{-17}$ (cm)	$\log \dfrac{S_n}{S_\beta}$	$\log S_\beta$	$\log S_n$	N_ϵ
NGC 3242	11″	0.2	1640	1.33	−1.00	−1.16	−2.16	3700
IC 4593	5″	1.0	2000	1.50	−1.14	−1.29	−2.43	2700
NGC 6543	10″	0.2	1080	0.785	−1.07	−0.87	−1.94	6400
NGC 6572	7″	1.0	1230	1.29	−1.17	−0.76	−1.93	5100
NGC 6818	9″	0.3	2380	2.1	−1.00	−1.55	−2.55	2000
NGC 6826	13″	1.0	1050	2.04	−1.12	−1.53	−2.65	1800
NGC 7009	9″	0.3	930	0.825	−1.06	−0.97	−2.03	5750
NGC 7027	5″	1.0	2130	1.59	−1.57	−0.82	−2.39	2700
NGC 7662	8″	0.2	1200	0.70	−1.21	−1.04	−2.25	4900

and confirm the photographic measures made some years ago by the writer.

Table 1 gives the details of the calculation of the electron densities. The second column gives the mean angular radius in seconds of arc. The third column gives the estimated thickness of the shell for those objects which can be even roughly approximated as shell objects. The distance r in parsecs is from the work of Berman. D is then calculated from the data of columns 2, 3, and 4. The sixth column gives the logarithm of the ratio of the intensity of the 20A stretch of the continuum at the Balmer limit, S_n, to the intensity of Hβ, S_β. The surface brightness in Hβ is taken from the data of Liller, who measured the surface brightnesses of the green nebular lines and adopted $S(\text{H}\beta)/S(N_1 + N_2)$ from the results of photographic photometry. The electron density N_ϵ is given in the last column for $T_\epsilon = 10,000°\text{K}$. If S_β and T_ϵ have been estimated too small, the electron density will be increased.

For typical bright planetaries the electron densities fall between 1000 and 6000 electrons/cm^3.

Medium-bright planetaries, such as NGC 40 or NGC 2022, appear to have densities of the order of 10^2–10^3 electrons/cm^3, while in the stellar planetary IC 4997, N_ϵ apparently approaches 10^5. The electron densities in the shells of novae and Wolf-Rayet stars seem to be much higher.

It is also possible to estimate N_ϵ from the surface brightness of Hβ. The number of hydrogen atoms in any level n may be expressed in terms of N_i and N_ϵ by the means of the dissociation formula for hydrogen [cf. eqn. (26) of Ch. ★4)], viz.,

$$N_n = b_n N_i N_\epsilon \frac{h^3}{(2\pi m k T_\epsilon)^{3/2}} n^2 e^{X_n} \tag{10}$$

where [see eqn. (102) of Ch. ★5]

$$X_n = \frac{hRZ^2}{n^2 k T_\epsilon} = \frac{1.57 \times 10^5}{n^2 T_\epsilon} \tag{11}$$

and b_n is a factor that expresses the deviation from thermodynamic equilibrium for the temperature T_ϵ. In strict thermal equilibrium, $b_n = 1$. The amount of energy emitted per cm^3 per sec in downward transitions from level n to level n' is

$$E_{nn'} = N_n A_{nn'} h\nu_{nn'} \tag{12}$$

where N_n is given by eqn. (10), $A_{nn'}$ is computed from eqns. (76) and (83) of Chapter ★5, and $\nu_{nn'}$ is given by eqn. (92) of Chapter ★5.

If we combine these expressions and make use of eqn. (104) of Chapter ★5, we can write

$$E_{nn'} = N_i N_\epsilon \frac{KZ^4}{T_\epsilon^{3/2}} b_n \frac{g}{n'^3} \frac{2hRZ^2}{n^3} e^{X_n} \qquad (13)$$

Now $n = 4$, $n' = 2$, $g = 0.822$ for Hβ. Putting in numerical values, we find

$$S_{H\beta} = 7.37 \times 10^{-20} \frac{N_i N_\epsilon}{T_\epsilon^{3/2}} b_4 De^{X_n} \qquad (14)$$

If T_ϵ can be estimated and b_4 found from theory or observation, N_ϵ can be obtained from $S_{H\beta}$. Similar formulae may be derived for other hydrogen lines. Measures of the surface brightness in Hα in diffuse nebulae, for example, provide estimates of the densities of these objects.

Hydrogen is the most abundant element in the nebulae. Hence $N_i = N_\epsilon$ is essentially the density of hydrogen ions/cm^3. If we know the size of the nebula in km, we can compute the mass of the luminous portion. The resultant masses turn out to be less than a tenth the mass of the sun. In many objects the outer, neutral envelope must have a comparable mass, so that an estimate of about a fifth of the solar mass for the entire nebula is probably of the right order of magnitude.

The metastability of the 2s level in hydrogen and the filamentary structure of the nebulae impose two limitations on the foregoing theory. Because of its long lifetime, atoms tend to accumulate in the 2s level, and, in extended objects such as the diffuse Orion Nebula, the population is great enough for absorptions from this level to play a significant role. Greenstein found the energy distribution in the continuous spectrum of the Orion Nebula to correspond to a color temperature of 12,000°K at the Balmer limit. If this energy distribution be interpreted as arising entirely from ions and electrons, T_ϵ would be 65,000°K. The relative intensities of the [O III] lines, however, suggest an electron temperature of about 10,000°K. The coloring effect by small particles will not account for the observed energy distribution. Greenstein showed that we could bring the two results into harmony if we assume that the optical thickness in the Balmer continuum is appreciable. When absorptions from the second level become prominent, the energy distribution is no longer given by eqn. (106) of Chapter ★5, but tends to approach the black-body distribution appropriate to the electron temperature. Taking into account the long lifetime of the 2s level (8.23 sec^{-1}), Greenstein finds the population to follow, very nearly, Boltzmann's formula and $N(2s)$ is of the order of $10^{-4}N_0$ (N_0 = number of neutral atoms in ground level). Outside the region of ionization,

N_0 is about 10^3, and, since $\alpha_r \sim 10^{-17}$/atom at the Balmer limit, a distance of 10^{18} cm or a third of a parsec is required to produce an optical thickness of about one. Since the bright part of the nebula has a radius of about 0.5 pc, we need a region of neutral hydrogen of the same size and density as the observed luminous part to produce appreciable self-reversal. Some years ago, O. C. Wilson found the sharp $\lambda 3889$ He I line superposed upon the spectra of several stars shining through part of the nebula. Thus he obtained direct observational evidence for an appreciable population in highly excited metastable levels.

Greenstein estimated the mass of the diffuse Orion Nebula to be about ten times that of the sun.

In planetary nebulae, the effect of the metastability of the 2^2S level is less pronounced. Suppose that a nebula such as NGC 3242 is surrounded by a shell of neutral material of the same density and thickness as the luminous portion. Now NGC 3242 has a radius of about 5×10^{17} cm and $N_i = 3 \times 10^3$ ions/cm^3, which we assume equal to the density of neutral atoms in outer portion. With $\alpha_r = 10^{-17}$ we find an optical depth of 0.07 if the electron temperature is 10,000°K.

We have treated the planetary nebulae as though they were shells of constant density. The filamentary character of objects such as NGC 6720, or NGC 7293, show that this approximation is not always tenable. Electron densities computed on the assumption of a uniform density apply neither to the filaments, nor to the over-all averages of such nebula. Let us compare a homogeneous shell with one of the same over-all dimensions and mass but which has all of the material concentrated in filaments that occupy a fifth of the volume. The density in the filaments will be five times as great as the density in the homogeneous nebula and, since the recombination goes as $N_i N_e$ or N_e^2, the emission will be 25 times as great. Since, however, only a fifth of the total volume is occupied by the radiating material, the total luminosity of the filamentary shell is five times larger than that of the homogeneous shell. The electron density derived on the assumption that the shell was uniform would be $\sqrt{5}$ times larger than the true density averaged over the shell. Until the actual volumes occupied by the filaments are known, our estimates of electron densities must remain as orders of magnitude. The scale of the fine structure varies from nebula to nebula and some, such as the Owl Nebula, appear smooth even under conditions of best seeing and highest resolution.

6. Collisional Excitation of the Forbidden Lines

The unusual appearance of the spectra of gaseous nebulae arises from the prominence of the forbidden lines, particularly those of oxygen, nitrogen, and neon in various stages of ionization. I. S. Bowen, who identified the well-known green nebular lines λ5007, λ4959 with [O III] suggested that electrons collide with ions in their ground term and excite them to nearby metastable levels a few volts above the ground level. The atom can return to the ground term either by giving up its energy to a passing electron in a superelastic collision, or by the emission of a forbidden line. In the nebulae, conditions are such that the production of forbidden lines is favored over the production of permitted lines.

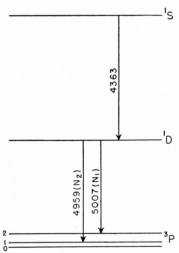

FIG. 6.—TRANSITION SCHEME FOR THE FORBIDDEN LINES OF O III

The $^1D_2$ and $^1S_0$ levels are excited by inelastic collisions with electrons. The forbidden lines are emitted as the ions return to lower levels by radiative transitions.

The collisional excitation of metastable levels proceeds at the same rate as in thermodynamic equilibrium at the same temperature T_e and density N_e. Since the electron temperature is only in the neighborhood of 10 or 20 thousand degrees, negligible fractions of atoms are excited to levels lying 10 to 30 volts above the ground level as compared to the numbers excited to metastable levels 2 to 5 volts above the ground level. Radiative excitations of permitted resonance lines are likewise usually negligible in number because of the dilution of the radiation.* Similarly, the excitation of the hydrogen and helium lines—by photo-ionization followed by recapture of the free electrons—is an inefficient process that occurs slowly at the temperatures and densities of the nebulae.

*An exception must be made for the lines of the Bowen fluorescent mechanism (see Sec. 8).

It appears that, although most of the visible light radiated by typical planetary nebulae is emitted in the green nebular lines, the concentration of hydrogen exceeds that of O III by a factor of a thousand or more! M. J. Seaton has recently recomputed the target areas for the collisional excitation of the forbidden lines of O I, O II, O III, N II, Ne III, Ne V, S II, and other ions of astrophysical interest.*

7. The Problem of the Electron Temperature

In all problems of interpretation of the planetary nebulae a knowledge of the electron temperature is desirable. There are four methods which might be employed to get estimates of this quantity.

(1) Energy distribution in the Balmer continuum
(2) Relative intensities of the "auroral" and "nebular" lines of ions such as O III
(3) Profiles of emission lines
(4) Magnitude of the Balmer discontinuity

If the energy distribution in the underlying continuum were known so that the true intensity of the Balmer recombination spectrum could be derived as a function of frequency, one could employ eqn. (4) to derive T_e. On the assumption that the intensity of this continuum is independent of wave length in the spectral region in question, T. L. Page obtained electron temperatures in the neighborhood of 10,000°K for a number of planetaries.

The relative numbers of atoms in the $^1S_0$ and $^1D_2$ levels of doubly ionized oxygen may be estimated from the intensities of $\lambda 4363$ ($^1S_0 - {}^1D_2$) and $\lambda 5007$, $\lambda 4959$ ($^1D_2 - {}^3P_{2,1}$) since the A values for these transitions are known.† The relative population of $^1S_0$ and $^1D_2$ depends on the density, the electron temperature, and the target areas for collisional excitation. M. J. Seaton's recent calculation of the necessary target areas for O^{++}, N^+ and other ions makes it possible to estimate T_e. These electron temperatures fall between about 8000°K and 20,000°K. With the earlier estimates of the target areas (which appear to have been too large) and the older photometric data, electron temperatures in the neighborhood of 10,000°K were found for most planetaries.

On the basis of the considerations of Section 6 of Chapter *3 we might expect that accurate measures of the profiles of the hydrogen lines would give an upper limit to the electron temperature. Turbulence and particularly the variation of the velocity of expansion in the nebula would seem to be the greatest obstacle to the application of this method.

*Phil. Trans. Royal Soc., London. **A**, **245**, 469, 1953. Proc. Roy. Soc. **218A**, 400, 1953.

†See Sec. 20 of Chapter *5 of Astrophysics—The Atmospheres of the Sun and Stars.

In addition to the usual recombination continua in the planetary nebulae, there is a strong continuous emission whose source has never been identified. It has been suggested that the simultaneous emission of two photons by a hydrogen atom in the metastable $2s$ level may account for this emission and the detailed dependence of the intensity on frequency has been calculated by Spitzer and Greenstein.* This bluish continuum would underlie the recombination hydrogen and helium continua and would produce a weakening in the discontinuity at the Paschen and Balmer limits. The magnitude of this Balmer discontinuity depends in a known way on the temperature. In IC 418 Minkowski finds a Balmer discontinuity that cannot be reconciled with a temperature as low as 10,000°K—perhaps T_e is 20,000° or 25,000°K in the region producing the strong continuum.†

Method (1) suffers from the fact that the frequency dependence of the underlying continuum is not known, method (3) has not yet been applied, and method (4) has only been used to establish the order of magnitude of T_e. The most promising method appears to be (2), but it utilizes results based on an extremely difficult quantum mechanical theory. Improved observational data are urgently needed.

The relation between the electron temperature and that of the central star, which is assumed to radiate like a black body of temperature T, has been considered theoretically. Let us first discuss the example of a pure hydrogen nebula in which only radiative processes occur. First there is the condition of radiative equilibrium which states that the number of photo-ionizations from the ground level equals the number of recaptures on all levels. Second, there is the condition of radiative equilibrium which specifies that the total amount of energy absorbed in a volume element must equal that emitted. The solution of the appropriate equations for an optically thin nebula is easily found by numerical methods. At the lower temperatures the theoretical electron temperature approximates that of the central star, but with increasing T_1, T_e lags farther and farther behind. At the higher electron temperatures, the dissipation of energy takes place largely by free-free emissions. At $T_1 = 20,000°$K, $T_e = 18,000°$K; for $T_1 = 80,000°$K, $T_e = 57,000°$K, while for $T_1 = 320,000°$K, T_e would be 132,000°K. The effect of a finite optical thickness does not change the qualitative picture very much, the electron temperature remains below that of the central star.

*The available observations on the energy distributions in the continuum do not yet permit a clear-cut decision to be made.

†If the two-photon emission mechanism is accepted, the measured Balmer discontinuity in NGC 7027 gives an electron temperature of the order of 10,000°K, whereas the intensities of the [N II] and [O III] lines interpreted with the aid of Seaton's cross sections give a temperature near 15,000°K.

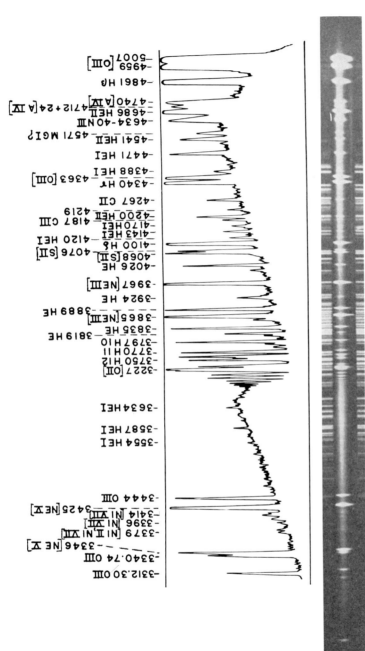

FIG. 7.—SPECTRUM AND TRACING OF *NGC 7027*

This nebula exhibits a high-excitation and an unusually rich, line spectrum. Notice also the strong continuous spectrum and the strong Balmer recombination spectrum. The stronger lines are overexposed to bring up the continuum and weaker lines. Lines of H, He I, He II, C II, C III, N III, [O II], [O III], O III, [Ne III], [Ne V], Mg I, [S II], [A IV], [Ni II], and [Ni VII] are found on the tracing. (Photographed with the Cassegrain spectrograph with quartz prisms and *f*/2 Schmidt camera at the McDonald Observatory, August 24, 1946; exposure time, 6 hr.)

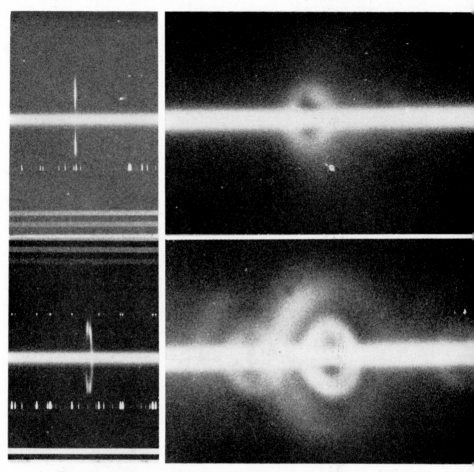

Fig. 8.—Slit and Slitless Images of [Ne III] and [Ne V] in *NGC* 2392

Top: Enlarged slit and slitless images of λ3426 [Ne V]. *Bottom*: Enlarged slit and slitless images of λ3868 [Ne III]

Notice that the [Ne III] line is split by internal motions in the nebula, whereas the higher excitation [Ne V] line is not. The slitless image of λ3868 is confused with that of λ3889 (H + He I). Both slitless spectra were taken without the image rotator and are somewhat blurred by the rotation of the image on the slit during the course of the exposure (after Olin C. Wilson). (Courtesy, *Astrophysical Journal*, University of Chicago Press, **108**, 205, 1948.)

Actually, even in a pure hydrogen nebula such high electron temperatures would never be reached. Electron collisions would tend to excite hydrogen atoms to discrete levels from which they would return with the emission of radiation. Thus line emission would arise at the expense of the kinetic energy of the electrons, the gas would be cooled, and the temperature would become stabilized somewhere, possibly between 20,000°K and 40,000°K.

Real planetary nebulae contain not only hydrogen and helium but also "impurities" in the form of oxygen, nitrogen, neon, etc., that produce strong forbidden lines.

The energy radiated in these forbidden lines is acquired at the expense of the kinetic energy of the electrons. Free electrons are constantly losing energy by exciting atoms to metastable levels. Almost no energy is regained by superelastic collisions. Consequently, this process acts as a thermostat upon the nebula. The amount of the cooling depends on the ratio of the sum of the intensities of all the forbidden lines to the intensity of the Balmer recombination lines. For example, in IC 418 where the ratio of the sum of the intensities of the forbidden lines to Hβ is about 3.5, the electron temperature may be as high as 20,000°K with a central star whose temperature (as estimated from its spectral class) is near 30,000°K. On the other hand, in nebulae where the aforementioned ratio is much higher, T_ϵ is lower even though the central star is hotter. The electron temperatures obtained from the observed $(N_1 + N_2)/(4363)$ intensity ratios with the aid of Seaton's cross-sections show that no close correlation exists between T_ϵ and the central star temperature T_1.

8. Fluorescence Effects in Oxygen and Nitrogen

High excitation planetaries, such as NGC 3242 and 2440, show a number of strong lines in the near ultraviolet. One of these, λ3202, arises from He II, the strong λ3346, λ3426 pair are attributed to [Ne V], but the remainder are permitted O III lines. Other O III lines, equally strong in the laboratory, are not observed in the nebulae.

Bowen noticed that all the observed lines originated from the single upper level $2p3d\,^3P_2$, either directly or indirectly by cascade. This level is connected to the $2p^2$ level of the ground term by a transition at λ303.799 which almost coincides with the resonance Lyα line of He II λ303.780. Fig. 9 depicts the cycle of events. An O III atom, raised to the $2p3d\,^3P_2$ level by the absorption of a quantum of λ303.8 (He II), may return either directly to the ground level of the atom or cascade back through the terms of the $2p3p$ and $2p3s$ configurations, emitting the observed lines in transit. Transitions to $3p^3P$ give λ3444 and λ3429 (blended with [Ne V]) those to $3p^3S$ give λ3133. Subsequent

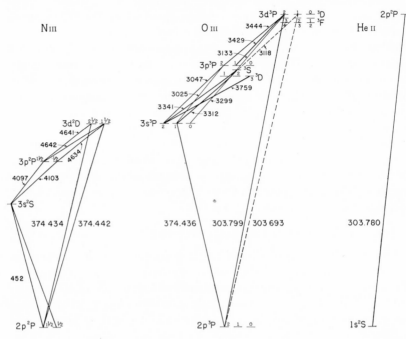

FIG. 9.—THE BOWEN FLUORESCENT MECHANISM

The diagram shows the terms of N III, O III, and He II that are involved in the production of the strong permitted lines of nitrogen and oxygen observed in high-excitation planetary nebulae. (Courtesy, *Astrophysical Journal*, University of Chicago Press, **81**, 4, 1935.)

transitions from $3p^3S_1$ to $3s^3P$ give λ3341, λ3312, and λ3299. Finally, jumps from $3s^3P$ to $2p^3P$ (ground term) give the unobservable λ374.436 line, which, curiously enough, excites a somewhat similar cycle in N III, where the λ4634–λ4641 and λ4097–λ4103 lines are produced by cascade from $3d^2D$ to $3p^2P$ and from $3p^2P$ to $3s^2S$, respectively. These lines are strong in the nebulae that show the strong permitted O III lines.

Thus the He II λ303.8 radiation supplies a rich reservoir of energy to the O III ions upon which the $2p^2 \; ^3P_2 - 2p3d^3P_2$ transition alone can draw. A quantitative discussion of the problem indicates that in nebulae where the O III lines are strong the intensity of the radiation in the O III λ303.80 line is between a hundred and a thousand times greater than that radiated by the central star in this spectral region. As the theory requires, the O III lines appear only in those nebulae with strong He II λ4686, and the images are never significantly larger than the λ4686 image. *NGC* 7009 provides an excellent example. The Bowen fluorescent lines, quite conspicuous in the main body of the nebula, are missing in the low-excitation ansae where He II ($\lambda 4686$) is absent. The green nebular [O III] lines do appear in the ansae, however, showing that some O III is present which could absorb the $\lambda 303.8$ radiation if it existed there. A consistency check on the Bowen fluorescent mechanism is provided by the relative intensities of the ultraviolet O III lines, which all arise by cascade from a single upper level. The observed and theoretical intensities agree within the limits of error of the observations.

The Bowen fluorescent mechanism illustrates the dangers of literal interpretation of spectral line intensities in terms of abundances. Similar special excitation processes appear to operate in the extended atmospheres of Wolf-Rayet stars, P Cygni stars, combination variables, and novae.

9. Internal Motions in Planetary Nebulae

Direct photographs or slitless spectrograms give significant clues to the spatial distribution of the radiating atoms, i.e., the stratification. We need, in addition, information about the kinematics of the nebular material. Are the planetaries expanding, contracting, or rotating; are the gases in equilibrium, in a steady state, or are they in turbulent motion?

Many years ago at the Lick Observatory, Campbell and Moore studied the internal radial motions of [O III] in the brighter planetaries. With high dispersion, the green nebular lines in many objects appeared broadened, distorted, or doubled. The large, high-excitation nebulae often showed evidence of considerable internal motion and turbulence. The irregular nebula *NGC 7027* appears to be a highly turbulent structure, whereas the ring nebula *NGC 7662* displays a more orderly type of internal motion.

The splitting of the lines cannot arise from rotation, as lines of different elements or stages of ionization of the same element give different internal velocities. The complexity of internal nebular kinematics is well illustrated in Wilson's observations of *NGC 2392*. See Fig. 8. Perrine and later Zanstra attributed the doubling to an expansion or a contraction of the nebular shells. One component arises from the near side, the other from the far side, as in a nova. Motion perpendicular to line of sight gives no doubling. Zanstra showed that the observed doubling and irregularities could be explained if different amounts of material were initially ejected in different directions.

A thorough study of the internal motions in the planetary nebulae has been made by Olin Wilson with the coudé spectrograph and 100-inch reflector. The mean component of separation, ΔV, for H, [O III], and [Ne III] are always in good agreement, and their average ΔV may be taken as the most reliable measure of the velocity of expansion. In many nebulae, the ΔV's for different ions show a considerable spread; when this occurs, the high-excitation ions show smaller than average separations, whereas the reverse is true for low-excitation ions. Hydrogen is the exception; it always agrees closely in ΔV with [O III] or [Ne III]. In five of the eight nebulae in which [Ne V] is observed, the lines are not resolvable into components, and ΔV probably does not exceed 10 km/sec, although for other lines the ΔV ranges from 37 to 107 km/sec. The low-excitation [O II] lines often show large ΔV's.

The correlation between the component separations and the dimensions of the corresponding nebular images appears to be of the utmost significance. [Ne V], which always shows a smaller splitting, also always gives a smaller monochromatic image. Numerically, no close correlation between differences in ΔV and image size exists. In *NGC* 2392, a large difference in ΔV corresponds to a small difference in image diameter, whereas the opposite is true for *NGC* 7662.

In low-excitation nebulae such as *IC* 418 the role of [Ne V] is played by [Ne III], and lines of ions such as O I or S II show a splitting. What interpretation is to be placed on the observed splitting of the nebular lines?

Strong theoretical reasons favor the expansion hypothesis. If the optical thickness of the shell is large, every quantum of the Lyman continuum will be degraded into a Lyman α quantum. Ambarzumian pointed out that since the absorption coefficient of Lyα is about 10^4 that in the continuum, the mechanical force exerted by radiation would vastly exceed the force of gravity of the central star and the nebula would be torn asunder. Its velocity of expansion would be about 200 km/sec instead of about 20 km/sec, as is observed. Therefore the actual Lyα radiation pressure must be much smaller than that which would result from ordinary scattering in a stationary nebula.

Zanstra suggested that differential motions within the nebula, such as would be produced by an over-all expansion, might greatly reduce this radiation pressure, provided the expansion velocity appreciably exceeded the thermal speeds of the atoms. In a rigorous solution of the problem, Chandrasekhar showed that the radiation pressure would be cut down by a factor of 10^4 as soon as the differences in velocities at the inner and outer boundary exceeded the undisplaced line width due to thermal motion and small scale turbulence by a factor of about 3.5.

Throughout the body of the nebular shell, selective radiation pressure approaches zero. At the edges it remains appreciable. Chandrasekhar suggests that an initially static nebula would start to expand until the regions over which the net radiation pressure is negligible would be extensive. In such a state the nebula would be quasi-stationary, and dissipation would occur only at the inner and outer edges. The effectiveness of radiation pressure depends critically on the rate of differential expansion. Once the nebula had adjusted itself to a steady state, it might persist in a pseudo-equilibrium condition for thousands of years. The Lyman continuum might produce a small dissipating force.

These discussions need to be modified in two ways. Because of the Doppler motion of the atoms there occurs a scattering with redistribution of frequency over the line. Furthermore, the line profile is not rectangular, but follows a Gaussian error curve corresponding to a Maxwellian distribution of velocities. Zanstra showed that the radiation pressure in a stationary nebula is much smaller than Ambarzumian had calculated. The nebula will expand, but the conditions on the ratio of expansion to thermal and turbulent velocity appear less drastic than formerly supposed. S. Miyamoto has estimated the contribution to the radiation pressure from the Lyman continuum.

An adequate theory of the dynamics of planetaries must account for the differing component separations of lines of ions of different degrees of ionization. Wilson suggests two alternative hypotheses to explain this effect. In one the material is assumed to be accelerated outward. The velocity given by any ion is a measure of the local velocity in the zone where that ion appears. Thus the low [Ne V] velocity means that in the innermost shell the rate of expansion is low. For some reason, such as the level of excitation, the hydrogen and helium velocity cannot be observed there. As the radiation from the central star is gradually absorbed in the outer shells, its momentum is transferred to the material which thereby acquires an outward velocity of expansion. Quantitatively, the hypothesis appears to check; the momenta carried by the absorbed quanta equals that acquired by the material, to within the uncertainties in the basic data. The second hypothesis is that the radiation pressure due to Lyman α in a shell causes the expulsion of matter in both the inward and outward directions in the fashion suggested by Chandrasekhar (see page 152). The material in high-excitation inner shells such as that of [Ne V] has a low-expansion velocity because it is retarded by radiation pressure while the ionized oxygen atoms in the outer part of the nebula are accelerated outward by the radiation pressure.

In many nebulae the line components are quite sharp, showing that large-scale turbulence does not exist and that the regions of line formation contain no large velocity gradients. In every instance, however, the hydrogen lines are more diffuse than those of other elements. Possibly an estimate of the upper limit of the electron temperature may be obtainable from the profiles of these lines.

The study of internal radial velocities is greatly helped with the aid of a multiple slit on the spectrograph instead of a single slit. The multi-slit consists of a series of parallel, closely ruled, lines. Instead of a single slit image of a narrow strip across the nebula, there are obtained images of a number of such strips. With a single exposure, velocities can be measured in many different parts of the image. Photometric measures of the intensities of the split-lines combined with isophotal contours may be used to get clues to the three-dimensional structure of a nebula. Such studies are in progress for *NGC* 7662.

10. Stratification and Ionization

For an adequate interpretation of the planetary nebulae it is necessary to take into account both the velocities and localizations of the various radiating atoms. Different ions tend to concentrate in different parts of the nebula. The monochromatic images of He II and [Ne V] are usually small; those of He I, [Ne III], [S II], and [O II] tend to be large. The explanation was given by Bowen who pointed out that the quanta of highest energy tend to be absorbed in the inner part of the nebula, whereas those of less energy may persist to the outer parts. Quanta capable of ionizing helium would be absorbed first; hence the He II images would be smallest. Lower energy quanta, capable of singly ionizing oxygen, might reach the outer portions of the shell. Hence emission of [O II] or [S II] would be found in the regions farthest from the center.

Although the general forms of most nebulae are thus qualitatively explained, it must be emphasized that the observed features probably depend on the optical thickness of the nebular gases, and upon the details of the initial ejection process. Different images often have different shapes. The λ3727 [O II] radiation in *NGC* 7009 shows a concentration at the ends of the spindle, whereas the He II λ4686 radiation is strongest near the middle portions.

Figure 10 shows the intensity distribution across the major axis of *NGC* 6720, the Ring Nebula in Lyra. Notice the concentration of He II λ4686 to the center of the nebula and the shell character of the [O II] λ3727 image. The H I and [Ne III] images are similar but smaller than that of [O II]. The ionization potentials of oxygen and hydrogen are nearly equal and we might expect H I and O II to appear in the same regions. Their coefficients of continuous absorption differ, however. The O I absorption coefficient remains large well beyond the series limit (Fig. 17 of Ch. ★5) while that of hydrogen falls off as ν^{-3}. As soon as hydrogen starts to become neutral in the outer zones, radiation beyond the Lyman limit is rapidly depleted and the hydrogen-ionization region has a sharp boundary in the manner indicated by Strömgren. In objects like *NGC* 6720, the hydrogen shell may not be completely opaque in the ultraviolet, and much of the radiation capable of ionizing oxygen may escape. The [O II] lines are collisionally excited while Balmer lines are produced by recombination. The intensity of the hydrogen lines depends on $N_i N_\epsilon = N_\epsilon^2$, whereas that of $\lambda 3727$ depends on $N_\epsilon N(\text{O II})$ for low densities. If N_ϵ falls off faster than $N(\text{O II})$ in the outer strata, $\lambda 3727$ should fall off more slowly than does hydrogen,

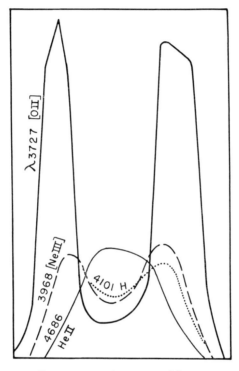

Fig. 10.—Intensity Distribution Across the Monochromatic Images of NGC 6720

The curves show the measured distribution of intensity across the major axis of the image, uncorrected for guiding errors. The scale of ordinates differs for each image since corrections for plate sensitivity and atmosphere extinction have not been applied. Compare with Fig. 3. (From a plate taken at the Lick Observatory.)

as is observed. Quantitative discussion is difficult because of the filamentary structure of the ring, and the unknown geometry of the nebula itself.

Wisps and filaments are prominent in many nebulae that are photographed on a large scale. Since all planetaries are of such a size, the internal motions are of such a speed, and the kinematical viscosities are so low that the Reynolds number [see eqn. (46) of Ch. ★3] is very large, turbulence should exist in all of them. Minkowski calls attention to seemingly smooth objects such as the Owl Nebula in which turbulence does not appear to be present or is on such a small scale as to be invisible. What seemingly suppresses the turbulence in such objects? Magnetic fields tend to suppress turbulence and might explain some of the planetary nebulae forms, but it is difficult to see how such fields can have originated.

A nebula of filamentary structure may show a spectrum markedly different from that of a homogeneous nebula of the same mean density and illuminated by a central star of the same temperature. Within the filaments, ionization may be less because of the higher density, whereas in regions of low density the emissions of the more highly ionized ions will be favored. Furthermore, the radiation fields may differ from one filament to another, an effect which is further complicated by the differential expansion of the nebula.

Finally, if we employ the ionization formula appropriate for a gas subject to dilute temperature radiation, we can find no combination of a black-body source, electron density N_e, or dilution factor W which will explain the observed distribution of atoms among different stages of ionization in an object such as NGC 7027 where appear the forbidden lines of atoms and ions as diverse as neutral nitrogen and [Ne V]. (Ionization potential of Ne IV is 97 ev.) Clearly the radiation field within the nebula must differ appreciably from that of a black body. There are the strong resonance Lyα lines of H I and He II, and of other elements as well, which are produced by the primary mechanism. Also the radiation of the central star may very well depart from that of a black body in the ultraviolet. (See Sec. 11.)

Are the shell structures actually hollow as the spectrograms suggest, or do they contain matter which is not in a condition to radiate? In other words, do hydrogen and helium exist in considerable quantities within the [Ne V] shell but at so high an electron temperature that their radiation is negligible? Probably the electron temperature is higher within the [Ne V] shell but it is difficult to see how it can be so high as to completely suppress the Balmer lines or He II λ4686 by slowing down the recombination rate. It seems more likely that the shells are actually relatively hollow.*

Olin Wilson has suggested that the material is ejected from the central star with velocities $\sim$5 km/sec. He supposes that during this stage the excitation and electron temperature are so high the nebula

---

*In IC 418, ions of H, Ne III and O III may persist to short distances from the central star. He, N II, O II, and S II exist in the outer ring but not near the center of the nebula. (The ion-density distributions for N II and S II should go to zero near the nucleus in Fig. 3, $Ap.\ J.$ **114**, 429, 1951.)

emits very little visible radiation and is transparent to the ultraviolet radiation from the central star. Ultimately the gas cools to the point where Ne V becomes common, the electron temperature is lowered, and hydrogen and helium recombination sets in. As the nebular material flows through the Ne V zone it cools, neutral H and He are formed and tend to block the outgoing radiation and permit the formation of O III. The electron temperature is still further lowered and the edge of the luminous zone is reached when the blocking of the ultraviolet radiation is complete or the nebular material ends. The inner visible boundary expands slowly; the various bright shells maintain a fixed distance from the nucleus as the gas flows through them. The outer boundary expands rapidly if it marks the physical edge of the nebular gases. If the mass of the shell is so high that the radiation is all extinguished (cf. discussion by Strömgren for the interstellar medium, Sec. 5 of Ch.6) the boundary is fixed. The ejection of material from the star ceases after a time, the inner boundary of the material reaches the Ne V zone and there results a large nebula of low surface brightness, e.g., perhaps *NGC* 7293.

Olin Wilson now prefers, however, the alternative suggestion that the originally ejected shell expands in size as it increases in radius as a consequence of the radiation pressure in Lyman α.

11. The Chemical Composition of the Planetary Nebulae

The interpretation of nebular line intensities in terms of the abundances of the constitutient elements must take into account the particular excitation mechanism for each line. The hydrogen, helium, and C II λ4267 lines are excited by recombination and subsequent cascade. The forbidden lines of oxygen, neon, nitrogen, argon, and other elements are produced by the collisional excitation of the metastable levels from which the atoms return to the ground level with the emission of radiation. With the best available values of the electron temperatures, of the target areas for collisional excitation, and of theoretical line strength one may estimate the abundances of many ions from their forbidden lines. The proportions of carbon and helium must be estimated from their recombination lines by a method akin to that employed for hydrogen. In *NGC* 7009, the O III abundance, as well, may be calculated from the recombination O II lines and compared with results from the [O III] lines.

The distribution of the atoms of a given element among the various stages of ionization is one of the most difficult parts of the analysis. Only one or two ionization stages are observed in most elements, and the contribution of the unobserved ions to the total number must be estimated. An empirical procedure appears best. For example, one may assume that the abundance ratio of atoms in successive stages of ionization, e.g., O II/O III, Ne III/Ne IV, etc., depends only on the ionization potentials involved and not on the type of ion.

From their study of *NGC* 6572, 7662, and 7027, Bowen and Wyse found the chemical composition of the planetaries to be similar to that of the sun. More accurately, we can state their result as follows: A mass of gas, similar in composition to the sun, attenuated to the density of a planetary nebula, would emit the same spectrum as a planetary. Subsequently, Wyse studied the spectra of additional planetaries and of the Orion Nebula and published eye estimates of intensities on a calibrated scale. More elaborate treatments of Wyse's observational data substantiate these conclusions; revised numerical values are given on page 229 for comparison with the stellar data in Chapter *8. Improved abundance estimates will require not only good collisional cross-section parameters but also a knowledge of the distribution of atoms in various ionization stages. This means we must have more information on stratification and the distribution of the radiating ions.

12. The Nuclei of the Planetary Nebulae

The central stars of the planetary nebulae show a variety of spectral characteristics. Some show continuous spectra with no apparent trace of emission or absorption lines, e.g., the nuclei of *NGC* 4361 or *NGC* 6720. The spectra of others are predominantly of the absorption type with few emission lines, e.g., the nuclei of *NGC* 2392 or *IC* 2149. Some show combined absorption and emission features, e.g., the nuclei of *IC* 418 or *NGC* 6543. A few central stars are of the Wolf-Rayet type, e.g., *BD* + 30° 3639.

Estimates of the luminosities and dimensions of these stars depend on their temperatures and distances. Both quantities are uncertain and the best we can do is to give orders of magnitude.

In 1926, Zanstra proposed a method for the determination of the temperatures of these stars from a photometric comparison of the continuous spectrum of the central star with that of the nebula. The essential idea is this: All the radiation of the planetary nebula arises from the degradation of energy received from a high-temperature star. In an optically thick nebula, composed primarily of hydrogen, each quantum beyond the Lyman limit ultimately is broken down into a quantum of Lyα and a quantum of the Balmer series or continuum. Hence a measurement of the total number of quanta radiated in the Balmer lines and the energy radiated in a small region of the visible continuum of the central star will permit a comparison of the total stellar energy radiated beyond the Lyman limit with that emitted in

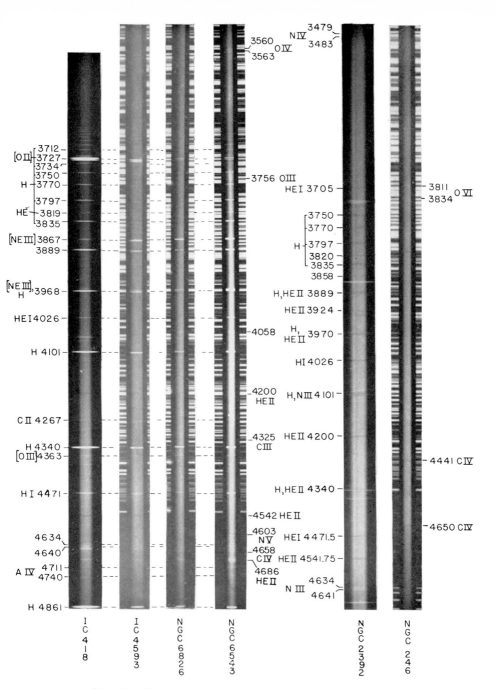

FIG. 11A.—SPECTRA OF THE NUCLEI OF PLANETARY NEBULAE

The long emission lines arise in the nebulae. *NGC* 2392 shows a central star with well-developed absorption lines, while the central star of *NGC* 246 shows O VI in emission and absorption lines of C IV. The nucleus of *IC* 418 has emission lines of both carbon and nitrogen, and absorption lines of the He II Pickering series. In the *IC* 4593 and *NGC* 6826 nuclei faint Balmer absorptions can be observed underlying the strong nebular emission. The *NGC* 6543 nucleus has numerous sharp emission lines in its spectrum.

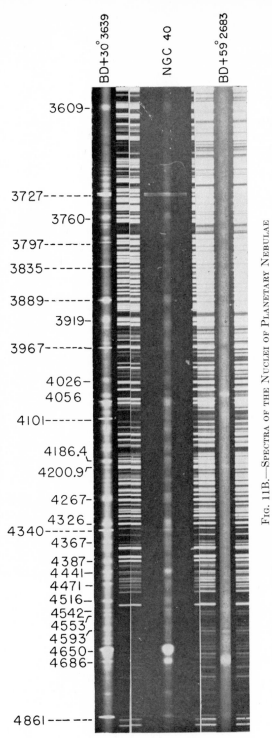

BD+30° 3639

NGC 40

BD+59° 2683

3609—

3727------

3760—

3797------

3835------

3889------

3919—

3967------

4026—

4056

4101------

4186.4

4200.9

4267—

4326

4340------

4367—

4387—

4441—

4471—

4516—

4542

4553

4593

4650—

4686—

4861----- ---

FIG. 11B.—SPECTRA OF THE NUCLEI OF PLANETARY NEBULAE

The planetary nebulae *NGC* 40 and *BD* + 30° 3639 have nuclei which show relatively sharp lines of the Wolf-Rayet type. The star *BD* + 59° 2683, the nucleus of *NGC* 7635, is a more typical Wolf-Rayet star with broad emission lines. The emissions of nebular origins are indicated by dotted lines. (Photographed at the McDonald Observatory.)

a known frequency interval in the neighborhood of say λ4000. For an object radiating as a black body this ratio will depend only on the temperature. If the star does not radiate as a black body, or if our assumptions about the absorption of starlight are not fulfilled, the temperatures derived will be in error.

Let L_p denote the total amount of energy radiated in the nebular image and H_s the intensity of the continuous background of the star. If the latter radiates as a black body of temperature T and radius R, the total energy radiated in $d\nu$ in all directions will be

$$H_s \, d\nu = 4\pi R^2 \pi B_\nu \, d\nu \tag{15}$$

where B_ν is the Planckian function. The factor is $4\pi R^2$ instead of πR^2, since one must compare the total amount of nebular and stellar radiation emitted toward all directions in space. If $y = h\nu/kT$, the corresponding number of quanta radiated in $d\nu$ will be

$$\frac{4\pi^2 R^2 B_\nu \, d\nu}{h\nu} = D \, \frac{y^2}{e^y - 1} \, dy \tag{16}$$

where

$$D = \frac{8\pi^2 R^2 k^3}{c^2 h^3} \, T^3 \tag{17}$$

and the total number of quanta emitted beyond the Lyman limit will be

$$N_{u1} = D \int_{\nu_1}^{\infty} \frac{y^2}{e^y - 1} \, dy \tag{18}$$

Recalling the discussion in Section 3, we see that N_{u1} will be the total number of quanta in the Lyman continuum plus the number of Balmer quanta. If the nebula is thick all the Lyman continuum quanta will be absorbed and eqn. (3) will hold. Zanstra also neglected the Balmer continuum. Let us define

$$A_\nu = \frac{L_p}{\nu H_s} \tag{19}$$

This quantity is determined by the observations. Then the number of quanta in a particular Balmer line image will be:

$$N_p = \frac{L_p}{h\nu} = \frac{A_\nu H_s}{h} \tag{20}$$

From eqns. (15), (17), (19), and (20) it follows that

$$N_p = D \, \frac{y^3}{e^y - 1} \, A_\nu \tag{21}$$

The total number of Balmer quanta $\sum N_p$ equals the number of "ultra-violet" quanta. Thus

$$\int_{\nu_1}^{\infty} \frac{y^2}{e^y - 1} \, dy = \sum \frac{y^3}{e^y - 1} A_\nu \qquad (22)$$

is Zanstra's fundamental equation for the determination of the temperature of the central star. It must be solved by trial and error. He gives tables of the integral on the left and the coefficient of A_ν as a function of temperature, so that the latter may be found by a process of successive approximations.

Zanstra also proposed a method based on the assumption that the energy of the photoelectrically liberated electrons was used up in inelastic collisions with the O III ions. The energy absorbed per second from the ultraviolet radiation output of the star is

$$E_{ul} = \int_{\nu_1}^{\infty} H_s \, d\nu = kTD \int_{\nu_1}^{\infty} \frac{y^3}{e^y - 1} \, dy \qquad (23)$$

The energy required for the ionization of the electrons is $E_1 = h\nu_1 N_{ul}$, while the energy of the free electrons themselves is

$$E_f = E_{ul} - h\nu_1 N_{ul} \qquad (24)$$

Zanstra supposed that this energy was dissipated in the collisional excitation of the green nebular [O III] lines. Thus he obtained yet another method for estimating the temperature of the central star.

In a third method of temperature determination, Zanstra employs the magnitude difference between star and nebula. He assumes that all the ultraviolet stellar energy above that necessary to detach the electrons goes into the excitation of the green nebular lines. Furthermore he supposes that the photographic magnitude of the star corresponds to its brightness at a fixed effective wave length which is independent of temperature. Actually there are other strong forbidden lines besides the green nebular pair, and sometimes most of the nebular light may not even appear in the green lines, as, for example, in *NGC* 40 where λ3727 is the strongest emission. Further, the effective wave length of a Wolf-Rayet nucleus may differ from that of a star which radiates a continuous spectrum.

In practical applications, Zanstra employed not only the hydrogen lines but also lines of neutral and ionized helium. In the latter instance we do not know the fraction of recombinations that give rise to the observed lines. In a thick nebula we can be reasonably sure that for hydrogen each ultraviolet quantum will be degraded into a Balmer quantum, but for the Paschen (λ4686) and Brackett (Pickering) series of He II no such simplification is available. The He I and He II "temperatures" tend to be higher than the H I temperatures.

The Zanstra method gives a lower limit to the ultraviolet color temperature of the central star, since it assumes all ultraviolet quanta are degraded to Balmer quanta. This condition can scarcely be fulfilled in many nebulae of low surface brightness or pronounced filamentary structure where much of the radiation may escape between the filaments.* Moreover, it seems likely that the nuclei of planetary nebulae do not always radiate like black bodies in the far ultraviolet. Strong emission lines may appear there.

On the practical side, the method has the advantage that one may compare the star and the nebula at the same wave length, thereby avoiding one of the more troublesome phases of spectrophotometry. Yet, one must compare the narrow, frequently faint, spectrum of the central star with the nebular image upon which it is superposed.

K. Wurm has proposed a method which is based on the ratio of the nebular emission in the Balmer continuum to the nuclear spectrum at the same wave length. It is essentially similar to Zanstra's first method, although the observational data are independent. Applications of this method have been made by T. L. Page who finds that it gives a temperature higher than 120,000°K for the central star of the Ring Nebula, *NGC* 6720. Since leakage of the ultraviolet radiation may be important in this object, the temperature may be appreciably higher.

Stoy suggested a method for the determination of nuclear temperatures based on comparison of the intensities of the Balmer and forbidden lines. He postulated that in each instant as much energy is fed into the ionized gas by electrons photoelectrically detached from hydrogen as is removed by the collisional excitation of the nebular lines. Temperatures estimated by the Stoy method tend to come out higher than those found by the Zanstra method.

Some planetary nuclei show absorption lines from which spectral classes may be estimated. Spectra of the highest dispersions are required in order to eliminate the effects of the nebular spectrum. Table 2 gives the results obtained by O. C. Wilson and the writer for four planetaries observed at the Mount Wilson and Palomar Observatories. The spectral class is estimated from the hydrogen and ionized helium line-intensity ratios by the method proposed by R. M. Petrie. If the excitation-temperature–spectral-class relationship is assumed to be the same as for normal, Type I *O*-stars, we obtain the values listed in the third column of Table 2. Notice that the excitation temperatures

---

*Thus Wurm has suggested that the central star temperatures are probably much higher than the H I theory gives; i.e., they may correspond to the values given by He II.

exceed the Zanstra temperatures for the nuclei of the bright, optically thick planetaries *IC* 418 and *IC* 4593, whereas the reverse is true for *IC* 2149. Seemingly, the agreement is good for *NGC* 2392 but for this object something else is wrong. The three *IC* objects are low-excitation nebulae, whereas *NGC* 2392 exhibits a high level of excitation with strong He II λ4686 and [Ne V]. The Zanstra temperature of this object obtained from ionized helium would be in the neighborhood of 100,000 °K! Deviations of the stellar ultraviolet from a black-body energy distribution and an error in the spectral-class–temperature relation may account for some of these discrepancies. If the helium/hydrogen ratio is larger in these stars than in Type I objects, the assigned excitation temperatures in column 3 are too large. The electron density, estimated with the aid of the hydrogen lines and the Inglis-Teller formula, is given in the last column.

Calculations of the radii of these stars based on their apparent magnitudes, excitation temperatures, and distances as estimated by Berman with the aid of eqns. (10), (11), and (14) of Chapter *6 show that most of these stars are comparable in size with the sun. The corresponding surface gravities implied by the intensities of the hydrogen lines and log N_ϵ strongly suggest masses not much larger than that of the sun.

TABLE 2

CENTRAL STARS OF 4 PLANETARY NEBULAE

Nucleus	Spectrum	Temperature (Spectral class)	Temperature (Zanstra)	log N_ϵ
IC 418	*O*7	33,200	25,000	13.5
IC 2149	*O*7.5	32,500	40,000	13.3
NGC 2392	*O*6	34,500	35,000	13.5
IC 4593	*O*7	33,400	25,000	13.4

The nuclei of planetaries of higher excitation are often so hot as to show only continuous spectra. If we trust the temperatures estimated by the Zanstra or Stoy methods, such stars must be smaller than the sun, perhaps comparable with old novae and the faint, Type II blue stars discovered by Humason and Zwicky. As a class, the planetary nuclei appear to show appreciable spread in surface temperature and radius, and perhaps in luminosity and density as well.

The limited number and extremely diffuse character of the absorption lines in the planetary nuclei make abundance determinations extremely difficult. We cannot exclude the possibility that in some of these stars the He/H ratio may differ from that in Type I objects. The nucleus of *NGC* 246 seems definitely to be a helium star. In this respect the planetary nuclei may resemble the bluest stars in the horizontal zero-absolute-magnitude branch of the Type II Russell diagram (the Humason-Zwicky stars). Münch finds that these objects with color indices of -0.3 to -0.4 often show a helium-rich, hydrogen-poor spectrum.

Further evidence that the planetary nuclei fall near the blue end of the horizontal branch of the Type II Russell diagram is provided by the planetary nebula in the globular cluster Messier 15. This object is one magnitude brighter than the RR Lyrae stars. The available, scanty, evidence suggests that planetary nuclei are relatively rare, bright, Type II objects. Although Sandage and Schwarzschild have interpreted the fainter end of the globular-cluster color-magnitude array in terms of evolutionary processes, the upper part of the diagram has not been so interpreted. The blue-white horizontal sequence undoubtedly represents stars that are more advanced in evolution than are the bright giants. We would conclude that the regular course of evolution is perhaps through the RR Lyrae stars to the novae. Perhaps a few objects are sidetracked en route to become planetaries. The nuclei with high helium contents are possibly those in which the carbon-nitrogen cycle has worked its way to the surface and the last bit of hydrogen is being used by the rapidly aging star.

An analysis of the spectrophotometric measures of *NGC* 7027 obtained by Minkowski and the writer with the aid of Seaton's target areas (footnote, page 211) and the methods of *Ap. J.* **102**, 239, 1945, give the following estimates of log N to replace those given in Table 17 of Chapter *8, viz.: H, 13.04; He, 12.04; N, 9.56; O, 10.00; F, 7.4; Ne, 9.48; S, 9.21; Cl, 8.39; A, 8.22; K, 6.5; and Ca, 6.6. There is an indication of a pronounced filamentary structure with $N_\epsilon \sim 7.7 \times 10^4/\text{cm}^3$, and $T_\epsilon = 14{,}500°$ K in these filaments.*

PROBLEMS

1. Consider a filament of completely ionized hydrogen $N_\epsilon = 10^4/\text{cm}^3$, $T_\epsilon = 10{,}000°\text{K}$. If the exciting radiation is cut off, how long will it take for half the ions to recombine? Assume the mass density to remain constant.

2. What is the optical thickness of a static homogeneous planetary nebula in the radiation of the center of the λ5007 line of [O III], if $N(\text{O III}) = 1 \text{ ion}/\text{cm}^3$, diameter of nebula $= 2.0 \times 10^{17}\text{cm}$, $T_\epsilon = T_i = 10{,}000°\text{K}$. The Einstein A for the transition is 0.021.

*This paragraph added in proof, March 4, 1954.

3. Assume that the central star of a planetary nebula radiates as a black body at 80,000°K. If the radius of the shell is 10,000 astronomical units and there are 10 neutral and 1000 ionized hydrogen atoms per cm³, calculate the momentum communicated by the radiation to each volume element and derive the acceleration of the nebular material.

4. Show why the central star temperature derived from the He II radiation will be greater than that found from the H I radiation if the shell has an optical thickness of about one at the Lyman limit. Assume hydrogen is five times as abundant as helium by numbers of atoms.

5. Show that if the electrons lose all their energy in the excitation of the green nebular lines, and all the ultraviolet energy is absorbed in the nebula, the temperature of the central star will be given by

$$\int_{y_1}^{\infty} \frac{y^3}{e^y - 1} \, dy - y_1 \int_{y_1}^{\infty} \frac{y^2}{e^y - 1} \, dy = \sum \frac{y^4}{e^y - 1} A_\nu$$

where A_ν is defined as in eqn. (17), except that L_p here refers to the [O III] lines.

REFERENCES

Textbook:

Wurm, K. *Die Planetarische Nebeln.* Berlin: Akademisches Verlag, 1951.

The classical researches on the structure and spectra of the planetary nebulae are contained in:
Publ. Lick Obs. **13**, 1918.

For accounts of more recent spectroscopic investigations see:
Bowen, I. S., and A. B. Wyse. *Lick Obs. Bull.* **19**, 1, 1939.
Wyse, A. B. *Ap. J.* **95**, 356, 1942.
Minkowski, R. *Ap. J.* **95**, 243, 1942.
Minkowski, R., and L. H. Aller. *Publ. Astron. Soc. Pac.* **58**, 258, 1946.
Swings, P., and J. W. Swensson, *Ann. d'Ap.* **15**, 290, 1952.

Spectrophotometric studies have been made by:
Berman, L. *Lick Obs. Bull.* **15**, 86, 1930.
Page, T. L. *Ap. J.* **96**, 78, 1942.
Aller, L. H. *Ap. J.* **113**, 125, 1951.
Minkowski, R., and L. H. Aller. *Ap. J.* (in press).
Liller, W., and L. H. Aller. *Ap. J.* (in press).

For catalogs of planetary nebulae see:
Verontsov-Velyaminov, *Russ. Astron. J.* **11**, 40, 1934.
Minkowski, R. *Publ. Astron. Soc. Pac.* **58**, 305, 1946; **59**, 257, 1947.

In our illustrative calculations we have employed distances determined by:
Berman, L. *Lick Obs. Bull.* **18**, 57, 1937.

See also:
Oort, J. *M.N.* **99**, 376, 1939.
Minkowski, R. *Publ. Obs. Mich.* **10**, 25, 1951.

For the interpretation of the spectra and structure of the planetary nebulae see:
BOWEN, I. S.   *Ap. J.* **67**, 1, 1928; **81**, 1, 1935.
WILSON, O. C., and L. H. ALLER.   *Ap. J.* **114**, 421, 1951; Wilson, O. C. *Ap. J.* **117**, 264, 1953 (structure of *IC* 418).

The theory of the planetary nebulae has been treated by:
AMBARZUMIAN, V.   *Pulkova Bull.* **13**, 3, 1933; *M.N.* **93**, 50, 1932.

Series of papers by Menzel and his collaborators entitled: "Physical Processes in Gaseous Nebulae" in:
Ap. J. I, **85**, 330, 1937; II, **86**, 70, 1937; III, **88**, 52, 1938; IV, **88**, 313, 1938; V, **88**, 423, 1938; VI, **89**, 587, 1939; VII, **90**, 271, 1939; VIII, **90**, 601, 1939; X, **92**, 408, 1940; XI, **93**, 178, 1941; XII, **93**, 195, 1941; XIII, **93**, 230, 1941; XIV, **93**, 236, 1941; XV, **93**, 244, 1941; XVI, **94**, 30, 1941; XVII, **94**, 436, 1941; XVIII, **102**, 239, 1945. See also
BOHM, D., and L. H. ALLER.   *Ap. J.* **105**, 131, 1947.

The transfer of radiation in a planetary nebula has also been treated by:
CHANDRASEKHAR, S.   *Zeits. f. Ap.* **9**, 266, 1935.
HENYEY, L.   *Ap. J.* **88**, 133, 1938.
HAGIHARA, Y.   *Japan. J. Astron. Geophysics* **20**, 113, 1943.
HAGIHARA, Y. and T. HATANAKA.   *Japan. J. Astron. Geophysics* **19**, 135, 1942; **21**, 45, 1945.

Continuous emission in planetary nebulae is discussed by:
SPITZER, L., and J. L. GREENSTEIN.   *Ap. J.* **114**, 407, 1951.

The role of radiation pressure in planetary nebulae has been discussed by:
CHANDRASEKHAR, S.   *Ap. J.* **102**, 402, 1945.
ZANSTRA, H.   *B.A.N.* **11**, No. 401, 1949.
MIYAMOTO, S.   *Publ. Astron. Soc. Japan.* **2**, 23, 1950.

The internal motions in the planetary nebulae have been surveyed by:
WILSON, O. C.   *Ap. J.* **111**, 279, 1950.

Spectroscopic studies of the nuclei of planetary nebulae have been made by:
SWINGS, P.   *Ap. J.* **92**, 289, 1940.
SWINGS, P., and O. STRUVE.   *Proc. Nat. Acad. Sci.* **26**, 454, 548, 1940; **27**, 225, 1941.
CILLIÉ, C. G.   *M.N.* **94**, 48, 1933.
ALLER, L. H.   *Ap. J.* **108**, 462, 1948.
WILSON, O. C.   *Ap. J.* **108**, 201, 1948. *Mt. Wilson Contr.* No. 749.
WILSON, O. C., and L. H. ALLER, *Ap. J.* **119**, 243, 1954.

The temperatures of the planetary nuclei were first determined by:
ZANSTRA, H.   *Pub. Dom. Ap. Obs.* **4**, 15, 209, 1930; *Zeits. f. Ap.* **2**, 1, 1931.

Subsequent investigations are due to:
AMBARZUMIAN, V.   *Pulkova Obs. Circ.*, No. 4, 8, 1932.
STOY, R.   *M.N.* **93**, 588, 1933.
WURM, K.   *Naturwissenschaften* **10**, 306, 1949.
PAGE, T. L.   *Astron. J.* **55**, 77, 1950.

Studies of the Orion Nebula have been made by:
GREENSTEIN, J. L.   *Ap. J.* **104**, 414, 1946 (continuous spectrum).
BAADE, W., F. GOOS, P. KOCH, and R. MINKOWSKI.   *Zeits. f. Ap.* **6**, 355, 1933; **9**, 202, 1934 (intensity distribution in the spectral lines).
BAADE, W., and R. MINKOWSKI.   *Ap. J.* **86**, 119, 1935 (Trapezium).

CHAPTER 6

THE INTERSTELLAR MEDIUM

1. The Grains and Gas Between the Stars

In addition to the stars, our galaxy contains vastly extended clouds of unorganized dust and gas. In regions like Monoceros the stars are evenly spread upon the sky, but elsewhere the rich star fields are invaded by wisps of occulting material. The great rift in the Milky Way, the inky filaments that hide much of the bright Sagittarius cloud, and the dark areas in Taurus and Cepheus are examples of these obscuring masses.

In some regions—e.g., Orion, the Trifid Nebula, Messier 8, and IC 5146—both dark obscuring clouds and bright nebulosity appear. There appears to be no fundamental difference between these two dissimilar objects. If a mass of obscuring material is illuminated by a star, a diffuse nebula may result. Many years ago Hubble found that if the illuminating stars are cooler than 22,000°K, the nebulosity tends to shine purely by reflected light; otherwise it may shine by fluorescence as well. Actually most emission regions in the Milky Way appear to be produced by clusters of O and B stars. The stars behind a reflection nebula are as completely hidden as those concealed by a dark cloud.

Extinction of starlight occurs not only in recognized dark areas but also in the "clear" regions of the Milky Way as Trumpler pointed out twenty years ago. The bright Milky Way from Perseus to the Sagittarius star clouds is all a region in which general absorption occurs when tested by the colors of distant early B stars. The obscuring material appears to be scattered hither and yon over the whole plane of the Milky Way in so irregular a fashion as to make a mean coefficient of extinction meaningless. Stebbins, Whitford, and Huffer found the colors of the B stars to vary irregularly even in small areas.

The effects of this general absorption appear in the measured distribution of external galaxies. Although these galaxies are probably randomly scattered in outer space, they seem to concentrate near the galactic poles and are almost completely absent from an irregular band about 30° wide around the whole galactic circle, the *zone of avoidance* of the spiral nebulae.

In addition to the absorbing medium, interstellar space also contains gas which leaves its imprint upon the spectra of distant stars or contributes a faint glow in certain regions of the Milky Way where electrons and protons recombine and faintly emit the Balmer lines.

Historically, the investigation of the interstellar medium was inspired by studies of galactic structure. We want to know the distances of faint stars whose spectral classes can be found. These stars are dimmed by interstellar matter, and we need to know the amount of the extinction. Unfortunately, we usually cannot measure the extinction directly. All we can find is the reddening produced by the medium, so we need the ratio of extinction to reddening.

This ratio may be found from the extrapolation of the wave-length law of extinction, but the character of the extrapolation will differ for metallic and dielectric grains. Hence we need to know the composition of the interstellar grains. Some information about the grains comes from a study of the diffuse light scattered by the particles between the stars and some clues come from a study of discrete clouds of material. Further help may come from a theory of the building of the grains, but the latter requires a knowledge of the composition of the gas, the temperature of the grains, etc. Hence purely astrophysical studies of the properties of the interstellar medium yield data of great value for the interpretation of the galaxy.

Some of the principal observational data for the study of the grains and the gas are the following:

I. Grains

    A. Average effect of all obscuring clouds
        1. Observations of the interstellar extinction as a function of wave length
        2. Scattering by diffuse interstellar material
        3. Polarization of the light of distant stars observed through the medium
    B. Effects of separate clouds
        1. Extinction and coloring of starlight by discrete dark clouds (e.g., dark lane in Aquila)
        2. Scattering of starlight by a diffuse-reflection nebula (e.g., Pleiades)
        3. Polarization of light by diffuse nebulae (e.g., *NGC* 7023)—not to be confused with the polarization of the light of remote stars observed through the medium

II. Interstellar gas

    A. Absorption lines
        1. Identifications which give the constituents of the medium

2. Measures of displacements which give the motions of the gases

3. Intensities giving the amount of material and its distribution in the line of sight

B. Emission lines

1. Extent and brightness of bright-line nebulosities and emission areas in the Milky Way, and the character of their spectra

2. The 21-cm radio-frequency emission giving important clues to the distribution and temperature of the neutral hydrogen gas

In the immediate neighborhood of the sun (which falls in a spiral arm) the total mass of the interstellar medium is of the order of that of the stars themselves. This is not true for the interarm regions or central bulge of our galaxy.

Baade's study of the Andromeda galaxy, Messier 31, shows conclusively that the spiral arms are arms of interstellar material—gas and solid particles. The gaseous nebulae and bright supergiant and blue stars that populate the arms are consequences of the presence of the particles and gas. The interstellar medium is absent between the arms and in the central bulge where the Type II population dominates. The Andromeda Spiral seems to be structurally similar to our galaxy. In the Triangulum Spiral, Messier 33, on the other hand, the gas and solid particles seem to be spread throughout most of the volume containing the stars. See Fig. 1.

Oort and his associates at Leiden find from the 21-cm radio-frequency radiation that the gas is confined to the spiral arms in our own galaxy. (See Sec. 9.)

Recently, W. W. Morgan, S. Sharpless, and D. Osterbrock have located the spiral arms of our own galaxy in the neighborhood of the sun. In order to accomplish this they studied the hydrogen emission nebulosities (many of which were of very low surface brightness) that are caused to shine by hot O and B stars associated with them. The distances of the B stars can be found from their spectroscopic parallaxes, with the criteria developed by Morgan. The distances of the O stars may be found from the intensities of the Ca II K line, the relation between K-line intensity and distance being determined from the data for the B stars. The resultant plot of the galactic longitudes and distances of these nebulosities serve to define two spiral arms in the neighborhood of the sun. Unfortunately the southern sky could not be reached, and evidence for a third arm closer to the center of the galaxy than the sun is fragmentary. The sun appears to be displaced about a

Fig. 1.—Emission Nebulosities in the Spiral Nebula, Messier 33

Each arrow indicates an Hα emission nebulosity measured on objective prism plates secured on Eastman 103a–E emulsion through a red plexiglas filter with the Curtis Schmidt telescope. Many of these objects were discovered by G. Haro with the Schmidt telescope of the Astrophysical Observatory, Tonanzintla, Mexico. (*Astron. Journal* **55**, 66, 1950.) Densities ranging from 10 to 50 ions/cm³ are found in most of these patches. The photograph upon which these emission nebulosities are marked was obtained by N. U. Mayall with the Crossley reflector at the Lick Observatory.

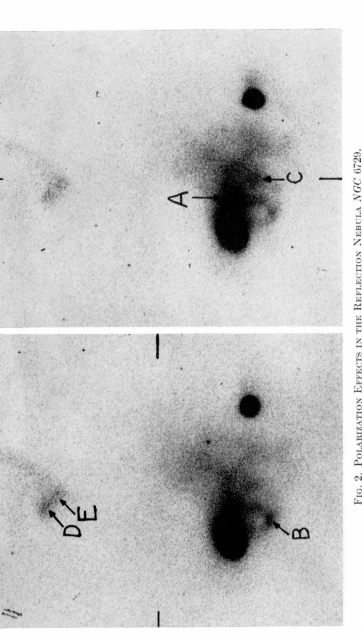

FIG. 2. POLARIZATION EFFECTS IN THE REFLECTION NEBULA *NGC* 6729.

The lines near the edges of the above pictures indicate the orientation of the axis of transmission of the Polaroid filter for each exposure. The presence of polarization can be readily seen when the intensity of *B* is compared with *C* in the two photographs. Also, compare *D* with *E*. The measured apparent polarizations are: *A* (the main body of the nebula, 12%; *B*, 17%; *C*, 3%; *D*, 17%; and *E*, 6%. Each feature is identified on that photograph (above) on which it has the higher intensity. With different settings of the axis of transmission of the Polaroid filter, the observed polarization of *B* probably would have been much larger. (Courtesy, E. B. Weston and W. T. Whitney, photograph from the McDonald Observatory.)

thousand light-years toward the galactic center from the center of one spiral arm which includes the S Monocerotis, Orion, ξ Persei and North America nebulosities, the great rift in the Milky Way, and the southern Coal Sack. A second spiral arm, parallel to the first, includes IC 410, NGC 281, NGC 7635, and NGC 7380, and is about 6000 light-years distant at its nearest point. Both arms are marked by supergiant and O and B stars that are not associated with any nebulosity.

2. The Extinction of Light by Small Particles

The absorbing medium between the stars extinguishes light selectively; i.e., it dims blue light more effectively than red light. In the visual region, the extinction varies roughly as $1/\lambda$, rather than as λ^{-4} as would be true for dielectric particles much smaller than the wave length of light. The particles responsible for extinction must be smaller than gross rocks, which would simply block the light, and yet much larger than molecules. They must obstruct, scatter, and diffract light.

Mie developed the theory of the optical effects of small spherical particles. Though the interstellar particles are probably rough, irregular and perhaps even crystalline in structure, rather than spherical in shape, the Mie theory may yet help us learn something of their size and character.* Schalén, Greenstein, van de Hulst, and others have studied this problem. Extensive calculations of the scattering and absorption properties of small particles have been carried out by Frank Gucker at Indiana University.

The problem to be solved is this: A plane light wave falls upon a spherical object of given size and refractive index. What amount of energy is taken away from the incident wave and how is this energy scattered in different directions or absorbed within the sphere itself? The problem is a straightforward one; the rigorous treatment involves a solution of Maxwell's equations for electromagnetic waves interacting with spherical obstacles. The solution comes out in terms of the parameters:

$$x = \frac{2\pi a}{\lambda} \tag{1}$$

*Experimental tests of the scattering in colloidal suspensions by small metal particles agree with the predictions of the theory, in so far as the wave-length dependence of scattered and transmitted intensities is involved. In a qualitative way, the Mie theory may be expected to predict the general optical behavior of the interstellar particles. The application of the optical properties deduced from large specimens of a given substance to predict the properties of the irregular tiny interstellar particles may not be entirely valid. The absorptivity of a metal depends on the surface polish and the existence of thin films on the surface, as well as on the purity of sample.

(where a is the radius of the sphere) and the complex index of refraction,

$$\tilde{n} = n + i\kappa \tag{2}$$

The Mie theory gives the dependence of the intensity and polarization of the scattered wave upon the angle θ between the direction considered and the direction of the incident beam. In general, the calculations are quite complicated. When x is small ($x < 0.6$), we may employ the generalized Rayleigh formula for small solid particles. If ρ is the density of the particles, the scattering coefficient per gram of the interstellar materials will be

$$S_\lambda = \frac{32\pi^4 a^3}{\rho\lambda^4} \left| \frac{\tilde{n}^2 - 1}{\tilde{n}^2 + 2} \right|^2 \tag{3}$$

where the vertical bars indicate that the absolute value must be taken. In a dielectric κ is negligible with respect to n. In a metal, κ will be large and there will be a large internal absorption which must be taken into account to get the total extinction coefficient. If $x < 0.3$, the mass absorption coefficient will be

$$k_\lambda = \frac{6\pi}{\rho\lambda} \operatorname{Im} \left| \frac{1 - \tilde{n}^2}{2 + \tilde{n}^2} \right| \tag{4}$$

where Im denotes that the imaginary part of the quantity in brackets is to be taken.

The optical properties of the spheres will depend on the sizes and the composition. The chemical composition determines n. In an ideal dielectric substance n is real, and the extinction coefficient is simply the scattering coefficient. When a light wave falls upon a metal, the electric field in the wave causes the free electrons to oscillate. As they do so, they dissipate energy in ohmic heating. Hence the energy of the light wave becomes absorbed and converted into heat. An ideal dielectric has no free electrons and therefore no ohmic heating. Such a substance must scatter, transmit, or reflect light without absorption.

For a perfect reflector, $\tilde{n} = \infty$, whereas for a perfect absorber, $\tilde{n} = -i\infty$. In either event, the electric field of the light wave never penetrates the sphere; the energy is all reflected or is all absorbed on the surface.

We define the *efficiency factor* Q as the ratio of the flux lost to the beam by scattering and absorption to the flux that is geometrically obstructed. That is

$$Q(x) = \frac{k_\lambda(x)}{N\pi a^2} \tag{5}$$

Here k_λ is the extinction coefficient, N is the number of particles per gram having a radius a. We may write

$$Q = Q_s + Q_A \tag{6}$$

where Q_S is the scattered component, and Q_A is proportional to the flux which is absorbed in the particle and transferred into heat.

For a given value of n, one may compute $Q(x)$. The curve starts with $Q = 0$ at $x = 0$, rises to a maximum where Q is about 4 or 5 and finally approaches 2 for $x = \infty$.* Fig. 3, due to van de Hulst, gives Q for values of $\tilde{n}$ ranging from 1.25 through 4/3 (ice crystals) to 2, which corresponds to heavy glasses, silica, and certain common rocks.

The corresponding curves for metals rise above the dielectric curves for $x < 1$. Thus for $x = 0.1$, $Q = 0.27$ for iron at $\lambda4430$, and 0.00034 for a perfect reflector. The scattering of any small particle ($a < < \lambda$) goes as a^6. The true absorption in a dielectric particle is negligible. On the other hand, the absorption due to ohmic heating in a similar metal grain is proportional to its volume and therefore to a^3. See Chapter *5,† page 124. Hence small metal particles are more effective at blocking radiation than are dielectric particles of the same size.

In the range of sizes where particles are most efficient in blocking radiation, the Q's of the dielectric particles exceed those of the metals and are much higher than either dielectrics or metals at $x < 1$. The dependence of extinction on wave length follows from Q. Let

$$\gamma = \frac{d \log Q}{d \log x} = \frac{dQ}{dx} \frac{x}{Q} \tag{7}$$

but

$$\frac{d\lambda}{\lambda} = -\frac{dx}{x} \tag{8}$$

whence

$$\frac{dQ}{d\lambda} = -x \frac{dQ}{\lambda \, dx}$$

$$\frac{dQ}{Q} = -\frac{d\lambda}{\lambda} \gamma$$

$$Q = C\lambda^{-\gamma} \tag{9}$$

*Diffraction causes the scattering efficiency to remain at twice the cross-section even for large objects. With increasing particle size, the diffraction pattern shrinks. For $a = 10^{-4}$ cm the first ring falls 18° from the central ray; at $a = 0.01$ cm, it has shrunk to 1', while for larger particles, the deflection of the scattered light from the beam is negligible. This explains the paradox that $Q = 2$ for large particles where the observed blocking cross-section obviously equals the geometrical cross-section.

†All references to chapters in the author's *Astrophysics—The Atmospheres of the Sun and Stars* (New York: The Ronald Press Co., 1953) will be designated in this volume by * before the chapter number.

When the particles are small compared with the wave lengths, the metallic absorption falls off less rapidly with λ ($1 \leq \gamma \leq 2$) than does dielectric extinction ($\gamma \geq 4$). This means that beyond $\lambda 10,000$ the increase in transparency will be smaller for metals than for dielectrics. Fortunately, it is possible to make observations as far in the infrared as

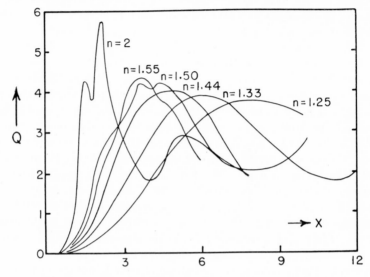

FIG. 3.—EFFICIENCY FACTOR FOR DIELECTRIC PARTICLES

Extinction curves showing the efficiency factor Q as a function of the size parameter, $x = 2\pi a/\lambda$, for various values of the refractive index n. (Courtesy, H. C. van de Hulst, *Utrecht Researches* 11, 21, part 2, 1949.)

$\lambda 20,000$ with the lead sulfide cell and thus to distinguish between these two alternatives.

Furthermore, metallic particles (not pure polished metals) have low reflectivities whereas many dielectrics such as ice will tend to have high reflectivities.

3. The Character of the Interstellar Grains

Earlier workers in the field of galactic structure supposed that absorbing material was confined to discrete dark clouds and that space elsewhere was clear. By 1930 it became evident that this picture had to be abandoned as it led to contradictions. The existence of a general absorbing medium was recognized and efforts were made to determine the mean coefficient of absorption as an aid to studies of the gross features of the galactic system. Considerable attention was paid to the law of reddening, and, subsequently, efforts were made to ascertain the size distribution and nature of the grains responsible for the extinction of light.

Presumably, diffuse reflection nebulae, such as those near the Pleiades, are composed of small particles of the same character as those of the interstellar medium. Hence we may learn important facts, not only from the wave-length extinction law in the general interstellar medium, but also from studies of the diffusion, reflection, and polarization of light in reflection nebulae.

Although the grains responsible for the interstellar reddening must fall in the range 10^{-5} to 10^{-3} cm radius, we must ask if there can be appreciable amounts of material in the form of larger particles that would contribute to the mass of the interstellar medium and simply block the light of distant stars. Chunks with diameters exceeding an inch can play no important role. A dark cloud which owed an appreciable fraction of its opacity to such fragments would be so massive as to have a pronounced effect on the motions of included stars.

The fact that the total mass of the interstellar material in the neighborhood of the sun is less than 3×10^{-24} gm/cm^3 implies that if the blocking of distant starlight were due entirely to grains, their sizes would be less than 4×10^{-3} cm radius. Such particles might exist in clouds. Were grains of some fixed radius between 0.01 cm and 0.001 cm numerous, bright stars seen through such clouds would show diffraction rings. Such haloes have never been observed, and we may conclude either that grains of these dimensions are not present in appreciable numbers or that a range of sizes exists.

In a reflection nebula, such as one in the Pleiades, we observe not only the reflected light of the star, but also light that is thrown in our direction after repeated scattering by particles in the nebula. The Rayleigh law

$$I_{\text{diff}} \sim \text{constant} \times \lambda^{-4} I_{\text{incident}} \qquad (10)$$

could be expected to hold only for a thin nebula composed of particles much smaller than the wave length of light. An exact interpretation of the colors, however, requires a theory of scattering of starlight in a nebula such as that developed by Henyey and Greenstein.

Rayleigh scattering requires that the illumination observed at right angles to the incident ray be completely polarized. In reality the polarization could never be complete because the particles receive light scattered from one another as well as from the central star. W. F. Meyer found polarization effects of less than 10 per cent in *NGC* 2261, and studies of the nebulosity around ρ Ophiuchi by Struve, Elvey, and Roach, and of the γ Cygni Nebula by Henyey indicate not more than 12 per cent polarization. In most objects it could not be detected.

In *NGC* 6729, W. T. Whitney and E. B. Weston found a maximum polarization of 15 per cent. See Fig. 2. Thus the polarization effects also speak against a high percentage of scattering by particles according to Rayleigh's law. We must not confuse these polarization effects with those recently discovered by Hall and Hiltner for *transmitted* starlight!

In connection with the absorption of light in space we are interested in two questions: What is the wave-length law of absorption, and what is the ratio of the coloring effect of the medium to the total amount of absorption as measured at some particular wave length, e.g., λ4400?

The standard procedure for the determination of the wave-length law of absorption is to compare the energy distribution of a reddened star with that of an unobscured star of the same spectral class. The earlier work was done mostly by photographic photometry. For example, W. Baade and R. Minkowski measured the energy distribution in several reddened stars in Orion and Perseus, while W. W. Morgan and G. W. Wares compared the reddened star 13 Cephei with the normal star σ Cygni, stars which have a similar spectral type and absolute magnitude and distances. These researches indicated that the extinction in most instances is nearly a linear function of 1/λ.*

The most precise determination of the wave-length law of interstellar absorption is that by Stebbins and Whitford who measured the magnitudes of stars in six colors from λ3350 to λ10,300 by photoelectric photometry. They compared reddened and unreddened *B* stars by forming the differences between the observed magnitudes at six effective wave lengths. Although the 1/λ law may serve as a rough approximation, they remark: "the deviation of the selective absorption from the 1/λ law is not subtle; it is conspicuous in the galvanometer readings of every strongly reddened *B*-star."†

Whitford has extended the study to λ21,000 in the infrared with the aid of a lead sulfide cell, while Stebbins has made measurements at λ3200 with a silver filter. We give here the extinction in magnitudes found from a comparison of ε Persei with the reddened star, ζ Persei, reduced to an extinction difference (V − I) between λ4220 and λ10,300

Filter	Silver	U	V	B	G	R	I	I₂
Wave length (Angstroms)	3200	3530	4220	4880	5700	7190	10,300	21,000
Δ magnitude	+1.30	1.18	1.00	0.81	0.64	0.35	0.00	−0.14

*For example, see the discussion by J. Hall, *Ap. J.* **85**, 145, 1937.
†*Ap. J.* **102**, 318, 1945.

of one magnitude.* Whitford combines these data with observations of other stars in the infrared and with his and Stebbins' previous measurements of reddened B stars to obtain the final curve shown in Fig. 4. Notice that although the curve approximately follows the dashed $1/\lambda$ line, deviations seem to occur both in the ultraviolet and in the infrared. The leveling off of the absorption in the far infrared indicates an approach to the λ^{-4} law. In the far infrared, the particle sizes are much smaller than the wave length of light. This strongly suggests that dielectric particles rather than metallic particles are responsible for the extinction of starlight. The shape of the curve also throws some light on the size distribution of the particles. (See Sec. 7.)

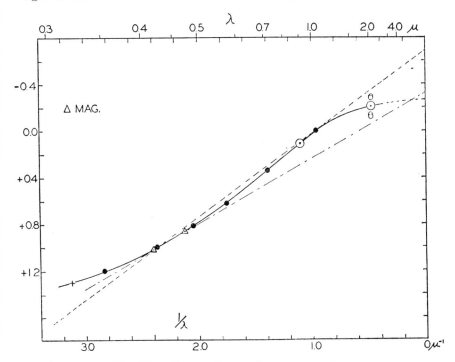

Fig. 4.—The Wave-Length Law of Interstellar Absorption

The curve shows the mean interstellar absorption in magnitudes from four pairs of stars reduced to $V - 1 = 1^m00$. Filled circles are six-color observations; small open circles are individual lead sulfide observations with large open circles showing the mean; and the cross is the silver-filter observation on one pair only. The triangles show the baseline of the E_1 colors. Notice that the dotted line extrapolation of the previously existing data (represented by the black dots) leads to an improbably high value of the ratio A_{pg}/E_1, whereas the extrapolation of the base line of the E_1 colors gives a value much closer to the correct one. (Courtesy, A. E. Whitford, *Astrophysical Journal*, University of Chicago Press, **107**, 105, 1948.)

*Ap. J., **107**, 104, 1948.

Although the reddening law appears to be pretty much the same from one part of the galaxy to another, an important exception must be mentioned. Baade and Minkowski found that certain stars in the Orion Nebula did not follow the usual law. θ Orionis and other stars were affected by a strong selective absorption that increases rapidly from $\lambda 9000$ to $\lambda 6000$ and shows a less rapid variation in the interval $\lambda 6000$ to $\lambda 4000$ than do normally reddened stars. Baade and Minkowski found the average particle size to be larger than for other clouds and suggested that in Orion radiation pressure drove the small particles away from the stars. From the theoretical dependence of the absorptivity upon the particle-size distribution, van de Hulst concluded that the particles in front of θ_1 Orionis are larger than those in ordinary clouds by a factor of about 1.3 and have a somewhat stronger internal absorption than the ordinary interstellar grains. Apparently the hot stars expel many of the small particles by radiation pressure. If we exclude the Orion region and the highly excited central parts of certain other nebulae, the reddening law seems to be uniform throughout the Milky Way to the first approximation. Further spectrophotometric checks are, however, desirable.

The effect of the interstellar light absorption on the color index of a star is measured by the *color excess E*. This quantity is the difference between the observed color index c, which may be affected by space absorption, and the intrinsic color index, C, viz.:

$$E = c - C \qquad (11)$$

The true color index C can usually be estimated from the spectral class. The color excess E will depend on the wave-length range employed. If photographic and photovisual magnitudes are employed, the color excess E is a measure of the differential absorption between $\lambda 4250$ and $\lambda 5500$—the effective wave lengths of the photographic and photovisual systems. The most extensive set of accurate color measurements are those by Stebbins and Huffer who employed a base line $\lambda 4170$ to $\lambda 4710$ for stars of effective temperature 20,000°K; the corresponding color indices are designated as E_1.

A quantity of fundamental interest is the ratio of total absorption A_{pg} at some specified wave length, e.g., $\lambda 4400$, to the color excess; viz.: A_{pg}/E or A_{pg}/E_1. If we can establish this ratio accurately and prove that it remains constant in different regions of the galaxy, we will have a powerful tool for the study of galactic structure. For any star of known spectral class we may measure the color excess E. If A_{pg}/E is known, it is possible to find the total extinction A_{pg} and hence the undimmed apparent brightness of the star.

Several methods have been proposed for measuring this ratio. One of them consists of comparing star counts in regions where the stars are reddened with counts in nearby supposedly unobscured regions where the actual stellar density is supposed to be the same. Another method utilizes the colors of stars of known luminosity behind a well-defined dark nebula. For a dark cloud in Auriga, Schalén found $A_{pg} = 1.9$, and $E = 0.21$ ($\lambda 3950 - \lambda 4400$), whence $A_{pg}/E_1 = 9.0$. Analysis of star count data secured by C. E. Smith led R. J. Trumpler and the writer to a value $A_{pg}/E_1 = 6.3$, which appears to be too small. In other analyses, ratios ranging from 6.7 to 13 have been found.

Stebbins and Whitford compared photoelectrically the brightness and color of one of the dark lanes in the Andromeda Spiral Messier 31 with the corresponding measure for a symmetrically placed region on the other side of the center. They find $A_{pg}/E = 4.0 \pm 0.2$. Unfortunately, the interpretation of these observations rests upon unproven assumptions.

From the photoelectric color work, Greenstein and Henyey derived $A_{pg}/E_1 = 8.1 \pm 0.4$. Van Rhijn found a value of 8.2 from a discussion of all the available material.

Whitford's data appear to settle the question. In Fig. 4 the wave lengths of the E_1 color system are indicated by triangles. Note that a straight line through these points cuts the $1/\lambda$-axis near the extrapolated intersection of the observed curve. By coincidence, the ratios between total absorption and color excess, $A_{pg}/E_1 = 9$, derived by Stebbins, Whitford, and Huffer in 1939-40 on the basis of the then-assumed $1/\lambda$ law, falls close to the true value. Since $E/E_1 = 1.81$, this result agrees reasonably well with that obtained for Messier 31 and with Greenstein and Henyey's results. W. W. Morgan, D. Harris, and H. Johnson found the visual absorption to be related to the color excess by $A_{vis} = 6.1E_1$.

H. C. van de Hulst showed that a good representation of the observed extinction law could be obtained with a distribution function of particle sizes given by the theory of grain formation and destruction (see Sec. 7). Particles of the order of 0.4 to 0.5μ are most effective in blocking the light and the average density of the grains in the neighborhood of the sun is 1.4×10^{-26} gm/cm^3. That is, the mass contributed per unit volume by the grains is about 1/300 that contributed by the inter-stellar gas.

What information can be found about the albedoes of the interstellar grains? If the albedoes are high dielectrics are indicated; if they are low, the particles may be metallic. The fundamental investigation on reflection nebulae was that by Hubble who established the relation between the luminosity of the nebula and the magnitude of the included star.

Consider a star of apparent magnitude m_1, and luminosity L_1 placed in a uniform medium of reflecting particles. Let us suppose that for a given telescope, exposure time, and photographic emulsion, the angular diameter of the recorded image is a_1. The intensity I_0 of the light reflected from the nebula at this point will be proportional to $L_1/R^2 a_1^2$, where R is the distance of the sun from the nebula in parsecs. The apparent luminosity l_1 of the star varies as L_1/R^2; hence, $I_0 \sim l_1/a_1^2$. Now I_0 is a constant which corresponds to the threshold of the instrumental arrangement. If we express the apparent luminosity l_1 in magnitudes, there results a relationship of the form $m_1 + 5 \log a_1 = K$, where K depends on the reflectivity and the spatial orientation of the nebula, and the limiting detectable surface brightness. The observed relationship was

$$m_1 + (4.90 \pm 0.13) \log a_1 = 11.02 \pm 0.10 \qquad (12)$$

Hubble calculated the theoretical value of the constant on the right-hand side of the equation on the assumption that the inverse square law is valid and that all the starlight intercepted by the nebula is re-emitted. The surface brightness is determined by spreading the luminosity of the central star over a spherical shell of radius a. In magnitudes per square second of arc, this surface brightness will be

$$m + 2.5 \log 4\pi(60a)^2 = m + 2.5 \log a^2 + 11.64 \qquad (13)$$

Seares found the limiting surface brightness of an exposure of one minute on a Seed 30 plate with an $f/5$ reflector to be 18.8 magnitudes per square second of arc. The limiting surface brightness of a 60-minute exposure (neglecting the reciprocity failure of the photographic emulsion) will be $18.8 + 2.5 \times \log 60 = 23.25$. Equating this number to the preceding expression we find

$$m + 5 \log a = 11.61 \qquad (14)$$

If one assumes a random distribution of directions from the star to the nebula, the mean observed a, projected on a plane perpendicular to the line of sight, would be less than the true a. Hubble concluded that eqn. (14) should be corrected to

$$m + 5 \log a = 10.63 \qquad (15)$$

whereas Zanstra later showed the constant to be 11.09. The agreement between observation and simple theory is good. Concerning the results of his observations, Hubble* remarks: "The general conclusion from this observation is that within the errors of observation, the data can be represented by the hypothesis that the diffuse nebulae derive their

*$Ap. J.$ **56**, 400, 1922.

luminosity from involved or neighboring stars and they emit at each point exactly the amount of radiation they receive from the stars."

The remarkable fact was that the emission nebulae appeared to follow the same law as nebulae with continuous spectra! This result is particularly surprising when we recall that bright lines originate by fluorescent processes and electron excitation, and their intensities depend on the far ultraviolet spectrum of the central star. Perhaps line radiation contributes relatively little to the total surface brightnesses of these objects. Hubble made a similar study of the planetary nebulae and found them to be systematically brighter than their central stars.

It is remarkable that Hubble's relation holds even for pure reflection nebulae. A shell thick enough to interrupt all starlight falling upon it would be sufficiently opaque for the scattered light to be somewhat dimmed. Possibly the extreme patchiness of the diffuse nebulae permits us to see relatively opaque slabs, which are themselves not obscured by material lying in front of them. Even so, some light loss must occur in these slabs.

Struve and Miss Story made a statistical study of the nebulae discussed by Hubble. They found that the nebulae with continuous spectra tend to be more opaque than emission nebulae. The optical thicknesses frequently amounted to only a few tenths.

The theory of the reflection and scattering of starlight in a cloud of discrete particles was first given by Seeliger and extended by Henyey, Greenstein, and others. (See Problem 4.) The scattering is governed by the albedo γ and the phase function $\varphi(\alpha)$, which determines the angular distribution of the scattered light. Here α is the angle between the initial and the scattered ray. For isotropic scattering $\varphi(\alpha)$ is 1; for Rayleigh scattering $\varphi(\alpha)$ varies as $(1 + \cos^2 \alpha)$. A determination of $\varphi(\alpha)$, if possible, would help determine the size of the particle, since $\varphi(\alpha)$ is a function of the ratio of the particle radius to the wave length of light. Backward-throwing phase functions correspond to particles with radii of 0.01 to 1 cm; forward-throwing phase functions to much smaller particles.

Henyey and Greenstein developed a theory of the colors of reflection nebulae on the basis of a detailed transfer theory. The spectral energy distribution of the scattered radiation depends on the absorption coefficient and the scattering efficiency of the grains. Since these properties depend on the intrinsic character of the material, the goal is to determine them from a study of the nebular colors. The theory should enable us to disentangle the color effects of physical interest from those which depend only on the fact that we observe not one, but many particles.

Starlight passes through part of the nebula before it is scattered by the grains, and the scattered light must pass through some of the nebula before it reaches the observer. The bluing by scattering may be counteracted by the reddening by transmission. Thus they find that if the star is in front of the nebula, the color of the nebula approaches that of the star as the opacity is increased. If the nebula is in front of the star, it will always be bluer, and if the star is immersed in the nebula, the partial obscuration of the star by the nebulous material will produce an additional bluing of the nebula relative to the star. If the albedo depends on wave length, and if the light is scattered several times in the course of its passage through the nebula, slight albedo variations will be greatly exaggerated.

Since the optical properties, including extinction coefficient, albedo, and phase function may be calculated by theory for different kinds of grains (metals or dielectrics), the Henyey-Greenstein theory may be employed to predict the colors and brightnesses of diffuse nebulae for comparison with observation.

Unfortunately, the complications of the problem, arising from the unknown position of the star with respect to the nebula and the orientation of the nebula in space, limit the amount of information obtainable from studies of reflection nebulae. The investigations do suggest, that the albedo γ of an interstellar grain is high; Henyey found $\gamma = 0.6$ for several nebulae. An application of Seeliger's theory to pure reflection nebulae suggests that γ is about 0.7 for the thick cloud near ρ Ophiuchi.

In addition to the bright reflection nebulae we must also consider the illumination of the obscuring clouds scattered throughout the galactic plane. It was realized some years ago that a large conspicuous dark cloud, such as the Coal Sack or Horse Head Nebulae, should have a high scattering power because of its great optical thickness. Since it is dimly illuminated, it should be brighter than the background between the stars in the nearby Milky Way, provided space is relatively transparent. However, in 1937 Struve and Elvey found the surface brightnesses of some of Barnard's dark areas to be fainter than the background of the sky between the stars in the star clouds. If the region of the star clouds were transparent, dimly reflecting dark nebulae should be brighter than they observed. Therefore, either the grains composing the nebula had low albedoes, or there existed scattering material in the star clouds of the Milky Way. From photoelectric measures of the surface brightness of the night sky, Elvey and Roach showed that this second hypothesis was correct. The diffuse galactic light amounted to 57 tenth magnitude stars per square degree. Henyey and Greenstein measured photographically the brightness of the galactic radiation over a wide range of galactic latitude in Cygnus and in Taurus. On the assumption that the scattering layers were stratified in parallel

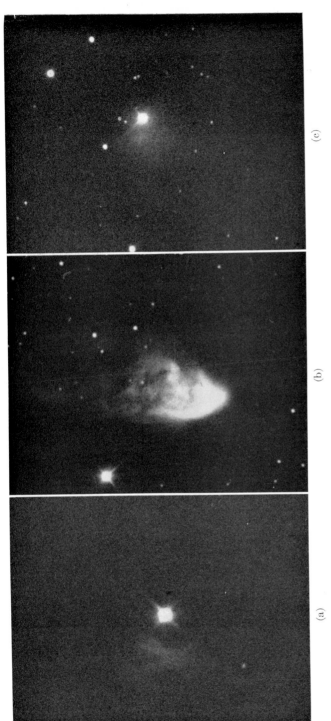

(a)

(b)

(c)

Fig. 5.—Three Stars of the T Tauri Type

(a) Hind's Nebula associated with T Tauri (Oct. 28, 1952). The brightness of the nebula changes slowly with time.

(b) Hubble's variable nebula, *NGC* 2261, associated with R Monocerotis (Oct. 26, 1952). The star is near the bottom of the nebula. The details of the nebula show conspicuous changes, evidently due to shadows cast by moving obscuring clouds passing close to the star. The same features reappear after several years.

(c) RY Tauri and its associated nebula (Oct. 28, 1952).

(Photographed with the 60-inch reflector at the Mount Wilson Observatory.)

(Continued on the following page)

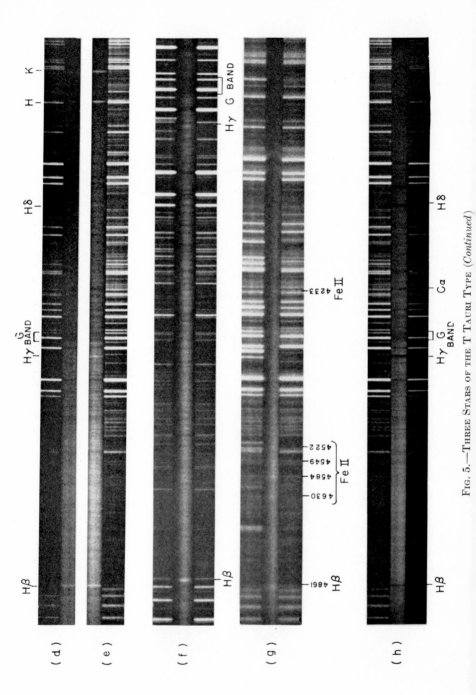

FIG. 5.—THREE STARS OF THE T TAURI TYPE (*Continued*)

planes, and by trying different hypotheses about the size and kind of particle, they showed that the phase function must be strongly forward throwing and that γ must exceed 0.3, a result in accord with those found from diffuse reflection nebulae.

Clues to the character of dense clouds of grains may eventually come from studies of the T Tauri variables. These stars have been studied in greatest detail by Joy, Herbig, and Greenstein. They appear as G, K, and M dwarfs which are immersed in dark nebulae and show bright lines of hydrogen and the metals. Giant stars in dark clouds do not show these bright-line characteristics. Presumably the material of the interstellar medium is being accreted by the stars; grains composed primarily of abundant elements may approach close enough to these stars for evaporation and subsequent line excitation of the liberated gases to occur.

A number of T Tauri stars and related objects are associated with small diffuse nebulae (see Fig. 5), e.g., T Tauri itself, RY Tauri, R Monocerotis, and R Coronae Austrinis. It is probable that in some of these objects we do not observe the spectrum of the star itself but simply the spectrum of an excited inner region of the nebula. Rapid, as well as long-term, changes are sometimes observed in the spectra of T Tauri stars.

4. The Interstellar Gas (Kinematics and Distribution)

Most of the interstellar material in our part of the galaxy occurs not in the form of small particles that block and color the light of distant stars, but rather in the gaseous state. In 1904 Hartmann noticed that sharp and narrow Ca II lines in the spectroscopic binary δ Orionis did not share in the periodic velocity shifts of the diffuse H and He lines which originated in the stellar atmosphere. Instead, they remained fixed in position. Subsequently, from measures of these so-called stationary lines in early type stars, V. M. Slipher suggested that the calcium lines originated in an extensive gas cloud widely spread among the stars. In 1919 Miss Heger found sharp stationary D lines of sodium

---

←——— Fig. 5.—Three Stars of the T Tauri Type (*Continued*)

(d) Spectrum of T Tauri (Sept. 6, 1950).

(e) Spectrum of T Tauri (Sept. 7, 1950). Notice the increase in the intensities of the emission lines. $H\gamma$ is nearly absent on Sept. 6 and strong in emission on Sept. 7. These rapid changes may be similar to the "flares" observed in M dwarf stars.

(f) Spectrum of T Tauri (Oct. 13, 1951). Notice the absorption lines characteristic of a G-type dwarf.

(g) Spectrum of R Monocerotis (Nov. 25, 1951). Upon a spectrum which is nearly continuous are superposed emission lines of hydrogen and Fe II.

(h) Spectrum of RY Tauri (Oct. 18, 1950). This plate shows no emission lines.

(Spectrograms secured at University of Michigan Observatory.)

in the spectra of certain O stars observed at the Lick Observatory. Since then, extensive studies at Victoria and Mount Wilson have revealed lines of other atoms and even molecules, as well as certain unidentified diffuse features.

Almost without exception, interstellar lines represent transitions from the lowest level of the atom or molecule in question. The Ti II lines observed by Adams and Dunham provide an example in point. Only absorption lines from the lowest $(J = \frac{3}{2})$ level of the ground a^4F term appear, while lines arising from the $J = \frac{5}{2}, \frac{7}{2}$, and $\frac{9}{2}$ levels are missing, even though the $J = \frac{5}{2}$ level lies but 0.012 ev above the ground level! Evidently, collisional excitation to the upper levels of the ^4F term must be infrequent, perhaps minutes or even hours apart, since the lifetime of the $^4F_{5/2}$ level is 28 seconds.

All that appear of the rich band spectra of the molecules are lines arising from the lowest rotational state of the lowest vibrational level. The radiation density is too low to excite appreciable numbers of molecules to higher levels. Inelastic collisions with electrons are so infrequent that the molecules always have ample time to return to the ground level before they can absorb a quantum of energy. Swings and Rosenfeld identified with CH the sharp λ4303.3 line observed by Dunham. Later, McKellar suggested this identification could be confirmed if other lines arising from the lowest level, viz., λ3886.3, λ3878.7, and λ3890.2, could be observed. Soon thereafter, Adams found these three CH lines with the expected intensities in the spectrum of ζ Ophiuchi. Since then, λ4232.57 and λ3745.33 have been identified with CH$^+$, while λ3874.63 is known to arise from CN. It seems likely that other hydrides, such as NH and OH and possibly also C_2, may exist in interstellar space. Expected lines of NH and OH fall in the observable ultraviolet at λ3357.8 and λ3078.4, respectively.

We can expect to observe only the ions of abundant elements whose lines fall in the observable range λ3000–λ10,000. A high ionization potential for the ion concerned, or at least for the next higher ionization stage, is necessary for the appearance of an interstellar line. Otherwise the atom in question will become highly ionized, and it will have no chance to recapture a free electron to form an ion which can absorb lines in the observable region. For example, aluminum exists mostly in the ionized condition, and its resonance lines cannot be observed. The effect of abundance plays an important role here. Detection of an ion is favored if it has only one or two lines with large f-values which arise from the ground level. Iron is an abundant element, but it has several lines from the ground level, each with a small f-value, and the observed lines are weak. On the other hand, Sc II, Sr II, and Ba II, whose lines fall in the observable range, appear to be too rare, cosmically speaking.

Among the unidentified interstellar absorptions are the diffuse features at $\lambda5780.4$, $\lambda5796.9$, $\lambda6283.9$, and $\lambda6613.9$, discovered by Merrill in 1934, and the broad, diffuse, symmetrical absorption extending from $\lambda4410$ to $\lambda4450$, which was discovered to be interstellar by Merrill and further studied by Beals and Blanchet, by Greenstein and Aller, and by Duke. See Fig. 6. The intensity of the diffuse $\lambda4430$ line is

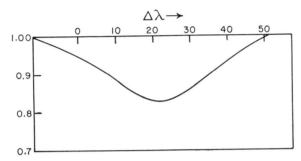

FIG. 6.—THE PROFILE OF THE DIFFUSE INTERSTELLAR FEATURE AT $\lambda4430$ IN
HD 183143

Notice the broad symmetrical character of the profile. (Courtesy, The McDonald Observatory.)

most strongly correlated with $\lambda6284$, is moderately well correlated with interstellar reddening, and may be connected with interstellar polarization. Such diffuse lines occur, for example, in the solid states of molecules that have incomplete inner shells of electrons. These substances are frequently paramagnetic, e.g., the iron alums. The $\lambda4430$ line is abnormally weak in the Orion nebulosity.

Among the first questions to be answered about the interstellar gas are these: Is the material spread uniformly or is it concentrated in discrete clouds? How are the line intensities to be correlated with the distances of the stars upon whose spectra they appear?

Direct observations of the diffuse nebulae suggest that grains and gas often tend to concentrate together.

Perhaps the best example in point is the vast diffuse Orion Nebula, which is about 500 parsecs distant from us. The inner bright region is about 4' in radius, or 0.6 parsecs. Greenstein has estimated the total mass of the hydrogen gas to be about ten times that of the sun. The gas density is high (about 10^4 ions/cm^3) at least in the bright part, and the heavy obscuration nearby shows that grains are concentrated in this region. The bright hot stars of the Trapezium excite a typical nebular spectrum in the luminous nebulosity. The whole Orion aggregate forms an association of hot stars and bright and dark nebulosity. The ratio $A_{pg}/E_1 = 14$ is abnormally high in the Orion region. In the nearby Taurus region, where the obscuration is also heavy, there are no hot stars to excite abundant gases such as hydrogen or oxygen, which may be present in large quantities.

Under these circumstances we might expect a strong correlation between reddening and interstellar K-line intensity. Actually, the correlation is weak, indicating that the density of Ca II ions is not strictly proportional to the particle density. Since the proportion of calcium atoms in the singly ionized state is strongly affected by the ionization equilibrium, the ratio of the number of Ca II ions/cm³ to the total number of gaseous atoms/cm³ is not constant from point to point.

Since 1928, when Struve demonstrated the intensity of the interstellar lines to be correlated with distance, many investigators have studied the problem and have shown that the intensity–distance relationship is complicated by the effects of galactic rotation, thermal motions of the atoms, occurrence of the gas in spiral arms, and the relative velocities of the discrete clouds in which the atoms are concentrated.

Consider the relationship between the equivalent width of an interstellar line and the number of atoms acting to absorb it. If the atoms are in thermal motion at a temperature T and the medium is at rest, a curve of growth computed for Doppler broadening and natural damping ought to represent the observations. Thus the D lines of sodium ought to show an intensity ratio of 2:1 when very weak, should be about equal in intensity when both are strong enough to fall on the flat part of the curve of growth, and show a ratio of 1.41/1 when so strong as to fall on the damping portion. Lines on the square root portion of the curve of growth have not been observed.

If the medium shares in galactic rotation, different parts will have different relative velocities. In those directions where the relative motions are zero (null points), our simplified picture should be valid; but where the relative motions are large, the effective absorption frequencies of atoms at different distances along the line of sight will be displaced, and the qualitative effect will be similar to an increase in v; hence the lines will be stronger than in stars at the null points, even though the number of atoms along the line of sight remains the same.

With these considerations in mind, O. C. Wilson and P. W. Merrill analyzed the intensities of the interstellar D lines in 200 stars well distributed over the Milky Way. As might have been anticipated, the observed intensities did not fit the theoretical curve of growth for the static medium. More specifically, the D lines in distant stars near the nulls of galactic rotation have much the same strength as in distant stars at other galactic longitudes. In other words, at all longitudes the D lines seem to increase in strength at about the same rate with increasing distance. Thus some widening effect other than galactic rotation must be present. The importance of this widening effect is evidenced by the fact that the D lines tend to be saturated at distances of only a few hundred parsecs; i.e., the ratio of D_2/D_1 falls below 1.2 for stars only 500 to 1000 parsecs away. If increasing distance simply increased the number of absorbing atoms, the intensity of the D lines would be changed only slightly, in view of this already high saturation. Actually, the intensity tends to increase in direct proportion to the distance. Wilson and Merrill suggested that the D lines were absorbed in separate clouds, moving with random velocities at speeds of some 15 km/sec.

Direct evidence for the existence of such discrete clouds had already been found by Beals, who noticed that interstellar lines in Orion show complicated structures. Subsequently, Adams has studied the complex structure of the H and K lines in 300 stars. In some regions as many as five components were observed. Their narrowness gives strong evidence for the discrete character of the clouds and the absence of any appreciable internal turbulence. Radial velocity measures serve to distinguish clouds lying in the same direction from us but at different distances. Thus in Lacerta there is a primary cloud with a velocity of -2 km/sec, and a second and thinner cloud with -24 km/sec; the cloud in Perseus had a residual velocity of $+5$ km/sec; while the stars near the belt of Orion reveal two clouds, one with $+7$ km/sec and the other with -15 km/sec.

By a comparison of the radial velocities of the other constituents of the interstellar medium with H and K, Adams was able to show which component belonged to which cloud. Thus Ca I and Fe I appear only in stars with strong interstellar H and K, while the diatomic molecules CN, CH, and CH^+ may occur when H and K are relatively weak. Neutral and ionized CH show marked differences in intensity in different stars; e.g., CH^+ is not found in Orion. With distances for the background stars supplied by W. W. Morgan, Whipple carried out a detailed analysis of Adams' data. He finds 6 to 8 gas clouds per kiloparsec along the line of sight near the galactic plane. From a comparison of the K line in different stars, Whipple found that lines of the same cloud would sometimes appear in two or more stars. In this way he identified 34 clouds and found a tendency for the clouds with weaker lines, presumably the less massive ones, to move with greater velocity. The smaller clouds had a root mean square velocity of 35 km/sec and the larger ones a velocity of 10 km/sec. Under this hypothesis the larger clouds might have been formed from the smaller ones by amalgamation.

A more likely explanation (Blaauw and van de Hulst) is that the stronger and least displaced lines are simply blends of several smaller components. There is no need to imagine amalgamated clouds. In addition, measurement of the radial velocities of the individual clouds indicates that on the average these share in the general galactic rotation. In fact, the radial velocities found for the D lines in distant stars far from the nulls of galactic rotation can be used to give an approximate indication of the distance of the star. The presence of galactic rotation in the interstellar clouds provides an additional widening produced by individual motions of the clouds.

With the Palomar coudé spectrograph Münch has investigated the interstellar K line in faint, remote B stars. He has been able to separate components arising in the two spiral arms located by Morgan and his associates. Multiple lines are produced because of absorption in distinct gas concentrations in the two spiral arms. Münch found one star that showed as many as nine components.

What can be said about the spatial relation between the gas clouds and the grains that produce the extinction? Spitzer's comparison of D line intensities and color excesses in remote stars indicates that a cloud of gas is also a cloud of solid particles. Analysis of the curve of growth shows that in reddened stars where E_1 exceeds 0.10, the D lines are produced in a number of relatively opaque clouds, each with an optical depth of about 5 in the center of the D_2 line. The density of neutral sodium atoms in a typical cloud appears to be about 5×10^{-8} atoms/cm^3. The color excess E_1 produced by one such cloud is between 0.02 and 0.03 magnitudes, and the cloud radius is between 5 and 10 parsecs. In stars with E_1 less than 0.01 the lines seem to be produced in less opaque clouds, and the optical depth through a single cloud at the center of the line is less than 1.0. The clouds in front of θ_1 Orionis, which shows the abnormal extinction law, have a high color excess but weak D lines. We have already seen that the smaller grains are apparently missing here and sodium atoms likewise seem to be relatively scarce.

The density of grains in the space between the clouds has been estimated as about one-fifth of the average density. For a fuller discussion the reader is referred to the arguments by Oort.*

The quantities of metals in interstellar space are small. The observed molecules show that carbon, nitrogen, and hydrogen are present, and if the composition of the interstellar medium is similar to that of stars

*B.A.N. **8**, 245, 1938.

and of gaseous nebulae we would expect these elements to be abundant. The atoms of these light elements would be detectable (if at all) only by their emission spectra, since the resonance lines all fall in the inaccessible ultraviolet.

With a specially designed nebular spectrograph, Struve and his colleagues looked for the Balmer recombination lines of hydrogen and the forbidden lines of oxygen. They found large regions of the Milky Way, some of which show a slightly milky background on the direct photographs of Ross and Barnard, where H, [O II] λ3727, possibly [N II] λ6548, λ6584, and sometimes [O III] λ4959, λ5007 appear in emission. No such regions are found in high galactic latitudes. The hydrogen emission regions in Cygnus, Cepheus, and Monoceros seem roughly circular, and sharply bounded on the outside. Although these faint emission areas seem associated with groups of the hot O stars, they differ from the ordinary gaseous nebulae in that they show little concentration to individual early type stars. When [O III] is observed in emission, it occurs in the central parts of the hydrogen regions without any sharp boundaries. The intensity ratio, λ3727/λ6563, i.e., [O II] to (H + [N II]?) is large in the Monoceros and Canis Major regions and small in the summer Milky Way, Cepheus to Sagittarius, showing that different physical conditions exist in different parts of the galaxy.

Strömgren and Hiltner have recently carried out observations with a photomultiplier and an interference filter that isolates the light of Hβ. They find that these emission regions, which are not visible in integrated light, show clouds comparable in density with the clouds of gas that are revealed by the absorption lines of sodium or calcium. The diffuse nebulae, observed in integrated light or in red filter photographs, are denser clouds comparable with the one in front of $χ^2$ Orionis and which produces strong interstellar lines. Brighter diffuse nebulae, like Orion, are ten thousand times more intense than the fainter emission regions.

With the Greenstein-Henyey wide-angle camera and appropriate plate and filter combinations, Sharpless and Osterbrock were able to photograph a number of faint hydrogen emission regions in which the electron density was of the order of 2 or 3 particles/cm^3.

5. Density and Composition of the Interstellar Gas

If we can suppose that they are both produced in the same region of space, the simultaneous presence of λ4226 of Ca I and the H and K lines of Ca II suggests a means of estimating the partition of atoms among the various stages of ionization. From the measured equivalent widths of various interstellar lines, or from theory, one may construct a curve of growth from which he can read the ratio of ionized to neutral calcium. Then, if the intensity distribution $I(\nu)$ of the radiation impinging upon the interstellar atoms can be obtained from the spectral types and temperatures of the surrounding stars, the electron density N_e can be found from the appropriate ionization equation. With N_e and $I(\nu)$ known, the distribution of other elements among their ionization stages may be found.

Dunham measured the equivalent widths of lines of Na I, Ca I, Ca II, and Ti II in the $cB1$ star, χ^2 Orionis, whose distance is 725 parsecs. He used the four sodium lines, $\lambda 3302$, $\lambda 3303$, $\lambda 5890$, and $\lambda 5896$, whose f-values are known, to establish the form of the empirical curve of growth, from a plot of the observed quantity, $F = 10^6 \, W/\lambda$ against $\log f\lambda$. To determine n, the number of atoms in the line of sight, he made use of the condition that for weak lines the relation

$$F = 10^6 \, \frac{W}{\lambda} = \frac{\pi \epsilon^2}{mc} \, 10^6 n f \lambda \qquad (16)$$

must hold. Thus, when W/λ is 10^{-6}, $\log nf\lambda = 6.055$. The four sodium lines define much of the curve; the slope through the $\lambda 3300$ doublet is steeper than through the D lines and must approach $45°$ for even weaker lines. The $45°$ portion is joined to the empirical curve by a judicious extrapolation. With the aid of this curve, one may read off values of $nf\lambda$ from the observed W/λ values of the lines of Ca I, Ca II, K I, and K II. (See Fig. 7.)

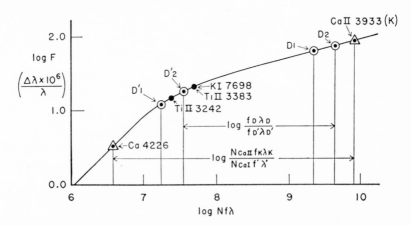

FIG. 7.—THE CURVE OF GROWTH FOR INTERSTELLAR LINES OBSERVED IN THE SPECTRUM OF χ^2 ORIONIS

Here $F = 10^6 W_\lambda/\lambda$. The shape of the curve is determined essentially by four obdium lines. The abundances of the other elements are determined by fitting the osserved points to this curve since $f\lambda$ is known for each line. (Courtesy, T. L. Dunham, *Proceedings of American Philosophical Society* **81**, 287, 1939.)

Since the f-values of these lines are known, one may find the number of ions n between the earth and χ^2 Orionis.

Strömgren has derived a theoretical curve of growth for the interstellar lines. The problem differs from the stellar one discussed in Chapter *8 in that pure extinction occurs. Hence the observed intensity I_λ at a wave length λ within the interstellar absorption line is:

$$I_\lambda = I_\lambda^o\, e^{-t_\lambda} \tag{17}$$

where I_λ^o is the intensity in the nearby continuum of the background star. Here $t_\lambda = N\alpha_\lambda$ where α_λ is the atomic absorption coefficient at the wave length in question. The equivalent width in wave-length units is:

$$W = \int \frac{I_\lambda^o - I_\lambda}{I_\lambda^o}\, d\lambda = \int \left(1 - e^{-t_\lambda}\right) d\lambda$$

$$= \Delta\lambda_0 \int \left(1 - e^{-(\alpha_\lambda/\alpha_0)t_0}\right) du$$

where the Doppler-width constant $\Delta\lambda_0$ is defined by eqn. (39) of Chapter *8 and u is defined by eqn. (29) of Chapter *8. Here $t_0 = n\alpha_0$, where α_0 is the absorption coefficient at the center of a line of zero damping [cf. eqn. (33) of Ch. *8]. For the interstellar lines in question, the ratio a, defined by eqn. (31) of Chapter *8, is about 0.001 or smaller. Strömgren shows that the observed intensities are such that one may take $a = 0$ without making any appreciable error in the calculation of a theoretical curve of growth. Then

$$\frac{t_\lambda}{t_0} = \frac{\alpha_\lambda}{\alpha_0} = e^{-u^2}$$

where

$$u = \left\{\lambda - \lambda_0\left[1 + \frac{V}{c}\right]\right\}\frac{1}{\Delta\lambda_0}$$

V denotes the velocity of the gas cloud in the line of sight, and u has the same physical meaning as in eqn. (29) or (40) of Chapter *8, i.e., it is the distance $\lambda - \lambda_0$ measured from the center of the line in units of $\Delta\lambda_0$.

Since α_λ/α_0 is a known function of the variable of integration u, the ratio $W/\Delta\lambda_0 = Wc/\lambda v$ can be computed as a function of t_0. It will be proportional to t_0 for small values of t_0, but as the optical thickness at the center of the line increases, the equivalent width grows slowly with n. Since $t_0(D_2) = 2t_0(D_1)$ one can calculate theoretical values of the doublet ratio $W(D_2)/W(D_1)$ as a function of t_0. Also n/W can be tabulated as a function of t_0. Hence from W and the measured doublet ratio one may obtain not only t_0 but also the most probable kinetic velocity of the atoms, v. When n is large, the doublet method fails since a small error in the observed ratio may produce a very great error in log n. Fortunately, the $\lambda 3302$–$\lambda 3303$ lines can be measured in a number of stars. The ratios of the f-values for the D lines and the $\lambda 3302$–$\lambda 3303$ pair equals 21.8. Hence the ratio $W(D_1)/W(3303)$ can be calculated as a function of log t_0 (last column, Table 1).

TABLE 1

THEORETICAL CURVE OF GROWTH FOR INTERSTELLAR LINES[*]

log t_0	$\log \dfrac{W}{\lambda} \dfrac{c}{v}$ (D_1 or H)	$\dfrac{W(D_2)}{W(D_1)}$ or $\dfrac{W(K)}{W(H)}$	$\log \dfrac{N}{W}$	$\dfrac{W(D_1)}{W(\lambda 3303)}$
−0.2	9.96	1.66	13.06	
0.0	0.11	1.53	13.11	
+0.2	0.24	1.39	13.18	
+0.4	0.34	1.29	13.28	
+0.6	0.42	1.21	13.40	81
+0.8	0.48	1.16	13.54	59
+1.0	0.52	1.13	13.70	42
+1.2	0.56	1.11	13.86	29
+1.4	0.59	1.10	14.03	20
+1.6	0.62	1.08	14.20	14
+1.8	0.64	1.07	14.38	10.2
+2.0	0.66	1.07	14.56	7.4

[*]B. Strömgren, *Ap. J.* **108**, 248, 1948.

Strömgren quotes the following examples to illustrate the use of this table.[†] "In χ^2 Orionis Dunham observed $W(D_1) = 0.39A$, $W(\lambda 3303) = 0.040A$. The ratio $D_1/3303 = 9.8$, when used in Table 1, gives log n/W for D_1 equal to 14.40; hence log $n = 13.99$. The number of absorbing sodium atoms is thus found from the strengths of D_1 and $\lambda 3303$ to be $n = 9.8 \times 10^{13}$. Also $\lambda v/c$ is found to be 0.09A. Next, consider an example in which measures have given equivalent widths of the interstellar D_1 and D_2 lines in a star equal to 0.16A and 0.24A, respectively. The doublet ratio is 1.50, and the table gives log n/W for D_1 equal to 13.12 so that log $n = 12.32$."

If the observed ions all occur in the same cloud, the next step is to investigate the ionization equilibrium and derive the partition of atoms among the various ionization stages. When the proportion of observed to total ions is known, the total number of atoms of the given element may be found.

[†]*Ap. J.* **108**, 249, 1948.

The interstellar atoms are all in their ground levels and exposed to the composite radiation of many stars. Although the energy distribution of this radiation may correspond to temperatures of several thousand degrees, the energy density is low because of the great distances of the stars and the presence of absorbing material. We write the intensity of the radiation incident upon the atoms as

$$I_\nu = W_\nu B_\nu(T_i)$$

where $B_\nu(T_i)$ is the Planckian function for some convenient temperature T_i, usually about 10,000°K, the dilution factor W_ν includes the deviation of the energy distribution of the composite source from that of a black body, the geometrical attenuation of the radiation, and the effects of interstellar absorption. The rate of ionization goes roughly as W times the corresponding rate for thermal equilibrium.

The rate of recombination depends on the electron temperature. We must emphasize that while ionization may occur only from the ground level, recombinations may occur on all levels. The contributions of stationary states of high quantum number turn out to be quite significant. The appropriate ionization formula may be written in the form

$$\log \frac{N_i N_e}{N_0} = -\chi \frac{5040}{T_i} + \frac{3}{2} \log T_i + \log \frac{2g_1}{g_0}$$

$$+ \frac{1}{2} \log \frac{T_e}{T_i} + 15.38 + \log D \tag{18}$$

where D includes the effects of the dilution of the radiation, and the fact that recombinations may occur on all levels, while ionizations take place only from the lowest. In the most elementary approach we put

$$D = W \frac{a_1}{\sum a_n} \tag{19}$$

where $a_1 / \sum a_n$ represents the fraction of recombinations taking place on the ground level.

Recombination rates for the different levels may be computed as a function of the temperature if the corresponding absorption coefficients are known (cf. Ch. ★5). Dunham calculated the composite radiation field of the stars, by grouping them according to temperature classes and calculating the contributions of each group to $I(\nu)$. He carried out solutions both with and without the effect of the interstellar absorption upon $I(\nu)$ being taken into account. The results show that a single O star, such as ζ Puppis, will outweigh all the other stars within a hundred parsecs of it. Sirius, which is visually the brightest star in our sky, makes but a small contribution to the total.

Dunham finds the energy density without absorption to be 5.24×10^{-13} ergs/cm^3. If we take $T_i = 15,000°$K, the energy density for equilibrium is then 387 ergs/cm^3, $W = 1.35 \times 10^{-15}$. As an illustration let us choose $T_\epsilon = 10,000°$K, which Spitzer finds appropriate for the regions where the interstellar hydrogen is ionized. For Ca I, $\sum a_n/a_1 = 2.6$, $2g_1/g_0 = 4$, $\chi = 6.09$ ev, and, upon substitution in eqn. (18), we find log $N_1 N_\epsilon/N_0 = 4.81$.

Strömgren has evaluated D with the effects of the variations of W, and the atomic absorption coefficients taken rigorously into account. We give part of his table herewith:

TABLE 2*

log $N_1 N_\epsilon/N_0$

T_ϵ	Na I	K I	Ca I	Ca II$^{(1)}$	Ca II$^{(2)}$
10,000	1.73	2.38	4.29	+0.44	+0.72
1,000	0.92	1.50	3.41	−0.21	+0.07
100	0.22	0.77	2.68	−0.82	−0.54

(1) Values for region where hydrogen is neutral; radiation beyond λ911 is absorbed.

(2) Values for region where hydrogen is ionized, so that no substantial radiation beyond λ911 is absorbed.

*$Ap. J.$ **108**, 258, 1948.

With Dunham's observed value of log N(Ca II)/N(Ca I) $= 3.55$ for the atoms in the direction of χ^2 Orionis, and $T_\epsilon = 10,000°$K, we get $N_\epsilon = 5$ electrons/cm^3.† To get the total amount of calcium present we must allow for the second ionization whose potential is 11.9 ev. The degree of ionization will depend on whether hydrogen is ionized or neutral in the region concerned. One can discuss the ionization equilibrium of each element and deduce the composition of the interstellar gas, as Dunham, Struve, and Strömgren have done.

From the interstellar lines observed in seven different stars, Strömgren finds N(Ca II)/N(Na I) $= 0.6$. The corresponding ratio of calcium to sodium is 0.04, which is much smaller than the value 1.5 found from studies of stellar atmospheres. The discrepancy has been recognized for some time; it may arise from errors in the assumed absorption coefficients and in the assumed intensity of the ionizing radiation from λ1000 to λ2000. Generally we assume stars radiate like black bodies in this region but it is more likely that the composite energy curve is cut by numerous absorption lines, which, however, may not be as strong as in the sun.

†In practice, the use of the Ca I/Ca II ratio to establish the ionization equilibrium is difficult because the Ca II lines tend to be saturated.

To make further progress, we must discuss the state of interstellar hydrogen. We ask this question: What will be the physical state of a tenuous, roughly uniform cloud composed primarily of hydrogen and containing one or more hot stars? Near these stars the hydrogen is ionized. With increasing distance the fraction of neutral hydrogen rises slowly. Bengt Strömgren showed that suddenly, at a critical distance s_0, the proportion of neutral hydrogen increases abruptly, and there is almost no ionization at greater distances. The critical distance s_0 depends on the absolute magnitude and temperature of the exciting star and the density of hydrogen. Strömgren employs an ionization formula essentially of the type of eqn. (18), and sets N_ϵ equal to the number of hydrogen ions N_i. The geometrical dilution factor is

$$W_g = \frac{R^2}{4s^2} \tag{20}$$

while dt is taken as the element of optical depth at the Lyman limit, viz.:

$$dt = N_0 \alpha_u 3.08 \times 10^{18} \, ds \tag{21}$$

since the parsec (3.08×10^{18} cm) is chosen as the unit of length. N_0 is the number of neutral H atoms/cm^3. Strömgren writes the ionization equation in the form

$$\frac{x^2}{1-x} N = C_1 \frac{e^{-t}}{s^2} \tag{22}$$

where,

$$N = N_0 + N_i \qquad C_1 = 10^{-0.51-\theta I} \sqrt{\frac{T_\epsilon}{T}} \, T^{3/2} R^2$$
$$N_i = N_\epsilon = xN$$
$$N_0 = (1-x)N \qquad \theta = \frac{5040}{T} \tag{23}$$

The numerical value of C_1 follows from the choice of a parsec as the unit of s, the solar radius for R, and cm^{-3} for N. Put $N_0 = (1-x)N$ in eqn. (21), solve for $(1-x)$ and substitute in eqn. (22) to obtain

$$e^{-t} \, dt = x^2 \frac{N^2}{C_1} s^2 3.08 \times 10^{18} \alpha_u \, ds \tag{24}$$

Employing the new variables,

$$y = e^{-t}, \quad z = \left[\frac{3.08 \times 10^{18} \alpha_u N^2}{3 C_1} \right] s^3 \tag{25}$$

where $0 \leq y \leq 1$, eqns. (24) and (22) become

$$\frac{dy}{dz} = -x^2, \quad \frac{1-x}{x^2} = \alpha \frac{z^{2/3}}{y} \tag{26}$$

with

$$\alpha = \left[\frac{9}{NC_1(3.08 \times 10^{18}\alpha_u)^2} \right]^{1/3} \tag{27}$$

Now $y = 1$ for $z = 0$ since $t = 0$ at $s = 0$. From the conditions of the problem, α is small, and when t is small, x is nearly unity and $y = 1 - z$. Hence $(1 - x)$ will remain small until y becomes small. Then x will decrease rapidly which means that hydrogen will become neutral. The value of s corresponding to $z = 1$ is called s_0. From eqn. (25)

$$s_0 = \left[\frac{3C_1}{3.08 \times 10^{18}\alpha_u N^2} \right]^{1/3} \tag{28}$$

Strömgren found the exact dependence of the degree of ionization x upon s by numerical integration. At first the number of neutral atoms increases because of the s-factor and e^{-t} does not become important until the number of neutral atoms is appreciable. Then the degree of ionization falls rapidly to zero. The ratio of ions to total hydrogen (ions plus atoms) as a function of distance from the star is shown in Table 3. From eqns. (23) and (28) we find for hydrogen

$$\log s_0 = -6.17 + \frac{1}{6} \log \frac{T_e}{T} - \frac{1}{3} \log \alpha_u - \frac{1}{3}\theta I$$

$$+ \frac{1}{2} \log T + \frac{2}{3} \log R - \frac{2}{3} \log N \tag{29}$$

TABLE 3*

IONIZATION OF HYDROGEN

s/s_0	$N_i/(N_0 + N_i)$
0.00	1.00
0.58	1.00
0.74	0.99
0.84	0.98
0.93	0.96
0.97	0.94
1.00	0.85
1.03	0.33

*Ap. J. **89**, 531, 1939.

If we insert $I = 13.53$ ev, $\alpha_u = 6.3 \times 10^{-18}$ cm^{-2} (the absorption coefficient at the Lyman limit) and make use of eqn. (13) of Chapter ★6 in the form

$$\log R = \frac{5700}{T} - 0.20M_v - 0.05 \tag{30}$$

we find

$$\log s_0 = -0.47 + \frac{1}{6} \log \frac{T_\epsilon}{T} - 3.75\theta + \frac{1}{2} \log T$$

$$- 0.13 M_r - \frac{2}{3} \log N \qquad (31)$$

For main sequence stars Strömgren tabulates s_0 as a function of N and the temperature of the illuminating star. If there are n such stars producing ionization, the volume will be increased n times; hence the radius will be $s_0 n^{1/3}$.

TABLE 4*

RADII OF IONIZATION REGIONS

Temperature	Spectrum	M_{vis}	s_0 ($N = 1/cm^3$)
40,000°K	O6	−3.9	58 pcs
32,000	O9	−3.6	38
25,000	B0	−3.1	20
20,000	B2	−1.8	8.3
18,600	B3	−1.2	5.7
15,500	B5	−0.8	3.0
10,700	A0	+0.9	0.45

*Compare: $Ap. J.$ **89**, 533, 1939.

Table 4 gives the temperature, corresponding spectral type, adopted visual absolute magnitude, and computed s_0 for $N = 1$ atom/cm^3 and an assumed $T_\epsilon = 10,000°$K. The dependence of the volume of the ionized region on the temperature of the illuminating star is so profound that the total volume ionized by all stars hotter than $B3$ is much larger than that ionized by all cooler stars, despite the overwhelming preponderance of the latter.[†]

In the ionized hydrogen H II region the continuous Lyman radiation is gradually degraded into Balmer and Lyman line radiation in the same way as in planetary nebulae. Throughout most of this region the Lyman line radiation is present mostly in the form of Lyman α, since the other quanta become converted by repeated fluorescent processes into Lyman α, Balmer lines, Paschen lines, etc. The H II region as well as the neutral hydrogen or H I region is transparent to the Balmer lines.

[†]The theoretical sizes of the ionized H II regions surrounding the hottest O stars are dependent upon the energy distribution beyond the Lyman limit in the O stars. Strictly, one should calculate the flux emergent from the atmosphere for a series of different excitation temperatures. Miss Underhill has done this for an $O5$ star. Calculations by Liller for the analogous problem in planetary nebulae suggest that the changes will not be great.

Once created, Balmer quanta simply escape from the H II region. Thus the hydrogen radiation passing through the surrounding H I region consists of Lyman α quanta, which are simply scattered until absorbed by grains, and Balmer and Paschen quanta that escape without further interference. The second level may be excited relatively often because of the absorption of Lyman α quanta, but the $n = 3$ and higher levels relevant to the production of the Balmer lines are not excited. Hence the observed Balmer emission must originate in the H II regions, which, as noted above, have sharp boundaries.

Strömgren identified the hydrogen ionization or H II regions with the extended areas of hydrogen emission observed at McDonald and Yerkes.* Detailed comparison, however, requires that the patchiness of the interstellar medium be taken into account. From observations of the surface brightness in the light of Hα, Struve estimated the number of atoms in the third level of hydrogen, N_3, to be about $5/cm^2$, in the line of sight, for the luminous patches in Cygnus and near λ Orionis. If the radiating volume had a thickness of 300 parsecs, N_3 would be $5 \times 10^{-21}/cm^3$. With the aid of such data and the theory of Balmer emission in gaseous nebulae worked out by Menzel and Baker, Strömgren derived an ionic density of $2-5/cm^3$ in good agreement with the electron density N_e found by Dunham. In the region near hot stars, hydrogen supplies most of the electrons.

In the hydrogen emission H II regions $N_i = N_e$ and there will be radiation available to ionize elements such as O I, O II, O III, He I, C II, N I, and Ne I, whose ionization potentials are greater than that of hydrogen. At distances greater than s_0 all the radiation beyond λ912 will have been absorbed, and O, N, Ne, and He will be neutral. Radiation longward of λ912 will be transmitted and C I (I.P. = 11.22 ev), Ca II (11.82 ev), as well as Ca I, Ti I, Na I, and K I, can be ionized in this neutral H I region. If, as Strömgren suggests, carbon supplies most of the free electrons in the H I region, the electron density will be between 10^{-2} and 10^{-3}, as Struve and Gerasimovic pointed out long ago. Here sodium would be singly and calcium doubly ionized since the rate of electron recapture would be extremely low, while titanium would appear mostly as Ti II. The ionizing radiation for these metals comes from the whole galaxy, not from just the O stars.

Adams's studies of the molecular lines indicate that CH$^+$ λ4232 and CH λ4300 originate not only in normal obscuring clouds responsible for selective absorption, but also in circumstellar clouds near late

*In the arms of the Andromeda Spiral, Messier 31, Baade has photographed (in the light of Hα) bright patches with sharp boundaries. These are evidently Strömgren spheres of ionized material but are similar to the nebulosity near S Monocerotis (described by Minkowski), rather than to the faint areas of hydrogen emission observed at McDonald and Yerkes.

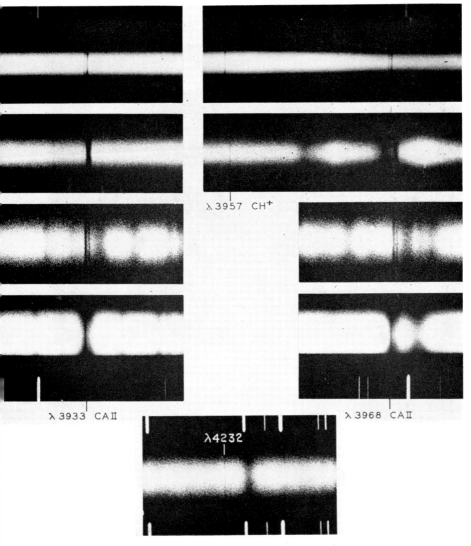

FIG. 8.—THE INTERSTELLAR LINES WITH HIGH DISPERSION

(From top to bottom)

ζ Ophiuchi (left) K   (right) λ3957 and H
P Cygni (left) K   (right) λ3957 and H
υ Sagittarii (left) K   (right) H
α Cygni (left) K   (right) H
υ Sagittarii λ4232

In P Cygni the two components are not fully separated and in α Cygni the lines are superposed on the K and H stellar lines. (Courtesy, Walter S. Adams, Mount Wilson Contribution No. 673 and *Astrophysical Journal* **97**, 107, 1943.)

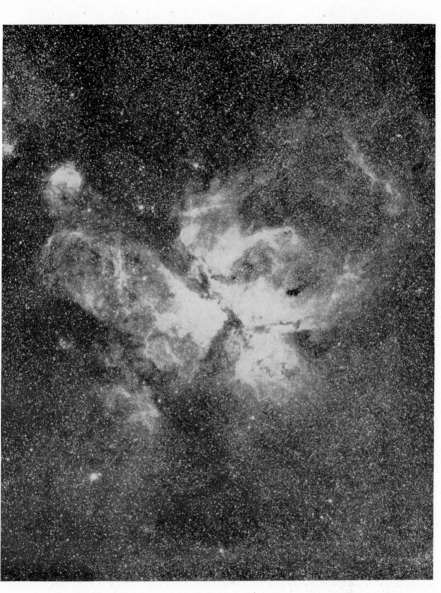

FIG. 9.—THE η CARINAE NEBULA AS IT APPEARS IN THE RADIATION OF THE RED HYDROGEN (Hα) LINE.

Photographed by Karl G. Henize, May 27, 1951, at the Lamont-Hussey Observatory of the University of Michigan, Bloemfontein, Orange Free State, South Africa, with the Mount Wilson 10-inch camera. North is at

B-type stars.   D. R. Bates and L. Spitzer suggested they originate from the dissociation of CH_4 in frozen grains that approach hot stars.

Observations by Struve and his colleagues show that [O II] $\lambda 3727$ is almost always present in regions where hydrogen is ionized and shows the same sharp boundaries—a result we might expect since the ionization potential of O I (13.56 ev) is nearly the same as that of hydrogen (13.54 ev).   Now [O III] is rarely observed, and then only in the inner parts of the H II regions, and it fades gradually outward. Its presence requires the double ionization of oxygen (34.94 ev).   On the other hand, [O I] has never been observed.   We might expect it in the H I regions but the combination of a low electron density and a possibly low collisional target area may not permit enough collisional excitations of the upper level.   The blending with the lines of the aurora or night sky may be serious.

From the observed intensity of the [O II] $\lambda 3727$ line, Struve estimated the population of the metastable ^2D level, to be 9.3×10^{11} atoms/cm^2 in the line of sight.   If the diameter of the radiating region is 9×10^{20} cm, the density of O II atoms in the ^2D level is 10^{-9}.   As in the planetary nebulae, electron collisions excite the atoms from the ground level to the ^2D term, whence they cascade back to the ground $^4S_{1/2}$ level with the emission of $\lambda 3727$.   If $T_e = 20,000°K$, we find the number of O II atoms/cm^3 to be 1.2×10^{-3}, whence the abundance ratio of hydrogen to oxygen is comparable with that found for stellar atmospheres (see Ch. *8).

We must now consider the modifications required by the extreme patchiness of the interstellar medium.   Recent investigations by Adams, Merrill, Spitzer, Strömgren, and others have emphasized the filamentary distribution of the interstellar dust and gas.   Probably about 5 per cent of the space in the neighborhood of the sun is occupied by the clouds of grains and gas.   Within one of these clouds the hydrogen atoms have a density of the order of 10/cm^3 and are predominantly neutral. Between the clouds the hydrogenic density may be as low as 0.08 atoms/cm^3.   Strömgren finds sodium to be even more strongly concentrated in the clouds.   In fact, the total mass concentrated there is appreciably greater than the amount distributed between them.

The irregularity of the interstellar gas affects the ionization of hydrogen.   Hydrogen concentrated in clouds is more efficient in stopping the ionizing radiation than a similar mass uniformly distributed in space.   In fact, if the central ray through a region intercepts two or more ionized clouds, the volume will appear as a roughly coherent, although somewhat patchy, emission region.   Strömgren writes:* "A number of clouds, each of density N_H, occupying together a fraction

*$Ap.\ J.$ **108**, 242, 1948.

α of space (thus having a large-scale average density $\rho = \alpha N_H$), when ionized by a clustering of O stars, yields a hydrogen emission region, which with regard to both extent and intensity is equivalent to the hydrogen emission region produced by the same stars in a homogeneous medium of density equal to the geometric mean $(N_H \rho)^{1/2} = \alpha^{1/2} N_H$ of the cloud density N_H and the large-scale average density $\rho = \alpha N_H$."

The numerical values suggested by Strömgren are $N_H = 10$, $N_H \alpha^{1/2} = 2$, $\overline{N} = N_H \alpha = 0.4$, $\alpha = 0.04$, and $s_0 = 90$ parsecs for an $O5$ star.

Merrill suggests there may be systematic differences between thick and thin clouds because of greater ionization in the surface layers than in the interiors of thick clouds. Although the sodium and ionized calcium line intensities increase statistically with distance, no such relation appears to hold for Ca I $\lambda4227$, nor for the molecular lines.

Within the errors of observation, the results of Struve, Dunham, and Strömgren suggest that the composition of the interstellar medium is the same as that of the stars and planetary nebulae. Discrepancies that exist can be attributed to the uncertainties in the physical parameters and also to the effects of the inhomogeneities of the interstellar medium. In so far as the atomic constituents of galactic space are concerned, the situation seems straightforward. What makes the problem more difficult than that presented by the purely gaseous nebulae described in Chapter 5 is that both gaseous atoms and solid grains exist in the same regions of space. Hence a complete understanding of the phenomena involved requires a knowledge of the interactions between atoms and grains.

Our information on the physical conditions in interstellar space is still inadequate. We need more data on the size distribution of the grains and their chemical composition. In addition we need to know more about the admittedly irregular distribution of the gas and grains in space.

6. The Kinetic Temperature of the Interstellar Medium and the Influence of Radiation Pressure

We must now consider the possible interactions between the components of the interstellar medium. This problem lies at the basis of all considerations concerning the formation of particles out of the gas and the possible evolution of the medium.

These problems have been investigated by a number of Dutch workers, and by Whipple, but in most detail by Spitzer. We assume a steady state. If there is a gradual building up of particles at the expense of the atoms (or vice versa) let us suppose that it proceeds so slowly that it does not seriously affect the "equilibrium."

One of our first questions concerns the "temperature" of the interstellar medium. Since the deviations from thermodynamic equilibrium are profound, it is clear that no unique temperature will characterize all processes affecting the dust and grains.

In Chapter *5 we saw that a hypothetical black body which absorbed and emitted equally well in all frequencies would assume a temperature of about 3.2°K in interstellar space. The temperature T of an actual small particle would be something different.

The absorption A by an actual particle will depend on the following factors: (1) the energy distribution of the impinging radiation; (2) the dimensions of the particle, since the efficiency factor depends on $2\pi a/\lambda$; and (3) its temperature, since the conductivity of metals, in particular, is temperature dependent. We recall that A is that part of the geometrically incident radiation which is absorbed by the sphere. Energy balance demands

$$\int_0^\infty W_\lambda B_\lambda(T) A(\lambda, x, T_p) \, d\lambda = \int_0^\infty A(\lambda, x, T_p) B(\lambda, T_p) \, d\lambda \qquad (32)$$

where T is the adopted color temperature of the stars, W_λ is the dilution factor (which may depend on the wave length, to allow for the fact a unique color temperature cannot be assigned for galactic starlight), and T_p is the temperature of the particle. A simple generalization of Kirchhoff's law shows that the factor A must appear in the emission term since absorbed and emitted energy must be equal at each frequency when $W = 1$ and $T_p = T$.

The starlight received by the particles has a maximum near 0.3–0.4μ, while the wave length of the maximum of the radiated energy lies in the far infrared ($\lambda = 100\mu$ for $T = 30°$). Small particles cannot radiate efficiently at long wave lengths.* Hence they will assume temperatures considerably above that of the hypothetical black sphere.

H. C. van de Hulst has estimated the temperatures of metallic and dielectric spheres of radii 0.0 to 1μ in interstellar space. The former assume temperatures of 30–$100°K$, while dielectric particles would have temperatures of the order of 10–$20°K$, considerably above the black sphere temperature of $3.2°K$. A parameter of considerable importance is the kinetic temperature of interstellar matter as defined by the root mean square of the particle velocities. Obviously such a temperature will have meaning only if there exists an equipartition of energy among the atoms and grains of the interstellar medium. Elec-

---

*If we regard the grains as tiny classical antennae which are required to radiate at wave lengths many times their linear dimensions, it is easy to understand why they may absorb like gray bodies in the visible regions but radiate as though they were nearly white in the far infrared.

trons and ions will set up an equipartition of energy and follow a Max-wellian distribution appropriate to some electron temperature T_e. Spitzer has found that interactions between grains and gas molecules will suffice to bring the kinetic energy of the grains into equipartition with the energy of the ions and electrons.

Interstellar grains may absorb light quanta and eject photoelectrons. The process efficiency is low and the available light quanta are few. Actually, the capture of electrons that tend to charge the grain negatively may more than compensate for the accumulation of positive charge by the ejection of electrons. In the H II regions where the temperature is about 10,000°K, the grain will be charged to −2.2 volts independently of its composition or radius. Then the number of positive ions reaching the surface equals the number of electrons that can get to the particle over the potential barrier. The problem is analogous to that of an insulated probe placed in an electric discharge tube; the probe becomes charged negatively until the number of positive ions and electrons reaching it are equal.

In the H I regions the charge on the grain is small and may even be positive. Spitzer finds that initial irregularities in the motion should be wiped out in a time small compared with the age of the galaxy.

In a steady state, the kinetic temperature is determined by the condition that the kinetic energy gained per cm^3 per second by all processes must equal the kinetic energy lost by all processes. Processes capable of increasing the average kinetic temperature of the interstellar atoms, molecules, and grains are: (1) photo-ionization of hydrogen and other atoms, (2) photoelectric emission from grains, (3) photo-dissociation of molecules and negative ions such as H$^-$. Processes extracting energy from the motions of free electrons, ions, molecules, etc., are: (1) excitation of metastable energy levels of ions like N II, O II, and O III by electron impact, (2) excitation of vibrational and rotational molecular energy levels by electronic or atomic impact, (3) free-free emissions in the field of a positive ion or neutral atom, (4) excitation of vibrational levels of a grain by inelastic collisions. The balance of these processes establishes the equilibrium temperature.

Spitzer concludes that in the H II regions the kinetic temperature is in the neighborhood of 5000°K to 10,000°K. In the H I regions the grains depress the temperature as electrons and atoms give up energy when they strike and heat the particles. Spitzer and Savedoff find that the kinetic temperature is probably about 60°K in these regions. The variation in the kinetic temperature from point to point in the medium has an important bearing on the problem of initial particle formation and the rate of growth of the grains.

Radiation pressure exerts an important influence on the components of the interstellar medium. Its effect has been discussed by Bok, Spitzer, Greenstein, Schalén, and others. One effect pointed out by Spitzer is that two particles in the more or less uniform field of galactic radiation will be urged toward one another. Each particle, as seen from the other, will block out a portion of the luminous Milky Way. That is, the shadow of each grain on the other will produce an uncompensated force along the line joining them. This shadowing effect causes the particles to be pushed together with a force which varies as the inverse square of the distance between them. For ice particles with a radius of 10^{-5} cm, the radiative force is ten thousand times the force of gravity. For any given pair of particles, this force is much less than the minor statistical fluctuations in the general field of galactic radiation. Since it always operates in such a way as to force the two particles toward one another, its cumulative effect will be statistically important. Although a dust cloud will tend to be blown about by radiation pressure from passing stars, the net effect of the general luminous background of the galaxy is to make the cloud contract.

In the immediate neighborhood of a star the behavior of the particles is more complicated. Near a cool supergiant the atoms will remain neutral and will be little affected by radiation pressure. The force acting upon the grains much exceeds the interactive force between the grains and gas. Hence a late-type star repels the grains without affecting the distribution of the atoms.

Near highly luminous hot stars, on the other hand, hydrogen becomes ionized and the interaction between the positive protons and negatively charged grains becomes large. The grains and gas tend to stick together, and the whole interstellar medium will be repelled provided the velocity of the star is less than 10 km/sec. Spitzer finds the effect of the radiation pressure on the grains to be much more important than on the atoms. The radiation pressure on neutral hydrogen atoms is not important. A quantum of Lyman α radiation will diffuse slowly through space and be absorbed by a grain before it has gone a fifth of a parsec.

The temperatures and physical interactions of the atoms and grains have an important bearing on the problem we now want to consider— possible mechanisms for building grains from the gas.

7. The Formation of Grains

The studies of the interstellar medium have shown it to be made up of two components: (1) gas of roughly the same composition as the solar atmosphere, often highly ionized but containing neutral atoms and sometimes a few molecules; (2) grains of about 10^{-5} cm in diameter of a presumably dielectric substance.

The problem is this: how can solid particles be formed in a medium

initially gaseous? We may distinguish three separate topics: (a) formation of diatomic and polyatomic molecules as nuclei of condensation
from which larger and more complex particles are eventually built
(main work by ter Haar and Kramers); (b) growth of nuclei to large
particles (Lindblad and ter Haar, and particularly van de Hulst);
(c) processes limiting the growth of particles (Oort and van de Hulst).

Topic (a) is a rather speculative subject. On the basis of the work
by Kramers and ter Haar it seems likely that the first step in the building
up of grains is the formation of molecules such as OH, CH^+, and CH
by a radiative capture process. If the molecule escapes photo-dissociation it may combine with another atom or molecule and gradually a
crystal of some sort is built up.

The lower the temperature, the less the chance for evaporation and
the more stable the crystal. Since we have a fair idea of the temperature of the grains and the density of the gas and other parameters,
step (b) is less uncertain than step (a). From experimental data on
the vapor pressure of a frozen gas and absorbed layers one would expect
a solid hydrogen particle to evaporate while a frozen oxygen one would
remain. From the composition of the interstellar gas we would expect
the grains to consist mainly of carbon, oxygen, and nitrogen with a
small admixture of metals. Finally, just as much hydrogen will be
retained as can be held by the other constituents. We may expect the
grains to be similar to ice crystals with impurities akin to ammonia and
methane. They probably have an irregular structure.

F. D. Kahn has treated the water molecule as the fundamental
structure and suggests that, at the low temperatures of the H I regions,
long crystals of parallel dipoles could be formed.

The Dutch investigators estimated the rate of growth of the grains
on the basis of the kinetic temperature, the average density of the
medium, and the rate of hydrogen and helium evaporation. They also
took into account slight electrostatic attractions between negatively
charged grains and positive ions. It appears that the grains would
attain their present radii of the order of 10^{-5} cm in about 3×10^7 years.
Since the interval is much shorter than the 3×10^9-year time scale of
our galaxy, some process must limit the growth of the grains. It cannot
be the exhaustion of the interstellar gas, since the latter is still widely
spread through the galaxy and appears to be actually concentrated in
clouds where the grains are numerous. Oort suggested that these grain
and gas clouds move with random velocities of the order of 20 km/sec.
When they meet one another and interpenetrate, many of the colliding
grains become evaporated or fused together. Evaporation would occur
when two grains strike one another with a relative velocity greater
than 3 km/sec. Calculation shows that with the adopted densities,

cloud velocities, and dimensions an average particle will survive a dozen encounters between clouds and will live about a hundred million years. Otherwise, the particles would grow to sizes larger than those observed. Oort suggested that the luminous edges of dark nebulae arise from collisions between such clouds.

On the assumption of a quasi-equilibrium, the distribution law of grain diameters may be computed in terms of n_0, the number of particles per unit interval of length r, at $r = 0$, and a radius r_1, which can be estimated by theoretical means. Here r_1 depends on the rate of growth of the particle and the velocities and dimensions of the cloud. Similarly, n_0 depends on the number of proto-crystals that have been built up, presumably by the mechanism suggested by Kramers and ter Haar. The final test of the theory is how well the predicted size distribution fits the observational data. On the assumption that the interstellar particles were dielectric with refractive indices of 1.33 (like water), van de Hulst calculated the law of selective absorption. The scale factors in the distribution law are fixed when the theoretical curve is fitted to the extinctions observed by Stebbins and Whitford. He found that the theory could represent the observations in a satisfactory way if $n_0 = 10^{-8}/cm^3$ and $r_1 = 2.8 \times 10^{-5}$ cm. The value of r_1 falls just within the range of solution of the theory. On the other hand, n_0 is smaller than the values suggested by theory.

This would indicate that the formation of polyatomic nuclei proceeds more slowly than the (rather inexact) theory would suggest.

Furthermore, the growth of the grains may proceed more slowly than has been supposed. Recent discussions by Bertram Donn have emphasized that our knowledge of capture cross-sections and of the rates of building of grains is still very unsatisfactory. This deficiency can be overcome only after careful low-temperature experimental studies have been made of condensation and evaporation rates, etc., in mixtures simulating the interstellar grains. Nevertheless, the picture presented by the Dutch astronomers shows internal consistency and a sufficiently good agreement with observation to encourage further studies along these lines.

8. The Formation of Stars

Much impetus for work on the interstellar medium stems from the strong evidence that stars are continually being formed from the grains and gas. We recall from the discussions of Chapter 2 that the supergiants and bright main-sequence stars characteristic of Type I population are younger than the galaxy. Hence we believe that these stars, and fainter objects on the main sequence as well, had been formed out of the interstellar medium.

Baade's study of the Andromeda galaxy Messier 31 shows that the highly luminous supergiant and main-sequence stars are found only in or near the spiral arms where gaseous nebulae and dark lanes indicate the presence of the interstellar medium. They are not found between the spiral arms where there is no obscuring matter, nor in the central bulge. Nearly all the stars in these regions must belong to the Type II population.

The mechanism by which stars might be formed from the interstellar grains has been considered by Whipple and particularly by Spitzer. Spitzer has examined the question of how an initially gaseous medium could have condensed into small solid grains, and finally how the grains and residual gas could have been concentrated into stars.

His problem is: Given an extended gaseous medium, mostly hydrogen and helium but with slight traces of heavier elements, how will it evolve in a period of the order of 2×10^9 years? The primitive gas cloud could not have been much more massive than the present interstellar medium, since the total mass of all the stars in the neighborhood of the sun roughly equals the mass of the grains and dust in the same volume. From such material many of the present stars presumably condensed in the more or less remote past.

Spitzer's picture of the formation of stars may be sketched briefly. A hot star moving through the gas produces temperature inequalities. The cooler regions will become denser and the hotter regions more attenuated. The building-up of grains is favored in regions where the density is highest and their formation accelerates the cooling. As the particles grow, their absorptivity increases, and we detect them as diffuse clouds upon photographs. Gradually the radiation pressure of galactic light forces the material together into small regions of high obscuration or dense clouds. As the cloud contracts, the density of the solid particles finally surpasses that of hydrogen, and finally the gravitational attraction of the mass becomes important. In each dense cloud are formed one or more of these pre-stellar masses or proto-stars. Finally, when the density exceeds about 10^{-15} gm/cm^3, the proto-star breaks forth into incandescence.

If the foregoing picture of star formation is essentially correct, we should find observational evidence for it from concentrations of dark matter in the interstellar medium.

Photographs of rich star fields or diffuse nebulae often show small dark globules superposed like inkspots on a luminous background. They are most plentiful in the Sagittarius-Ophiuchus-Scutum region of the Milky Way, particularly in the region of Messier 8 where 32 such objects were found by Bok and Miss Reilly. None are seen projected against the Orion Nebula.

Although globules with diameters up to 100,000 astronomical units are found in the anticenter region, those near Messier 8 appear to have diameters mostly between 10,000 and 35,000 astronomical units. Some of the smaller globules have minimum absorptions of 2 to 5 magnitudes while Bok finds the larger ones to absorb at the most about one magnitude. The great Coal Sack near the Southern Cross has a distance of about 150 parsecs and an absorption of about 1.5 magnitudes. Its linear diameter of 8 parsecs is 16 times greater than that of the larger globules. Larger systems of dark nebulae with diameters of 30 to 40 parsecs and total absorptions of 1.5 magnitudes appear in Taurus and Auriga. They are probably groupings of many small clouds and do not represent single dynamical units. Eventually they may evolve into structures from which stars can be formed. On the assumption that the observed absorptions of the clouds arise entirely from particles of the most efficient size for scattering and absorption (i.e., grains with radii of about 10^{-5} cm), Bok has derived minimum masses of the globules. For example, he finds a globule of 5-magnitude total absorption and 0.06 parsecs diameter to have a minimum mass of 0.002 that of the sun. One of 1.5-magnitude total absorption and 0.5 parsecs diameter will contain 0.05 solar masses while the Coal Sack will have 13 solar masses. A mixture of grains of differing sizes and gas atoms and molecules may give masses exceeding these figures tenfold or more. It seems probable that globules and the Coal Sack Nebula represent the closest approach to star formation. Their densities suffice to prevent them from being torn apart by the shearing effects of galactic rotation. Furthermore, their relatively opaque character allows radiation pressure from surrounding stars to squeeze them together. In such objects it seems likely that radiation pressure will exceed gravity by a factor between 10 and 100. A stationary globule would collect grains from the surrounding medium as they were driven in by radiation pressure, while a moving globule would sweep up both dust and gas. Bok finds that an average globule should double its mass in 3×10^8 years, the Coal Sack in 3×10^7 years. Once gravitational contraction starts, the proto-star will evolve rapidly, it will burst into incandescence and move speedily toward the main sequence.

Photographs of the Andromeda galaxy show numerous luminous stars on the edges of the dark clouds as though they had been formed in the clouds and escaped. Stars of all masses are formed in this process; the more luminous ones are naturally the easiest to detect. A star of solar mass may either be a recent creation or it may have existed for 2 or 3 billion years, whereas a bright star must be young. The T Tauri stars may be dwarf stars in the process of formation—objects that have not yet completed their evolution into normal main-sequence objects.

An alternative process is that luminous stars may have been enlarged from less massive objects by the accretion of interstellar material.

Eddington treated this problem on the assumption that the grains and gas were captured as independent particles which did not affect one another. If ρ is the density of the gas, v the relative velocity of the star and of the particles of the cloud, G the constant of gravitation, M and R the mass and radius of the star, the rate of accretion of matter will be*

$$\frac{dm}{dt} = \frac{2\pi GMR\rho}{v} \tag{33}$$

Eddington concluded that accretion could not play an important role in stellar evolution. Hoyle and Lyttleton argued that, despite the low density of the cloud, collisions produced by the gravitational action of the star may produce important dissipative processes so that the mass motion of the gas as it streams by the star is not the same as that of the independent particles. He found the accretion rate to obey the relation

$$\frac{2\pi G^2 M^2 \rho}{v^3} < \frac{dm}{dt} < \frac{4\pi G^2 M^2 \rho}{v^3} \tag{34}$$

and concluded that if the interstellar gas has a sufficiently high density (10^{-21} gm/cm^3 in some regions) massive stars could be built up. Accretion requires a low relative speed of star and medium. A high degree of internal motion in the medium severely cuts down the rate of this process.

At the moment, it appears that, although accretion might build up the mass of an already existing star under especially favorable circumstances, stars are more likely to be formed directly from the interstellar medium.

Spitzer and Schwarzschild have attempted to explain the composition differences between Type I and Type II populations. They suppose that when our galaxy was young, the interstellar matter had large random velocities corresponding to violent turbulence with large density fluctuations. The Type II stars were formed at this time. Subsequently, the velocities of the interstellar matter decayed to their present average values and Type I stars were formed. At the same time grains began to form abundantly, and the stars formed out of these grains were less rich in hydrogen.

The most convincing evidence for the formation of stars out of the interstellar medium is that provided by A. Blaauw's study of the

*The Internal Constitution of the Stars (Cambridge: Cambridge University Press, 1930), p. 391.

motions in the ζ Persei cluster of B stars. This group is some 40 × 20 parsecs in size and located some 300 parsecs from us. Proper-motion studies showed the group to be expanding at the rate of 12 km/sec, which would imply an age of about 1,300,000 years. The stars must have formed quickly out of the interstellar medium, whose turbulent velocities appear to have been about 5 km/sec. The region still contains dark and bright interstellar matter. A similar family found by Blaauw and W. W. Morgan in Lacerta appeared to have an age of 4.2 × 10⁶ years. The Scorpio-Centaurus cloud, with dimensions of 290 × 100 × 70 parsecs, contains no bright supergiants. With an expansion velocity of one km/sec the cloud would have attained the dimensions, amount of elongation, and spatial orientation that is observed today after an interval of 60 million years.

Lack of space prevents further discussion of the topics of stellar evolution. Mention must be made of the work of Ambarzumian who had suggested that stars were formed not only as early-type objects in bright and dark nebulosities (which he calls O associations), but also as dwarf stars in such groups as the T Tauri variables (T associations).

To summarize, Type I stars appear to be formed continually from the interstellar medium in the spiral arms, whereas the Type II population appears to have been formed about 5×10^9 years ago.

9. Galactic Radio-Frequency Radiation

An important new field of research was opened in 1931 by K. G. Jansky's discovery of radio-frequency radiation from the Milky Way. Subsequent studies have been made with frequencies ranging from 10 to 500 megacycles. The regions of strong radiation are fairly regular and symmetrical about the direction to the galactic center. The distribution suggests that the radiation comes from the bulk of mass of the galactic system.

Although the sun occasionally radiates a great amount of energy in the micro-wave region, the total emission from the stars (if the sun is typical) would fail by a factor of 10^9 to account for the galactic radiation. Some stars may be much more powerful sources of radio noise than the sun, but the factor required to bridge the gap is so very large that no adequate mechanism has as yet been suggested. Free-free transitions in the interstellar gas appears to account for some of the radio noise but does not give the correct intensity or dependence on frequency. Westerhout and Oort suggested that the bulk of the galactic radio noise is supplied by discrete sources that had about the same distribution as the mass of the galaxy. The general features of the radio-frequency emission appear to be well explained except that the intensity comes out to be systematically too low by about the same amount all over the sky. Considerable radiation appears to be contributed by external galaxies. Furthermore, there are some outstanding residuals; an intense radiation appears to originate in the spiral arms identified by W. W. Morgan in the region around the anticenter, and at high latitudes. Further investigations have been carried out by S. P. Wyatt, Jr., who finds that the observed intensities at 100 megacycles/sec can be best accounted for by an axially symmetric radio galaxy, with axis ratio 5:1 and emission density at the galactic center five times that near the sun.

Radio-frequency radiation from a few external galaxies including Messier 31 and the Magellanic Clouds has been detected. The ratio of stellar to radio-frequency radiation is sometimes, but not always, about the same as in our own galaxy.

In addition to the general galactic radiation field, there are observed certain small regions of high energy output, the so-called "radio stars," of which one of the best known is the small Cygnus source. Baade found this source to coincide with two colliding galaxies. The Perseus point source appears to coincide with two apparently colliding extragalactic nebulae which show high-excitation emission nebulosity. The unusual elliptical extragalactic nebula Messier 87 appears to agree in position with the Virgo source. This galaxy contains a bright jet-like protuberance with many condensations. B. Y. Mills concludes from his interferometric observations that the jet is not the source of the radio emission.

The Crab Nebula is a strong source of radio-frequency radiation which cannot be accounted for as thermal emission. The radio-frequency energy distribution with frequency does not resemble that of other sources. Tycho's supernova of 1572 (for which no visible remnants were ever seen) was found by the Manchester group. A number of relatively extended sources have also been located. The Australian observers found a source in Puppis which has a diameter of about 1°; direct photographs of this region reveal a wispy nebulosity of about this size for which Minkowski finds erratic internal motions up to about 100 km/sec. These wisps recall those photographed in the extended Cygnus source (Cygnus X), and in the Cassiopeia source which has a diameter of 5'. Baade and Minkowski point out that these wisps have a distinctive appearance that separates them from other nebulae. Minkowski has photographed the spectra of a couple of these filaments. In one of them each spectral line is split into a number of components showing an over-all range of velocity of about 1500 km/sec. Oxygen is represented by strong forbidden lines, but hydrogen is not present, possibly as a consequence of a collisional rather than a radiative excitation of the spectrum! These filaments may be remnants of supernovae but the question is far from settled as yet. It must be emphasized that the vast majority of point sources cannot be accounted for in this fashion, and we have no hints concerning their identification. In fact, these point sources show no appreciable galactic concentration; they resemble the bright stars or galaxies in distribution. On the other hand, no radio-wave emission has ever been detected from any bright star.

Thermal radio-frequency radiation similar to that emitted by the quiet sun and arising primarily from free-free emissions recently has been detected from a number of diffuse galactic nebulae. At the Naval Research Laboratory, Haddock, Mayer, and Sloanaker observed Messier 8, Messier 17, and Orion with 9.4 cm radiation. Most emission nebulae are too faint or too small to be detected.

The nonthermal radiation from the disturbed sun or the aforementioned strong sources invariably appears to be associated with *matter in rapid motion*. The exact mechanism for the emission of radio waves has not yet been worked out.

In Chapter ⋆2 we mentioned the hyperfine structure of certain spectral lines, which is due to the coupling between the angular momentum of the electron and the nuclear magnetic moment. The ^2S ground level of H is resolved into a single lower state and three coincident upper states. The magnetic dipole transition has a wave length of 21 cm and a transition probability $A = 2.85 \times 10^{-15}$. In 1944 van de Hulst suggested that the interstellar neutral hydrogen gas should emit this radiation and the radiation was actually detected by Ewen and Purcell in March, 1951. The importance of this discovery for studies of galactic structure and the interstellar medium can hardly be overemphasized.

The line is produced in the H I regions, and, where the optical depth is very large, the temperature of the gas may be deduced from the intensity at the line center. It comes out in the neighborhood of 100°K, in excellent agreement with the theoretical predictions of Spitzer and Savedoff. The average density of neutral H appears to be about one atom per cubic centimeter. Oort and his co-workers have measured the profile of the line in different galactic longitudes and have shown how one may separate the effects of galactic rotation and the peculiar motions of the clouds. In the directions of the galactic center (and also the anticenter) the profiles are symmetrical; galactic rotational effects vanish. The neutral hydrogen becomes optically thick in a few hundred parsecs and our 21-cm radio-telescopes do not "see" more than 300 parsecs toward the galactic center. In other directions, the galactic rotation enters, the lines are broadened and distorted by differential motions and the profiles are no longer symmetrical. It is then possible to detect radiation from great distances. The Leiden investigators confirm the spiral arms discovered by Morgan, Sharpless, and Osterbrock.   In the direction of Cygnus they have located not only the nearby spiral arm, but also two other H I regions with radial velocities -60 km/sec and -90 km/sec.   These condensations may belong to spiral arms 3,000 and 10,000 parsecs away.   Since the radial velocities can be measured with high accuracy, the dynamics of the galactic system can be studied at great distances from the sun.

An analysis of the 21-cm radiation profiles shows that the neutral hydrogen is confined to the spiral arms.   The gas density between them must be vanishingly small.   The radio astronomy data thus confirms Münch's conclusions from his study of the interstellar K lines that the gas is confined to the spiral arms.   These results are what one would expect from Baade's observations concerning the distribution of the gas in the Andromeda galaxy.

At Harvard, B. J. Bok, H. I. Ewen, A. E. Lilley, and E. S. Heeschen have studied the distribution of the neutral hydrogen gas away from the galactic plane.   They find strong 21cm radiation from the dark nebulae in Ophiuchus and Taurus.

F. J. Kerr and J. V. Hindman of the Radiophysics Laboratory in Sydney have measured the intensity and distribution of the 21cm radiation from the Magellanic Clouds.   They find the Small Cloud to contain a great quantity of neutral gas.   Their estimate of the density of hydrogen in the Large Cloud is in good agreement with that found from the emission nebulae by Henize, Doherty, and the writer.   Kerr and G. de Vaucouleurs find the Large Cloud to be in rotation with a maximum rotational velocity of 20 km/sec about 3° from the center of the cloud.

Although but a few years old, radio astronomy has established itself as perhaps the most active branch of the science and certainly one of the most exciting.   Lack of space prevents our doing justice to this topic and reference must be made to the excellent treatments by Lovell and by van de Hulst.

10. Polarization of Galactic Light

Some years ago Chandrasekhar pointed out that eclipsing binaries of early spectral type should show polarization effects during eclipse as a consequence of the fact that the opacities of their atmospheres arise largely from electron scattering.   In searching for this effect, W. A. Hiltner and John Hall found that the interstellar medium polarizes light passing through it.   Hiltner found polarizations as high as 6 per cent, while Hall found the polarization to be independent of the wave length.   The polarization direction tends to be correlated in stars which are at small angular distances from one another.   The polarization is not strictly proportional to the color excess, indicating that the particles which produce the interstellar reddening are not strictly identical with those that are responsible for polarization. The star, HD 183143, which shows strong polarization effects, has the strongest interstellar λ4430 line!

This polarization can be produced by the preferential absorption of one plane of polarization by small elongated particles whose axes point in a common direction over large regions of space. Lyman Spitzer and J. W. Tukey supposed the particles to be needle-shaped and of a ferromagnetic character, lined up in large-scale interstellar magnetic fields of the order of 10^{-5} gauss. They supposed that in the course of the building up and evaporation of grains, compounds involving iron, magnesium, silicon, and other heavy substances would be retained. Because oxygen is so abundant, we might expect such ferromagnetic substances as Fe_3O_4 and $MgFe_2O_4$. These tiny magnetic particles would tend to form elongated structures and line up in a weak magnetic field. Scattering would differ in different directions and a beam of ordinary light would become polarized. Since the scattering efficiency exceeds that of ice crystals, these particles need not be very numerous to provide detectable effects.

Disorientation of the particles is continuously being produced by collisions with gas molecules. In order for the mechanism to work, a temperature of the order of $10°K$ is required, which seems low even for interstellar space. Furthermore, the more abundant paramagnetic substances cannot be successfully frozen into parallelism.

Leverett Davis and J. L. Greenstein have proposed a process which may orient paramagnetic substances at the kinetic temperatures likely to prevail in interstellar space. The mechanism depends on the recent work by Gorter and his colleagues in Holland, on the high-frequency magnetic susceptibility of paramagnetic materials.

In a steady state, random bombardment by gas molecules at a kinetic temperature of $10,000°K$ will give a particle of 10^{-6}-cm radius an angular velocity of about 10^9 radians/sec. If the axis of rotation is inclined to the magnetic field, an observer on the particle would notice a high-frequency alternation of the field. The rapidly varying magnetization of the particle depends on the susceptibility which is complex for many paramagnetic substances. The imaginary component is analogous to the imaginary part of the dielectric constant, which is connected with the heating of a condenser in an alternating electric field. In the magnetic field there is a corresponding dissipation of kinetic energy of rotation which acts as a torque tending to bring the axis of rotation of the particle parallel to the field. In this picture, the shortest axis of the elongated particle coincides with the axis of rotation, i.e., the long axis is perpendicular to the field. In the Spitzer-Tukey theory the longest axis of the particle coincides with the field. Collisions with gas molecules tend to disorient the particles with respect to the field, so that a distribution of orientations will be set up.

Davis and Greenstein conclude that if the paramagnetic material makes up 1 per cent of the mass of a particle 10^{-6} cm in radius, a field of 3×10^{-5} gauss can produce appreciable orientation at a kinetic temperature of 10,000°K. With dielectric prolate ellipsoids of ratio of axes 0.64, the polarization divided by the total absorption in magnitudes is about 0.016, which is the approximate maximum observed value.

H. C. van de Hulst finds that interstellar grains of the size suggested by the reddening measures give a barely sufficient amount of polarization, unless these particles strongly absorb as well as scatter the incident light.

Thus the polarization appears to arise from the orientation of interstellar grains in a galactic magnetic field. Furthermore, this magnetic field seems to be approximately parallel to the direction of the nearby spiral arm. That it is not exactly parallel is shown by the large and seemingly irregular fluctuations in the polarization direction of the light from distant stars seen along the spiral arms. The magnetic lines of force therefore must possess an undulatory character. The average angle θ between the plane of polarization (which is interpreted as defining the magnetic field) and the spiral arm seems to be about 11°. This angle θ must be connected with the strength of the galactic magnetic field H.

The interstellar medium is a good electrical conductor. Accordingly, magnetic lines of force act as though they were frozen in the medium so that as the gas is dragged hither and yon in turbulent motions, the lines of force are twisted and warped. If the field is weak, it can exert little restraint on the turbulent motion, and θ can become large. If the galactic magnetic field is strong, the lines of force will tend to be straight, and θ will be small.

Chandrasekhar and Fermi showed that, if ρ is the density of the interstellar medium and v is the root mean square velocity of turbulent motion, H and θ are related by

$$ H = \frac{v}{\theta} \sqrt{\frac{4\pi}{3} \rho} \tag{35} $$

Using $\rho = 2 \times 10^{-24}$ gm/cm^3 from Oort's estimate based on the 21-cm line data, $v = 5$ km/sec (from an estimate by Blaauw), and $\theta = 0.2$ radians, they found $H = 7.2 \times 10^{-6}$ gauss. A second method requires that the spiral arm be in equilibrium with respect to lateral expansion and contraction. That is, the pressure due to gravitational contraction in the spiral arm must exactly equal the sum of the gas and magnetic pressure. In this way they found $H = 6 \times 10^{-6}$ gauss. A third method is based on the stability of the spiral arms. If no magnetic field were present, a spiral arm would disintegrate into a series of separate clouds in about 10^8 years. If the magnetic field were strong, the spiral arms would last for a long time. Actually, the arms exist, but appear to be starting to disintegrate. The magnetic field required for a spiral arm to last 5×10^9 years is near 7×10^{-6} gauss.

The close accord of these three determinations leads to a galactic magnetic field strength of 7×10^{-6} gauss and indicates that the orientation mechanism is more efficient than Davis and Greenstein suggested.

Fermi has suggested that these interstellar magnetic fields may be connected with the origin of cosmic rays. The required fields are of the same order of magnitude as indicated by the above arguments. In any event, the interstellar medium promises to play an increasingly important role in astrophysics.

PROBLEMS

1. If the number of Ca II atoms in the line of sight is 3.12×10^{14} per cm^2 while the number of hydrogen atoms in the third level per cm^2 in the line of sight is 5, compare the relative emissions in the Ca II $\lambda 3933$ ($^2S_{1/2} - {}^2P_{3/2}$) line and Hα. Assume $W = 10^{-16}$, $A(\lambda 3933) = 1.66 \times 10^8$, $A(\mathrm{H}\alpha) = 4.39 \times 10^7$. The excitation potential of $^3P_{3/2}$ in Ca II is 3.2 volts. Assume the color temperature of the radiation is 15,000°K.

2. Eddington estimated that for the wave-length ranges relevant to the ionization of calcium, the composite energy distribution of the stars could be represented by a black body at 15,000°K. The total light of all stars is equivalent to 2000 stars of the first apparent magnitude. Given the absolute bolometric magnitude of the sun (4.62) and its energy output, compute the energy density in interstellar space and the dilution factor compared with a black body at 15,000°K.

3. A particle of radius 10^{-5} cm is located on the edge of a globule so that it receives radiation from only one side. Assume that the illumination from this hemisphere is uniform and use results from Problem 2. If the efficiency factor is 2 (corresponding to iron) what is the radiation pressure upon the particle? The efficiency factor for ice is 0.10. What will be the radiation pressure upon an ice particle of this size?

4. Consider the scattering of the light of a distant star by a plane parallel slab of thickness D. Assume the illuminating star and the observer to be on the same side of the reflection nebula. Show that if the phase function for scattering is $\varphi(\alpha)$, and k is the extinction coefficient the intensity of the scattered light (neglecting multiple scattering) will be given by an expression of the form

$$I = \frac{E_0}{R^2}\,\varphi(\alpha)\,\frac{\cos r}{\cos s + \cos r}\left\{1 - \exp\left[-kD\left(\frac{\cos r + \cos s}{\cos r \cos s}\right)\right]\right\}$$

PROB 4.

5. Assume that the ionized inner portion of the Orion Nebula is surrounded by a zone of neutral hydrogen a third of a parsec thick, with a density of 10^3 atoms/cm^3. With electron temperatures of 100°K, 1000°K, and 10,000°K, calculate the optical thickness of this zone due to continuous absorption of the negative hydrogen ion at λ5000, λ6000, and λ7000A. Assume $N_\epsilon = 0.1$.

REFERENCES

For a general account of the problem of the interstellar medium, see:

HYNEK, J. A. (ed.) *Astrophysics, A Topical Symposium.* New York: McGraw-Hill Book Co., Inc., 1951, chapter 13 by J. L. Greenstein.

Annales d'Astrophysique, Vol. I, 1938, contains a summary of much of the earlier work in papers by Struve, Schalén, Swings, and others.

Centennial Symposia—*Harvard Obs. Monogr.* **7,** 1948. The section on the interstellar medium contains important papers by J. G. Baker, J. Stebbins, J. L. Greenstein, Bart J. Bok, H. C. van de Hulst, Lyman Spitzer, Jr., F. L. Whipple, and others.

STRUVE, O. *J. Wash. Acad. Sci.* **31,** 217, 1941; *Stellar Evolution.* Princeton: Princeton University Press, 1950, chap. ii.

BEALS, C. S. *Pop. Astr.* **52,** 209, 1944.

The physical theory for the scattering and extinction of light by small particles is treated by:

MIE, G. *Ann. Phys.* **25,** 377, 1908.

DEBYE, P. *Ann. Phys.* **30,** 57, 1909.

Further discussions of the theory with emphasis on astrophysical applications may be found in:

GREENSTEIN, J. L. *Harvard Obs. Circ.* 422, 1938.

SCHALÉN, C. *Ann d' Ap.* **1**, 60, 1938.
VAN DE HULST, H. C. *Utrecht Obs. Researches* **11**, Part 1, 1946; Part 2, 1949.

For studies of the law of space absorption see:
TRUMPLER, R. J. *Publ. Astron. Soc. Pac.* **42**, 267, 1930, and subsequent papers by him and his collaborators in *Lick Obs. Bull.*
STEBBINS, J., C. M. HUFFER, and A. E. WHITFORD. *Ap. J.* **90**, 209, 1939; **91**, 20, 1940.
STEBBINS, J., and A. E. WHITFORD. *Ap. J.* **98**, 20, 1943; **102**, 318, 1945; *Astron. J.* **52**, 130, 1947.
WHITFORD, A. E. *Ap. J.* **107**, 102, 1948.
BAADE, W., and R. MINKOWSKI. *Ap. J.* **86**, 123, 1937.

The ratio of photographic or visual absorption to color excess has been discussed by:
WHITFORD, A. E. *Op. cit.* 1948.
VAN DE HULST, H. C. *Op. cit.* 1948.
HALL, J. *Ap. J.* **85**, 145, 1937.
OORT, J. *Bull. Astron. Inst. Nether.* **8**, 248, 1938.
GREENSTEIN, J. L., and L. HENYEY. *Ap. J.* **93**, 327, 1941.
GREENSTEIN, J. L. *Ap. J.* **104**, 403, 1946.
MORGAN, W. W., D. HARRIS, and H. L. JOHNSON. *Ap. J.* **118**, 92, 1953.

The classical paper on the illumination of reflection nebulae is:
HUBBLE, E. *Ap. J.* **56**, 416, 1922.

Studies of the colors and illumination of reflection nebulae have been made, for example, by:
STRUVE, O. and HELEN STORY. *Ap. J.* **84**, 203, 1936.
STRUVE, O. *Ap. J.* **85**, 194, 1937.
STRUVE, O., C. T. ELVEY, and F. E. ROACH. *Ap. J.* **84**, 219, 1936.
CEDERBLAD, S. *Lund Meddelande*, Series 2, No. 119, 1946.

The theory of the colors and illumination of reflection nebulae is given by:
HENYEY, L. G. *Ap. J.* **85**, 107, 1937.
HENYEY, L. G., and J. L. Greenstein. *Ap. J.* **88**, 580, 1938.

Polarization studies have been carried out, for example, by:
HENYEY, L. *Ap. J.* **84**, 609, 1936.
MEYER, W. F. *Lick Obs. Bull.* **10**, 68, 1920. (No. 328)
WHITNEY, W. T., and E. B. WESTON. *Ap. J.* **107**, 371, 1948.

Studies of the T Tauri variables and their related nebulosity have been made by:
JOY, A. H. *Ap. J.* **102**, 168, 1945; **110**, 424, 1949.
HERBIG, G. H. *Ap. J.* **111**, 11, 1950; *J.R.A.S. Canada* **46**, 222, 1952.
GREENSTEIN, J. L. *Ap. J.* **107**, 375, 1948.
GREENSTEIN, J. L., and L. H. ALLER. *Publ. Astron. Soc. Pac.* **59**, 139, 1947.

For the determination of the thickness of a dark nebula by star-count methods, see e.g.:
BOK, B. J. *Distribution of the Stars in Space.* Chicago: University of Chicago Press, 1937.

Numerous observational studies have been made of the interstellar lines. One of the most extensive is that by:
MERRILL, R. W., R. F. SANFORD, O. C. WILSON, and C. BURWELL. *Ap. J.*, **86**, 274, 1937.

The interstellar sodium *D* lines are discussed by:
WILSON, O. C., and P. W. MERRILL. *Ap. J.* **86**, 44, 1937.
SPITZER, L., JR. *Ap. J.* **108**, 276 1948.

The interstellar λ4430 has been studied by, for example:

GREENSTEIN, J. L., and L. H. ALLER. *Ap. J.* **111**, 328, 1950.
DUKE, D. *Ap. J.* **113**, 100, 1951.

The fine structure of the interstellar lines has been studied in most detail by:
ADAMS, W. S. *Ap. J.* **97**, 105, 1943.

Among important recent discussions of interstellar line velocities are:
BLAAUW, A. *B.A.N.* **11**, 405, 1952.
MÜNCH, G. *Ap. J.* (in press).

For a discussion of the interstellar emission nebulosities see:
STRUVE, O., C. T. ELVEY, and G. VAN BIESBROECK. *Ap. J.* **87**, 559, 1938.
STRUVE, O., and C. T. ELVEY. *Ap. J.* **89**, 119, 1939; *Ap. J.* **88**, 364, 1938.
SHARPLESS, S., and D. OSTERBROCK. *Ap. J.* **115**, 89, 1952.
SHARPLESS, S. *Ap. J.* **118**, 362, 1953 (catalog of nebulosities).
SHAJN, G. A., and B. F. HASE. *Publ. Crimean Astrophys. Obs.* **7**, 87, 1951; **9**, 52, 123, 1952 (photographs with Russian text).

The ionization equilibrium, composition, and density of the interstellar medium are discussed by:
DUNHAM, T. *Proc. Amer. Phil. Soc.* **81**, 277, 1939.
STRÖMGREN, B. *Ap. J.* **89**, 526, 1939; **108**, 242, 1948.

Temperature and dynamics of the interstellar medium:
EDDINGTON, A. S. *Internal Constitution of the Stars.* Cambridge: Cambridge University Press, 1926, p. 371.
SPITZER, L., JR. *Ap. J.* **93**, 369, 1941; **94**, 232, 1941; **95**, 329, 1942; **107**, 6, 1948; **109**, 337, 1949.
WHIPPLE, F. L. *Ap. J.* **104**, 1, 1946.
SPITZER, L., and M. P. SAVEDOFF. *Ap. J.* **111**, 593, 1950.

Formation of grains:
LINDBLAD, B. *Mon. Not. R. A. S.* **95**, 20, 1954; Nature **135**, 133, 1935.
TER HAAR, D. *B.A.N.* 361, 1943 (or *Ap. J.* **100**, 288, 1944).
TER HAAR, D., and H. A. KRAMERS. *B.A.N.* **10**, 137, 1946.
OORT, J., and H. C. VAN DE HULST. *B.A.N.* **10**, 187, 1946.
OORT, J. *M.N.* **106**, 159, 1946.
KAHN, F. D. *M.N.* **112**, 518, 1952.

Accretion:
EDDINGTON, A. S. *Internal Constitution of the Stars.* Cambridge: Cambridge University Press, 1926, p. 391.
HOYLE, F., and R. A. LYTTLETON. *Proc. Camb. Phil. Soc.* **35**, 495, 1939.
HOYLE, F., and H. BONDI. *M.N.* **104**, 273, 1944.
HOYLE, F. *M.N.* **105**, 287, 302, 345, 363, 1945.

Evidence for the formation of stars from the interstellar medium was obtained by:
BLAAUW, A. *B.A.N.* **11**, 459, 1952.
BLAAUW, A., and W. W. MORGAN. *Ap. J.* **117**, 256, 1953.

Discussions of aggregates of high-temperature stars have been given, for example, by:
AMBARZUMIAN, V. *Astr. J. U.S.S.R.* **26**, 3, 1949.
ROMAN, NANCY. *Ap. J.* **114**, 492, 1951 (Cygnus).
SHARPLESS, S. *Ap. J.* **116**, 251, 1952 (Orion).
MORGAN, W. W., A. E. WHITFORD, and A. CODE. *Ap. J.* **118**, 318, 1953.

Galactic Radio-frequency Radiation. Excellent summaries are given by:
VAN DE HULST, H. C. *A Course in Radio Astronomy.* Leiden: Leiden Observatory, 1951.

LOVELL, A. C. B., and J. A. CLEGG. *Radio Astronomy.* London: Chapman & Hall, 1952.
RYLE, M. *Progress in Physics Reports* **13**, 214, 1950.

See also:
MINKOWSKI, R., and W. BAADE. *Ap. J.* **119**, 206, 215, 1954.
MINKOWSKI, R., and L. H. ALLER, *Ap. J.* **119**, 232, 1954.
GREENSTEIN, J. L., and R. MINKOWSKI, *Ap. J.* **118**, 1, 1953 (Crab Nebula).

The radio-frequency line spectrum of hydrogen has been discussed by:
EWEN, H. I. and E. M. PURCELL. *Nature* **168**, 356, 1951.
MULLER, C. A., and J. H. OORT. *Nature* **168**, 357, 1951.
WILD, J. P. *Ap. J.* **115**, 206, 1952.

The galactic-structure results obtained at Leiden from the 21-cm radiation are summarized in:
OORT, J. *B.A.N:* (in press), 1953.

Interstellar polarization (additional bibliography in references cited):
HALL, J. *Science* **109**, 166, 1949.
HILTNER, W. A. *Science* **109**, 165, 1949; *Ap. J.* **109**, 471, 1949.
SPITZER, L., and J. W. TUKEY. *Ap. J.* **114**, 187, 1951.
DAVIS, L., and J. L. GREENSTEIN. *Ap. J.* **114**, 206, 1951.
VAN DE HULST, H. C. *Ap. J.* **112**, 1, 1950.
CHANDRASEKHAR, S., and E. FERMI. *Ap. J.* **118**, 113, 116, 1953.

Many of the topics discussed in this and the preceding chapter are treated in:
DUFAY, J. *Nébuleuses Galactiques et Matière Interstellaire.* Paris: Albin Michel, 1954.

INDEX OF NAMES

INDEX OF SUBJECTS

Absorption coefficient (opacity) in stellar
interiors, 9–14, 45, 47, 58, 63, 73
Rosseland mean value of, 10, 12
Absorption of starlight in space, 230
ratio of, to color excess, 240, 241, 248
wave length, law of, 235, 238
Accretion of interstellar medium by stars,
270
Adiabatic
equilibrium, 16; see Convective equilibrium
gas law, 15, 18, 53
gradient, 16, 18
pulsations, 115–21
Alpha (α)-particle, 22, 23, 25, 29, 37
synthesis of C^{12} from, 41, 42
Andromeda Nebula (Messier 31), 196,
232, 241, 260, 268, 269, 272
Ansae of nebula, 197, 215
Apsidal motions in eclipsing binaries, 74,
76

Balmer continuum, in gaseous nebulae,
205, 206, 211, 225
Balmer decrement in gaseous nebulae,
203, 204
Balmer discontinuity, in planetary nebu-
lae, 211, 212
Barn, defined, 34
Barnard dark area, 244
B emission stars, 141–44, 150, 152, 155
Beta (β)-decay, 27–29, 36
constant, 28, 29
Fermi theory of, 28, 29
Gamow-Teller selection rules, 29
Beta (β)-ray, 24, 27
Bolometric corrections, 108, 109, 112
Bolometric magnitudes
for δ Cephei, 108, 109
for long period variables, 112
Bound-bound or line absorptions
from X-ray levels, 9, 13
Bound-free absorptions, 9, 11, 12, 201

Carbon cycle, 3, 18, 36–40, 46, 62, 72
Cepheid variables, 98
classical, 98–100
color variations of, 107
curves of growth for, 128
intrinsic luminosities of, 101
light curves and periods of, 98–101

period luminosity relation for, 100,
101, 103
phase relation between light and velocity curves for, 127
pulsation of, 106–10, 115 et seq.
spectral variations of, 106, 107
surface gravities of, 129
temperatures of, 108
variations in atmospheres of, 128, 131,
132
Cepheid variables of Type II population
light curves of, 100, 101, 106
period-luminosity relation for, 100,
101, 104
pulsation mechanism of, 132
velocity curves of, 131, 132
Chandrasekhar's Beta (β) Theorem, 6
Chandrasekhar's method of envelopes, 59
Chemical elements, origin of, 90–94
Chemically inhomogeneous models, 79
Chromosphere of sun, 141
Coal Sack, 232, 244, 269
Color excess, relation to
absorption, 240
interstellar line intensities, 250
Color index, 240
Compound nucleus, 24, 26
defined, 25
Contours, isophotal, 198, 199
Convection, 14–19
and stellar rotation, 79
criterion for, 16
in stellar interiors, 14, 17, 18, 42
zone of hydrogen, 17, 133
Convective core of stellar models, 47, 62,
71
Convective cores of stars, 15, 46, 66
Convective equilibrium, 16, 46, 54, 62,
133
Coriolis forces, 19
Corona of sun, 141, 181
Coronal lines in novae, 180
Counter, Geiger-Müller, 31
anti-coincidence, 31
coincidence, 32
scintillation, 31, 32
Crab Nebula
as a radio source, 188, 272
identification as a supernova, of, 186
interpretation of, 186–89
spectrum of, 185

287